* * *

"*The Green-Clad Kicker* is a wonderful extension of Jamie's first book, *The Yellow Sports Bra*, as she continues her journey to college wrought with the trials, tribulations, celebrations, and excitement. Humor is prevalent throughout, and Jamie has an innate ability to capture the nostalgia of everyday routine as it threads through the memories of life. Reading *The Green-Clad Kicker* felt like curling up to a good old early 2000 rom-com movie with some hilarious, some sensitive and sincere, and all the real-life of a small-town girl from Montana taking her next steps into this big world."

—Vanessa Bucklin, author of *The Penultimate Step*

"Jamie Graham Duprey's sequel to *The Yellow Sports Bra* does not disappoint! *The Green-Clad Kicker* continues in memoir-style writing and takes one on a journey of the transformational transition from adolescence through early adulthood. Jamie is masterful at transporting the reader back to their own coming-of-age story, and I could hear Jamie's infectious laugh throughout. Jamie's story about finding lifelong friends, navigating being on your own for the first time, and discovering the love of your life is a story for everyone."

—Brian Henderson, former RMC head
women's basketball coach

"*The Green-Clad Kicker* is an honest, gripping, hilarious, and sweet story of Jamie's college years. It is relatable and helpful to those currently experiencing life in college, and it will make other readers smile as they reminisce about their own memories from 'back in the day.'"

—Whitney Edwards, forward at
Dickinson State University

"Jamie paints an amazing picture of what it takes to be a successful student-athlete, while being an amazing influence on people who have crossed paths with her. Being a friend, studying for tests, going to practice, attending church, and being a positive influence through all of life's challenges. This book is very genuine, well-written, and inspiring. Jamie's positive attitude, her love for people, and her witty sense of humor make this a very enjoyable read. Thank you, Jamie, for sharing your secrets on how to be a great human being!"

—Jake Stuart, NAIA All-American (2004),
RMC Hall of Fame (2019)

"*The Green-Clad Kicker* is a delightful, heartfelt book about leaving the familiarity and comfort of home, overcoming obstacles, navigating life as a young adult, and finding new friendships and love. Jamie takes us from her small and beloved hometown of Chester, Montana, to Rocky Mountain College in Billings, Montana, where she experiences the highs and lows of being a college student-athlete. Her character, sense of humor, and heart shines throughout this entire book. You will laugh, cry, and find yourself once again rooting for Jamie."

—Kelley (Edwards) Rice, Youth Aware of Mental Health
Program Director, Montana State University

"Wow, once I started reading, I couldn't put it down! Jamie's story should be made into a Hallmark movie! This should be required reading for every college student-athlete. She's right when she said, 'Even though I love basketball, and I have always been all about basketball, it is not basketball that keeps me going. It is the people, the relationships.'"

—Bob Parsons, Coaches of Influence (COIN), co-author of
Larry Luitjens, A Coach of Influence

"Such a charming evolution of a love story, as well as classic vignettes of college athletics and shenanigans. Hurray, Jamie!"

—The Rev. Laura Loving

The
GREEN-CLAD
KICKER

A True Story of
Love, Sports, and College

Jamie Graham Duprey

Aubade Publishing
Ashburn, VA

This work is a true story, based on journal entries the author made during the time the story takes place and the author's best recollection of the people, events, conversations, and locales at that time of her life. At times during the story, the author's recollection of the people, conversations, events, and locales might not be perfectly accurate. The attempt was made to be faithful to the historical events as they occurred. In some instances, journal entries were condensed or sequenced for literary effect, but no names, places, or events have been changed, invented, or altered.

Edited by Joe Puckett

Cover design, illustration, and book layout by Cosette Puckett

The Rocky Mountain College Battlin' Bear logo is a trademark of Rocky Mountain College

Library of Congress Control Number: 2023940784

ISBN: 978-1-951547-23-3

Published by Aubade Publishing, Ashburn, VA

Printed in the United States of America

To my Grandma Barb & my Grandma Joyce

I like to think I am a good mix of the two of you

I miss you all the time and think of you both every day

CONTENTS

Peggy~

Enjoy!

~Jamie

Romans 12:4-8

PRESEASON

"The end of a matter is better than its beginning."

—Ecclesiastes 7:8

2001–2002 Chester Lady Coyotes, State Class C Champions

Chester High School graduation, May 19, 2002

# Chapter 1

August 2002, last night at home before college, Chester, Montana

His eyes lock fiercely in on mine with that intensity I have seen so many times before. Is he going to kiss me? I wonder nervously, yet admittedly excited.

How is this even happening? Why is this happening? Should this be happening?

I exhale in an attempt to steady my breath and settle my tumbling thoughts. My chest tightens. He leans closer. I hesitate and pull back slightly.

Why did I hesitate and pull back slightly?

Because we decided it was best for me to enter college single, that's why. That it made sense for me to be free and fully available to new people and new experiences. Sense, yes. Sensible. Rational. Responsible. All those grown-up things. I am eighteen after all. Thus, I am a grown-up. See? I even use words like "thus." So we made the right decision. Yes, right.

Right?

He doesn't seem to notice that I pulled back slightly. Now his inviting sparkly blue eyes close, and he bows closer still. My nose pulls in his familiar scent of Extra peppermint gum, Irish Spring soap, and Old Spice deodorant. Mmm. Smells so good. That zappy feeling works its way down my spine and through my stomach. Did my knees literally just weaken? So cliché. Wait, what was that about being sensible and grown up? His hands work their way around my waist, fingertips gently tickling the thin line of exposed skin on my lower back.

Sensible, schmensible . . .

"Sweetheart?"

Sweetheart? Since when has Brent ever called me "sweetheart"?

3

Puzzled, I furrow my eyebrows and listen carefully. I discern the lyrics of "Here Without You" playing faintly in the background: *But all the miles that separate disappear now when I'm dreaming of your face ...*

I open my eyes to look at the face of the person addressing me. No face. My eyes focus and realize the confusion. My palms press into the mattress, and I push myself upright against my pillow. I look toward the white popcorn-textured ceiling and drop the back of my head against the wall. My shoulders lower with a comprehending—and perhaps a bit disappointed—breath. Two figures enter my bedroom: Mom leading and Dad following right behind. Mom sits at the head of my bed on my pink, green, and blue pin-striped crisp cotton sheets, Dad at the foot.

"Oh, sorry, honey. Were you already asleep?" Mom asks affectionately and apologetically.

My head swivels slightly from side to side in response to her question, while also shaking away the dream. "Oh, no." I rub my eyes and temples slowly with the tips of my fingers.

I look at her and manage a small smile. "I was just listening to music."

She rubs my back. "I bet you are tired. We just wanted to come in and tell you goodnight."

This keeps happening. Things I have done a million times somehow suddenly feel completely different. Like my parents coming into my bedroom to tell me goodnight. We have done this every night for my entire life. Tonight, though, it feels . . . well, let's just say there are a lot of "feels." Like when we had our last team basketball meeting, our last volleyball game, last concert, last track meet, last day of high school, graduation, blah blah blah. Okay, point taken. Clearly there is a theme.

Dad pats a patch of the fluffy down comforter covering my shins. Mom continues to rub my right shoulder. "How are you feeling?"

Can we say "loaded question"?

"Fine," I reply weakly.

Mom and Dad both look at me, with closemouthed faux smiles. I know they wear those expressions to mask their sadness. Last night we all had a little meltdown after Dad deplored, with a catch in his throat, "Not sure what we're going to do without you here."

"You two will head out tomorrow at eight bells." Dad skips the sappy stuff tonight into territory he can control: the logistics of tomorrow's trip. "It will take five hours to get to Billings, and orientation starts at four o'clock. You need time to stop for lunch, and then to get all your stuff from the car to your dorm room before that."

I do some quick mental math and debate arguing that we may not need to leave quite that early. Just as quickly I decide against it. When Dad has a schedule figured out, it is best to just go with it. "Okay," I oblige.

They both continue looking at me, eyes swimming with emotion. Aw, cute parents.

I smile and look from Mom to Dad. These two. It seems they have so much to say yet aren't sure what to say. "Well I better get some sleep then, if we are going to get up that early," I say, smiling.

"I love you guys."

More faux smiling and shoulder rubbing. They take turns kissing my forehead. "We love you, too, sweetie," Mom manages.

"Proud of you," Dad whispers. "Love you, babe."

I cue, "Night," and offer another encouraging smile.

"Night, sweetie."

"Night, babe."

Dad gives one last look back as he follows Mom out of my room, before slowly pulling the squeaky wooden door shut.

It is after ten o'clock. My body is tired, but my mind whirs. I swing my torso over the edge of my bed and procure my current journal. Things have been happening so fast lately, days and weeks blurring by. I am glad I can read about all that has happened or I swear I would forget half of it. I flip lazily through the pages. Some stray letters and folded papers float out. Setting the journal beside me, I gather and stack the papers in a crooked pile.

On top is the card Coach VanDyke gave me on senior night.

Jamie #12
Dear Jamie,

As we celebrate senior night many thoughts come to me, and it is all good. Thank you for bringing so much joy to my coaching experience. It has been a wonderful journey (we are still traveling) watching you grow as a player and as a person. Thank you for working so hard and demonstrating what "team" really means. Basketball does teach us a lot about life. Think of all the words we defined such as commitment, discipline, poise, teamwork, hustle, attitude, heart, character, determination, perseverance, leadership, etc. Carry those words with you, set goals and attack life the same way you attack a basketball game. Hold on to all the good memories. When I turn the light on and off in the coaches room I'll always think of you. Thank you for all the enthusiasm you bring to practice, games, and life. Continue to have fun at whatever you do. Always remember you are a worthy person. God loves you, and so do I. It is time to spread your wings like an EAGLE.[1] Discover the world and discover you. You are at LIBERTY to do what you want, go where you want, and be the person you want. When life gets a little crazy remember UTAH—slow down, relax and go for the best shot. As far as KANSAS goes, watch "The Wizard of Oz." Maybe we should travel to HOUSTON with a smile, or is that HOUSTON with a screen? It won't be long until game time.

The coach is the team, and the team is the coach. I bet you were already thinking that![2]

Together,
Coach VanDyke

---

[1] All the capitalized words were names of offensive set plays our high school basketball team used.

[2] I frequently told Coach VanDyke I knew what she was going to say before she said it. One weekend, Coach Schlepp had his wisdom teeth taken out the morning before a game. He coached his JV game that night, but Coach VanDyke made him go home at halftime of the varsity game, as he was swollen up like a balloon. Then she rushed into the locker room to tell us what changes to make for the second half. When she started explaining the changes, everyone giggled then explained, "Jamie already told us all that."

I wipe my eyes and slide the basketball-stamp-covered card back in its Columbia-blue envelope. Next in the pile is a hastily folded printout of an email Brent sent a few months back.

April 16, 2002

hey there u,

sorry it's taken me so long to write u. i just don't know. the only thing i know now is that i love u and that im gonna wait because i want to. that night you started singing that song and then saying u don't know what else to do i really didn't think that it would come down like that u know. i mean it hit me really hard you sayin that and all and i didn't sleep and still can't sleep. i know how it is not knowing what the future has in store but if u focus too much on the future u kinna forget what's happening in the present. i want to be with you so bad but i know that it hurts you not to have something to hold onto and not knowing what the future has in store. and i know that ur gonna meet someone in college and that's why i didn't want to let go of you. it's hard to know that ur not mine anymore u know. "if you could only see," good song. i love u jamie.

p.s. this is brent and i will always love u

A few more tears slip out. I refold the paper and tuck it underneath Coach's letter. A legal-size envelope is next in the queue, and I know exactly what it holds. Richie presented this typed-out letter to me the night of my graduation party.

High school was fun
Life can be hard
Thought you'd like money[3]
Instead of a card

---

[3] Richie had tucked a crisp $50 bill in with the envelope, which I remember thinking was extremely generous, especially to an eighteen-year-old!

Dearest Jamie Marie,

Here are some of my revelations on how to survive and/or have a happy life after high school:

1. *Study habits. Let's face it, school in Chester vs. college courses. No real comparison. Think of how many valedictorians from small towns tank when they hit college land. Here is the secret to success. Really. Take your number of credit hours, double that and reserve that much time for study. I know this sounds soooo stupid, and at the beginning there really isn't much new stuff that you are learning. The key is learning how to learn. Even if it means rewriting your notes, re-re-reading your notes or outline chapters or your notes. This will guarantee B+ stuff.*

2. *Sit in the front. Be on time. Be visible. Know the professor enough that if you have trouble, you will feel comfortable enough to ask for help, or an extra point or two. This sounds unfair, but it is the sad truth.*

3. *Don't be stupid with drugs and/or drinking. It's too cliché to discuss. Don't p*ss your opportunity down your leg. However, if you ever are stupid and you need help, our # is 406-759-5860, and we are on call 24-7. People who are stupid die. The diagnosis code in the ER is "too stupid to live." Really.*

4. *Sex or "How to end up with a sexually transmitted disease without really trying." It's God's little joke or wonderful design that when you feel like maybe having sex, you are at the most fertile part of your cycle. This is how sooooo many one-timers get pregnant. Now, about the hydrodynamics (the study of fluid behavior). Take a full water bottle and stick it in a tub of water. Squeeze the water out of the water bottle. What happens? A vacuum is created in the water bottle which draws any fluid around the opening of the bottle back into the bottle. The term is "back-flush." In humans, when the man ejaculates, if the*

8

tip of his "hose" is in a fluid area, his "hose" works like a little vacuum and draws all sorts of things back into the body. The stuff he brings back incubates in his body until he has sex again. Then, all the stuff, which has grown up nicely in his plumbing, is dumped into the next victim. Remember, Montana is endemic with chlamydia. Hep B, Hep C, genital warts, herpes, HIV and the standard gonorrhea are on the rise. Don't be a chump. Use your good judgment.

5. *Date rape. It happens all the time. Even in Chester. GHP and roofies (rohypnol) are common in Havre and Shelby. Billings is worse. Watch your drink. Don't leave it unattended, and do not take drinks from someone else. Freshman girls, especially fresh faced ones from small towns are preyed on, and you have to be smarter than the predators.*

6. *Don't walk alone at night. Look under your car before you get close enough to unlock the door. Be aware at all times.*

7. *Men— their mothers and fathers. Here's the secret to finding someone you can love forever. Meet their parents. If you want to keep a strong faith in God and raise your kids together in church, look at the parents. If they don't go to church, unless you hitch up with a born-again, it's unlikely he will go to church with you. Look at his dad. There is a huge likelihood that he will grow up just like Daddy. Could you love this guy?? Plus, look at Mom. Does she iron underwear? Then you can bet you will be expected to iron underwear. You get my point? People try to change, but it is tough to overcome the conditioning plus the genetics. That's why wife beaters beget a * *holes.*

8. *In ten years you will realize that you will never know just how amazing your parents are. Enjoy them now. There are no guarantees how long you have them.*

9. *If you wake up in jail in Mexico and have nowhere to turn to . . . call us. We will love you forever, no matter what.*

"Be strong in the Lord. Put on the whole armor of God. Finally, whatsoever things are true, whatsoever things are lovely, whatsoever things are of good report, if there be any mercy, if there be any praise, think on these things."

Love,
The Hamel bunch

I reread a few parts of Richie's letter, considering the care she took to spell all that out for me, appreciating her trademark directness and blunt honesty. For the most part I have been feeling excited for college, but sometimes I do get a little nervous. It is fun to think about who I might meet and what experiences I might have, but sometimes those things feel scary.

A card from Kaitlynn is next. She gave it to me just before our youth group went on a mission trip to Minneapolis.

June 22, 2002

Hello my sweetie

i have been sitting in this store all day, wondering about you. ever since you left, my day seemed to get worse. i understand what you are going through and the dilemma of the whole thing. i cannot answer the questions you ask, but i can be here to guide you and help you along your ("our!") way! the pillow i thought was perfect, because that's what i told you to do: follow your heart. i'd like you to read the tag on the pillow carefully, it means something. the dreamsicle is to tell you i love you and send you kisses and so when you look at it, you know i am with you. the purple placemat is for you to put on one of your night stands perhaps. i saw the color and thought of you! i also thought this card was perfect . . . "sending you a world of wonder"! it's hard to know all the answers, but you need to take each and every day as they come. Remember. . .

"Yesterday is history, tomorrow is a mystery, and today is a gift, that's why it's called the present!"
Keep yourself in good spirits and <u>SMILE</u>. my eyes are full of tears, and my mind and soul are just as confused as yours. you're my best friend, and i don't want to see you hurt again. But i do want to see you happy!
Have a Great trip, have some fun. i wish i could be with you, but i'll be fine. You are a very special person, one of a kind. i wish you the best. Always and forever!

Love,
Kaitlynn Rae

Her words make me smile. I can hear her voice perfectly when I read this. I don't think I can be reminded too often how important it is to have friends by my side. This thought chokes me up as I consider the reality of not living with all of my friends in one place ever again. Unless we start a compound someday, which seems unlikely. This fact is impossible to fully wrap my mind around, but it makes me sad. The last item on the pile is a piece of torn-out notebook paper where I had scribbled a rough draft of the poem I read for my graduation speech. Heidi's speech was of course better, but I do like the poem.

May 19, 2002

Our journey started out back in Kindergarten
When everything was so brand new
Then we had absolutely no idea
Of together all we'd go through
We learned so much in elementary school
How to read and write and spell
Best friends were found, best friends were lost
Who does so-and-so like? They'll never tell
Junior high was a whole different world
With many new freedoms, but also new rules
We got to make floats for the Homecoming parade

And play sports against teams from other schools
Finally we made it to high school
What we'd all been waiting for
None of us could even fathom
What those four years would have in store
Word Power tests every Friday
Nine week tests each quarter, what a thrill
But we got to have fun on the weekends
Go to ball games, drive around, and just chill
We put on many concerts and plays
Competed in football, tennis and track
Memories were made that we'll never forget
Sometimes we wish we could just go back
We loved, we learned, we fought, we forgave
We laughed, and yes, we cried
We taught each other so many life lessons
That we will always carry inside
Four years may sound like a long time
But trust me, it really does fly
It seems like yesterday we were just freshmen
Now all of a sudden it's time to say good-bye
My classmates are my family
We have been through everything together
And though now we are taking separate paths
I will remember you all forever
This important chapter in our lives is closing
But a new one is about to start
We can get whatever we want out of life
If we use our heads and follow our hearts

Carefully I refold this last page, stack it with the others, and stuff the stack in the top drawer of my bedstead. I sigh, bleary-eyed, and pick up my journal again. As I study it I notice that the three-subject college rule purple notebook is only halfway filled out. I wonder what—and who—will fill the pages of the second half. . . .

My eyes instinctively scan the walls of my bedroom, littered with posters and pictures. They land on the latest addition: my "State" wall. The images immediately evoke another inundation of emotion (listen to that fancy alliteration). I grin as I see Maci, Savannah, Amanda, Courtney, and Jillien singing intensely into water bottles while standing on a hotel bed; Chasi and Michele looking truly alarmed as they pretend to climb a rocky cliff between the restaurant and hotel parking lot (it was just a decorative bed of rocks, but we turned the camera for effect); Kaitlynn, Heidi, and I posing in our pregame dresses before the final game; Coach VanDyke and Coach Schlepp feigning frustration, dripping after being thrown into the hotel pool; and picture after picture of me with family members, community members, and team members clutching the coveted first place State C basketball trophy.

Four members of the 1979 state Class B runner-up Chester Lady Coyotes girls' basketball team pose with us after the 2001 state Class C championship game.

My eyes shift to my trusty alarm clock, shining fixedly under my lamp, its red LED displaying 11:07 in block numbers. Tomorrow I leave for college. Time for a new chapter, I think, as I gently toss the purple notebook on top of my green Wilson duffel bag, so I will remember to pack it before we leave, and click off my lamp. I close my eyes and allow myself to relive that momentous weekend. My mind works hard to recreate the scene of the big gym, faces of my teammates and coaches and fans flickering into view. Then it conjures a blurry image of my recent dream. Scenes and faces swirl in my mind as my heavy eyelids finally close and succumb to sleep.

FIRST QUARTER

*"Forget the former things; do not dwell on the past. See, I
am doing a new thing! Now it springs up; do you not
perceive it? I am making a way in the wilderness."*

—Isaiah 43:18-19

2002–2003 RMC Battlin' Bears

Chapter 2

*August 2002, leaving for college from Chester, Montana to
Billings, Montana*

7:00 The harsh, unwelcome blare of my alarm forces my eyes open, like when someone pulls the cord on a set of blinds and too quickly lets go. How can it already be time to wake up? It feels like I have been sleeping for five minutes. I grope for the clock perched on my bedstead, find and press the snooze button, and try to hang on to scenes from dreams that were so rudely interrupted: Emily picking me up outside my house, but when she starts driving we don't know which way to turn; Michele throwing me a great pass—Chasi and Maci are both wide open—but my hands grip the ball tightly, and my feet are stuck to the gym floor and won't move, no matter how hard I try; Kaitlynn and Heidi laughing about something, but I don't get the joke; Mari and Brent walking down the long bare hallway, but when I shout and wave my arms they don't seem to hear, don't turn around, just keep walking. . . .

7:09 Another shrill buzz. I have to get up or Dad will have an aneurysm. He is already stressed enough about me leaving. The least I can do is be ready on time. I manage to will myself to throw off my safe cozy covers and climb reluctantly out of bed. One last time, before everything changes. The familiar soft blue-gray carpet envelops my feet as I stride slowly and comfortably across my childhood room.

Goodbye childhood room.

8:00 Right on time! As usual. I smile proudly out the front window seat of our white 1994 Ford Taurus. Dad's rigid shoulders suggest he is not so thrilled with our departure time happening right at the last second, but his clenched jaw remains shut, and he raises his hand in a last wave as Mom and I pull slowly out of the garage. Dad has football practice today and tomorrow, and then he will head to Billings to meet us. I wave and recognize that look, where he is trying so hard not to cry.

17

Sweet Daddy. I look out my passenger window as Mom snakes through our alley and out onto Monroe Avenue. My eyes well up as we pass by Emily's house, then the hospital, and then turn onto Highway 223. Goodbye Chester.

1:08 After carrying us about 280 miles north to south across Montana, with a lunch stop at Eddie's Corner, obviously, the trusty Taurus climbs off Highway 3 onto Zimmerman Trail and zigzags cautiously down the steep winding road. My eyes sweep across the beautiful yet intimidating Yellowstone River Valley.[4] More people live in these neighborhoods on Rimrock Drive than my whole town. Probably my town plus Joplin, Inverness, Kremlin, and Gilford combined. Bonkers. We drive past multiple stoplights. I thought the four-way stop (with signs, not lights, mind you) in Chester was a big deal. Billings, Yellowstone County, my new home.[5] Chester is my home. An uneasy—yet slightly excited—sensation swirls my stomach.

Mom hangs a right off Rimrock at the light on Seventeenth. Then she turns left onto Poly Drive. I glance at the baseball field, and then study the cozy-looking grassy green bowl surrounding Herb Klindt Field (according to the large sign welcoming visitors).[6] Aluminum bleachers stand perched on both the home and visitors sides, and bright gold goal posts mark the end zones. A football spins through the uprights on the south end of the field. I watch absently as a green-and-gold-clad athlete with curly blonde hair retrieves the football and nonchalantly jogs toward his tall skinny teammate. The curly-haired player[7] takes a knee and situates the ball just so between his finger and the grass, laces out (*Ace Ventura*) of course. The taller player, also donning green-and-gold practice gear, carefully sets up and concentrates as he prepares to kick again. Green, huh? That might take some getting used to, as I am partial to Columbia blue. At least I get to stick with gold.

---

[4] The Yellowstone River is the longest free-flowing river in the lower 48 states (American Rivers, 2019).

[5] Billings is the largest city in Montana, with a population estimated at 117,116 as of 2020. Located in the south-central portion of the state, it is the seat of Yellowstone County. Billings was nicknamed the "Magic City" because of its rapid growth from its founding as a railroad town in March 1882 (City of Billings, n.d.).

[6] Rocky, n.d.

[7] Matt Kimmet from Laurel, the Bears' holder and a wide receiver.

Mom takes one more left that leads into the parking lot of the Widenhouse and Anderson dormitories. It is no Hogwarts, but it will do. Mom finds a spot facing Alden Hall. "Now what? Should I grab my bag?" "Let's just go to the desk first to check in and get your keys," Mom decides.

Like staying in a hotel. But this is where I live now. So weird. We walk up the sidewalk that leads to a glass door to an annex connecting the two halls. Widenhouse Hall is a long brick building that runs west to east. Anderson Hall sits perpendicular, creating an 'L' shape and pointing toward the beautiful Rims.[8] A smiling resident director greets us enthusiastically from behind a table that is covered with pens, papers, and clipboards. I try to focus and listen to all the information the RD is imparting, but my eyes and mind wander, actively taking in my new environment. Mom hands me a clipboard. I fill in spaces asking for my name, rank, and serial number. (I read that in a book once and found it funny. Don't get the wrong idea, I am excited to be here and do not feel like a prisoner.)

Finally we are given my key and very official-looking Rocky student-ID-slash-meal-swipe card with the ferocious battlin' bear next to my photo, hanging from a green lanyard. I pull the lanyard over my neck. Note to self: do not lose lanyard. I follow Mom back out the door and to the car. She punches in the five-number key code on the door that pops the trunk.

"We should be able to go in that door," Mom says, nodding toward a heavy-looking plain brown door that leads to my new dorm room, 130, according to the key in Widenhouse Hall.

I lift my duffel and place the wide black strap across my chest, leaving both hands free to carry other miscellaneous bags. Dad is bringing a few last odds and ends, but for the most part we were able to pack all my stuff. Mom carries a box where I threw in my journal this morning, packed with yearbooks and picture frames. My new roommate Kat has been living on campus all summer, and there is not a ton of space in our 140ish-square-foot room; I tried to pack light.

---

[8] The majestic "Rimrocks" are sandstone cliffs that line the north side of Billings (Billings365, n.d.).

19

My very official-looking Rocky Mountain College ID card, 2002

We start down the long, bare hallway, reading numbers as we go. "Left here, it looks like," Mom calls as I keep walking forward before making an abrupt about-face.

There is a short hall within the long hall lined with a few doors just before another door on the north side of the building. When we reach room 130 I drop my backpack and awkwardly handle the silver key, trying to figure out the easiest way to unlock it. I attempt to act smooth and casual but inadvertently jerk my neck forward, letting out a low blurty grunt when I misjudge the length of the lanyard in relation to distance to the keyhole. Sigh. Perhaps I will never be smooth.

I manage to successfully unlock the door to my new quarters and wedge my foot between the door and the jamb. I press my shoulder against the wood and backpedal in order to prop it for Mom. She sidles in and starts a pile on the short gray carpet below the sink and mini fridge.[9]

* * *

After several trips and some creative reorganization, we have found space for all of my stuff to cohabitate with Kat's in our cozy little cove.

---

[9] The Widenhouse dorms at Rocky were pretty chic, as far as dorms go. They came with a small fridge, sink, and a bathroom with shower that someone cleaned on a consistent basis!

I look around approvingly. We tucked in the extra-long purple sheets on my high top bunk, and my down comforter hangs like a canopy over Kat's bottom bunk. There is a plain wooden desk below the large picture window that gives us a beautiful view of the sidewalk and lawn leading to Alden Hall, and then on to "the sub."[10]

"Do you need anything else?" Mom asks, also taking a look around.

"I don't think so," I reply. "Maybe a nap."

Mom smiles but is serious in her response. "Yes, you should take a little nap. Then that orientation dinner is in a couple hours. I am going to head to Gary and Linda's."

"Okay, thanks for everything, Mama."

"You're welcome, sweetie." Mom rubs my back then gives me a big hug. "Dad will be here tomorrow by lunch. We will give you a call then. Have a good night. I love you."

"Love you, too, Mama."

* * *

My alarm, uh, alarms and informs me it is time to walk over to the sub for the orientation dinner. I sit up abruptly, momentarily startled by how close the ceiling is. It takes a second for me to remember where I am. I lie back and roll over on my stomach, extending my left arm down toward the very heavy—trust me, I know—wooden desk sitting below our lone window. This is an extraordinarily high bed. I manage to hit the snooze button then slide the little thingy that's not a button, but I don't know what to call it, to "off" without toppling out of the bunk. Kat is still working, and I am not sure when Maci is going to get here. I do know we are going to meet at seven o'clock and go play some ball at Senior.[11]

I carefully climb down out of my new bed and change into my yellow Freshmen Experience shirt that came in my welcome bag. Apparently each freshman receives a shirt like this, color coded based on major, and we are encouraged to wear them these first couple days. I go to the bathroom, then stand in front of the mirror and redo my

---

[10] "The sub" is McDonald's common, where the mail room, bookstore, a few offices, and the cafeteria are located.

[11] Billings Senior High School is one of the three public high schools in Billings; the other two are West and Skyview (Billings Public Schools. n.d.).

21

messy bun into a . . . nicer messy bun. I grab the green lanyard off the counter by the sink, pull on my navy-blue-and-orange Nike Air Presto sneakers (I specifically picked the color scheme to match my new basketball ankle tattoo), and make sure to press in the lock before letting the heavy door close.

I wave and smile at a couple students I pass in the long hallway. I open the west-end door and follow the sidewalk past one giant stone building, then up the curving stone walk leading to the sub. There are a few carpeted stairs just inside the entrance, and then I turn right into the cafeteria. This is where I need my ID card. Act cool. Maybe I should take the lanyard from around my neck this time, so as not to repeat the mishap earlier of pulling my neck forward when trying to unlock my dorm room. I absently exchange pleasantries with the nice lady manning the food card swipe station (that's probably what it is called) while I sweep the room, searching for a familiar or friendly face. My eyes land on a small sea of yellow shirts at a long table on the far side of the dining area.

I keep an eye on the yellow shirts while making my way through the buffet. After filling a thick, indestructible, translucent plastic cup with chocolate milk from the glorious, giant, shiny stainless-steel dispenser, I saunter toward those whose shirts match mine. This place has endless chocolate milk and endless Wilcoxson's ice cream. What more could one want? I have been watching a guy who is sitting a bit away from the others, not engaged in conversation with anyone in particular yet looking perfectly content. He has thick brown hair and some stellar facial hair, a nice goatee and sweet mutton chops. He kinda looks like that guy from *Shallow Hal*.

I stand next to him and greet, "Hi. Mind if I sit here?"

Mouth full and chewing, he politely gestures with an open hand that the seat is mine. I slide in next to him and introduce myself. "I'm Jamie. I'm an education major, too."

He calmly swallows his bite, and his response makes me chuckle. "I'm Peter. They forced me to choose a major."

There is a pause as he looks down and takes a small drink of milk. He looks back up and explains simply, "I liked this shirt color best."

"Nice," I reply, and laugh.

We continue with small talk while I work through the food on my tray. I find out this guy is from Waukesha, Wisconsin. Both his parents are pastors, and he is the middle child of an older sister and younger brother. He explains that Rocky was the only campus on his list he did not visit, so he picked it. I find myself giggling with everything he says. I fill him in on the basics of Chester, my path here, via basketball, and that my extended family lives close. He tells me earlier today he found Rocky in the phone book and randomly made a call from a payphone at the airport, somehow reaching Dean of Student Life, Brad Nason.[12] He had no ride here, very little money, and the soccer coach, Coach Richard Duffy, was sent to pick him up and drive him over to the dorms. I keep laughing.

Get to college, check. Make new friends, check.

* * *

My first weekend here has been pretty good. Friday morning I had to meet with my advisor, Dr. DeSilva, to go through my schedule. I hope I can handle all these classes. Psychology starts at a quarter to eight Mondays, Wednesdays, and Fridays; that sounds extremely early. Maci and I had a few meals with my parents, and we played basketball a couple different times. Kat's parents were here, too, and they are so sweet.[13]

Sunday morning I ate breakfast with Mom, Dad, Uncle Gary, and Aunt Linda. Dad, Mom, and I then went to Smith's and bought some food for our dorm room; we stocked up on Easy Mac and Top Ramen. My parents filled the Taurus up with gas at the station on Poly and Seventeenth. They hugged me goodbye and both cried. The only reason I cried a little was because they were so sad, and I felt bad they were crying. I did not really feel sad at all. I hope that is a good sign.

So that was it. Now I am on my own.

---

[12] Brad Nason, Dean of Student Life at Rocky, is an RMC alumnus, graduating with a degree in Sociology/Anthropology in 1983. Following graduate school, he worked at Yakima Valley College in Washington, returning to RMC in 1987. He has been associated with RMC for more than 38 years (Rocky, n.d.).

[13] Galen and Zana Bitz, Kat's parents, truly were such kind and loving souls. Whenever they visited us in Billings they would take us to lovely dinners, and Zana sent us notes and cards for every special occasion. Galen died in 2016, and Zana died in 2021.

Chapter 3

September 2002, settling in, Billings, Montana

The last couple weeks have flown by. So many new people, professors, classmates, teammates—whew! Classes are okay so far. After receiving my sixth syllabus I was feeling overwhelmed, but I finally feel like I am starting to get my classes figured out. I have foundations of education, first year writing, beginning stage acting, algebra, psychology, and freshmen seminar.

Maci and I have been lifting and working out every day. We took Kat with us to lift one day, and I am pretty sure she was really sore the next day. There are a lot of other awesome freshmen on our team. We have been playing together a lot. Our assistant coach, JD Gustin, has had us do some ballhandling and such a few times early in the morning. I do not love the early morning. Often I am the only one who shows up, so the other day he and I played full court one-on-one. It was as insane as it sounds. We were both sucking air.[14]

The other day, instead of practicing we had "team bonding." We did a bunch of teamwork-focused exercises, kind of like things we would do in cabin groups at Bible camp.[15] I felt like I got to know my teammates a lot better, and we have freakin' awesome people. Thank goodness they are not Bs. I know I was so lucky in high school to have amazing teammates. So I have been a little nervous about what that might look like here, not gonna lie.

Maci and I spent Labor Day weekend in Big Timber. It was so fun being with the grandparents and cousins and all, and it was such an easy trip to make. That is why I wanted to come to Rocky, to be closer to my

---

[14] JD Gustin was an assistant coach at Rocky from 2001–2003, and he coached our Rocky JV squad for the 2002-03 season (Utah Tech, 2023). I still shake my head and laugh when recalling playing full court one-on-one with him.

[15] I attended Flathead Lutheran Bible Camp (https://flbc.net/) near Kalispell in Lakeside, Montana most summers.

family! We have also been hanging out with a lot of people from the Hi-Line, like Kevin Jurenka, Jeri Matter, Roger Larson, Ericka Diede, and Brent Petrick, to name a few. The other night we were all sitting around in Brent and Kevin's room. I pointed my finger and swept my arm around the room at everyone and emphatically announced, "I used to hate all of you in high school, but now we are best friends!"

Roger, Kat, and Megan

We have had dinner with my aunts and uncles a couple times, too. I love getting to see all these family members. Gary and Linda[16] made us some yummy spaghetti, and we had those delicious little wafer cookies for dessert, Branae-style, and even some decaf coffee.[17] I am so grown up

---

[16] Gary is my mom's brother. He and my aunt Linda lived in Billings for forty-one years. Linda taught elementary in the Billings school district for nineteen years, after teaching seven years in Washington State. Gary taught for thirty-three years, three in Red Lodge, three in Washington, and twenty-seven at Billings Senior—as a math teacher then a counselor—and retired from teaching in 1999. Then Gary worked as a youth director at American Lutheran Church where first a college roommate of Jeremy's, Travis Dregne, worked part time, and then Jeremy took over the position. Now Gary and Linda live in Vancouver, Washington and are full-time grandparents!

[17] My mom's family, the Branaes, love to serve dessert after every meal.

now. Mel and George[18] had us over for pizza, which we scarfed, and my cousins Jarred and Clint were there, too.

Last weekend Jenny[19] and I tried to drive to Helena to watch the Rocky football game at Carroll, but my poor Taurus stopped working like twenty miles out of Townsend. Perhaps it was vapor locked or something? A lot of car problem jargon was flying around. Aunt Kathy and Uncle Jimmy saved the day with Triple A—I should write commercials for them—and took me to Bozeman. Then Skye Coughlan[20] picked up Jenny so she could get to Helena and see Jeffrey. The silver lining was that I got to spend the weekend in Bozeman. It was a bummer to miss the game, kind of, but apparently we got the snot kicked out of us. Heidi and Matt walked me around the MSU campus—giant compared to Rocky.[21] I waved and said hi to everyone I saw. Heidi and Matt sort of giggled sheepishly and were like, "What are you doing? We don't know any of these people!"[22]

Mom has already sent me a couple letters, which I love. It is kind of crazy how nice it feels picking up mail at the sub. It just feels really good to know someone has been thinking about you. On the outside of her last letter she wrote a reminder on the envelope: *Make sure you write a thank you for that French's scholarship.*

---

[18] Melanie Anglin is my dad's cousin, and she—"Aunt Mel"—and "Uncle George" have lived in Billings for thirty-eight years. George worked for oil refineries for forty-two years, when he had to settle down after rodeoing professionally. Mel worked in banking and accounting for thirty-four years. They are now also full-time grandparents!

[19] Jenny Balgua played her freshman year at Northern and transferred to Rocky after that. She and my brother Jeff dated for over two years. Jenny was a stud athlete—faster than everyone—and is such a kind, genuine, fun person. She married Tyler Holly, another Rocky football player!

[20] Skye dated and eventually married Zach Bumgarner. Zach played football at Carroll and was Jeff's roommate in Helena. Jeff and Zach played against each other in high school—Zach and Skye were both from Belt—and were in each other's weddings.

[21] Montana State University, home of the Bobcats, is one of two universities in Montana. The University of Montana—UofM—in Missoula is the other and is the home of the Grizzlies. In Montana, most people consider themselves either Cat fans or Griz fans. Sixteen universities and colleges make up the Montana University System, collectively enrolling over forty thousand students (Montana University System, n.d.).

[22] Rocky Mountain College had just under one thousand students when I attended. It didn't take long to feel like one knew most everyone while walking across campus, if not by name at least by face.

September 10, 2002

Dear Jamie,

Hi! Just got your letter today—it made me cry! We are so proud of you! We know you will do well out in the world because you have so many talents and are such a wonderful person.

Enclosed are a few things I thought you might be interested in. The letter from Cell One explains your new plan which starts 9-23. The $10 from Vanity expires on 10-27. They must have one of those stores in Billings. I need to write to Robin.

At school tonight they had sort of a "bring your parents to school day." School let out at 1:00 pm, and then the parents came to their kids' classes. Dad said it was pretty fun and a fairly good crowd. I think he said it was sort of his idea.

Richie organized a songfest for tomorrow evening at 8:00 in honor of the 9-11 anniversary. So some of us have been practicing the last couple nights. We'll do patriotic songs. Miss Goodheart brought a version of "Dona Nobis" (you would recognize it) that is very simple and really cool. Is the college doing anything?

It finally warmed up around here. Last week we had close to an inch of rain, which is good, but harvest is really getting messed up.

I ordered flowers for Amanda for her birthday in one of those magnet vases like you got from the Clarks on your birthday.

Lots of people ask how you are doing. Everyone asks me how I like the "empty nest." I was going to change the message on our answering machine to say, "You have reached the empty nest of Jim and Karen Graham," but I didn't. The evenings are what are the worst cuz they seem so long! I think what I miss most about you being gone is not hearing you come in after practice and yell, "I'm home!" and not being able to kiss you and tell you goodnight. It is an adjustment.

I dusted and vacuumed your room last week. I boxed up some of those books—Berenstain Bears, Babysitters Club, etc. I also hung up the wall hanging Mary made you, and the KSEN player of the week plaque.

The football team plays in Hays on Saturday. I am not going. That night J-I is here for varsity volleyball. I really don't know if I can handle watching that, especially if they would even beat us in one game, that would be awful! I know Dad won't go to that one.

Well, hopefully you'll get to come home for Homecoming. If you don't, I'll mail you a package—your bra and other stuff that has accumulated, and maybe some goodies! We haven't heard anything from the Ullmans about the car yet.

Give us a call sometime this weekend. We love you very, very much and miss you terribly!

Love,
Mom and Dad

* * *

I have gone to a couple parties at houses off campus. Can we say overrated? Last weekend Maci and I went to this party that this guy—who is apparently my cousin, turns out—invited us to.[23]

---

[23] Leif Stephens graduated from Sweet Grass High School in Big Timber, Montana, attended Rocky his freshman year, then transferred to Montana State University. He was visiting Rocky that weekend. His grandfather and my grandmother were second cousins, making him and me fourth cousins!

Leif introduced us to a lot of people, including one of his best friends from last year that he refers to as "Kicker," and uses a French accent whenever he says it. I cannot remember Kicker's real name right now, but he seemed really nice. I think he thought Maci was cute. Probably a player.

I went to the backyard during the party because my brother called. I love having a cell phone. You can just walk around backyards, talking on the phone. Wild. Then that party got broken up. People were running all over the place. I somehow scaled this ridiculously tall wooden fence American Gladiator style and ended up walking with Helvik and this Matt kid. [24] They helped me find Kat, as her brother and cousins were driving around looking for me. [25] Sounds like another group ended up bailing someone out of jail or something? Something about littering? I do not know if that was really the reason, or if someone was just quoting *Super Troopers.* I think the guy they bailed out is the one on the football team that looks like John Belushi. Oh, football players. Oh, college.

Kelley Edwards from Denton is on my team, and she is the funniest person I have ever met. The other day we were in this room near my math class looking at this giant framed picture of the Rocky football players. Kelley pointed at two players, out of like eighty some, and told me they were the only two I would ever be allowed to date. She said the quarterback currently has a girlfriend, so that left just one. [26] It was the kicker Leif introduced me to the other night. She reminded me that his name is Jeremy. He looks like Jim Carrey, sits by this other football player, Mike, in my psychology class—he seems like he might be Mike's goofy sidekick—wears an Arizona Diamondbacks baseball cap, and always smiles and says "Hi, Jamie!" when I pass him to and from class. After hanging out with Doug [27] for a couple weeks, I am thinking it might not be the best idea to date any football player. Ever.

---

[24] Matt Hagedorn, from Broadus, and Justin Helvik, from Wibaux, were football players at Rocky, each a year older than me.

[25] Henry and Matt Bitz.

[26] Adam Sanchez was the quarterback at that time, and was dating Kayla Neubauer.

[27] Doug Evenhus graduated from Centerville with my teammate Jessica Workman. We went to the lake and hung out a few times the first couple weeks of college.

Chapter 4

September 14, 2002, Kat's nineteenth birthday, Billings, Montana

"**H**appy birthday dear Ka-at! Happy birthday to you!" I finish my lovely solo serenade. Kat blows out the single candle on the brownie delight the nice waitress here at Mackenzie River Pizza presented to her.[28]

"Thanks, Jame," Kat says, smiling at me before taking a large bite.

We already devoured almost all of our large Rancher pizza and an order of cheesy, garlicky lodgepoles. I always thought I could eat a lot. And then I met Kat. Just another reason we are roommate-soulmates. We share the delicious giant brownie delight. Mmm, brownie delight (Homer Simpson). Then I take care of the check. How classy of me. We grab our coats and scooch out of our romantic booth. As we weave our way toward the door, the waitress hurries up behind us with our Styrofoam container of leftovers. Whew! Thank goodness she remembered. We are going to be needing those leftovers in a few hours.

As we drive home, we start and restart the song we are currently working on memorizing. I listen to the intro and begin, in a singsong talking voice, "Is she really going out with him?"

Kat replies, in her best Brooklyn accent, "Well theh she is, let's aska."

"Betty, is that Jimmy's ring you're wearing?" I demandingly query, shooting a sharp look at my driver.

Kat nods and gives a sideways glance. "Mm-hmm."

"Gee, it must be great riding with him. Is he picking you up after school today?"

"Uh-uh."

"By the way, where'd you meet him?"

---

[28] Mackenzie River Pizza is a delicious gourmet pizza chain that began over twenty-five years ago in Bozeman, Montana (Mackenzie River Pizza, 2020).

She belts out, "I met him at the candy store!"

She continues, and I smile and giggle while waiting for my next line.[29]

Kat and me in our freshman dorm room

* * *

"Here you go, Kev. I'm gonna take a walk." I hand Kevin a half-full bottle of strawberry Boone's Farm, and Deana Carter's song immediately starts running through my head. I wave goodbye to Maci, Alex, Megan, Roger, and Brent. As I lazily amble toward the door, I hear Kevin and Maci adamantly insisting—again—that Megan *must* try a Rocky Mountain hot dog. "Yes, they are red!" Maci says. Her raised voice carries out of the room as I smile while opening the door. I proceed to enter the deserted dorm hall.

---

[29] When we drove together I made Kat memorize and sing "Leader of the Pack" and other similar, awesome songs from various burnt CDs, and Kat had me memorize and sing songs by bands like Weezer. We had so much fun together!

Julio stopped by a few minutes ago to take Kat outside for some fresh air. I figure I better go check on her. I grab the handrail and make my way carefully down the one flight of stairs in this building. As I carelessly meander down the long, quiet hallway I glance from one door to another, wondering who might be awake. I nearly reach the exit when a soccer ball rolls rapidly out of room number 123. I reach down to pick it up as, simultaneously, two long tan arms reach out from the open dorm door. I grab the ball first, then look up to see who is attached to those arms. A gap-toothed smile greets me, below kind green-brown eyes and a worn Arizona Diamondbacks baseball cap covering wispy brown hair. "Hello, Jamie."

"Hi, Jeremy." I promptly respond to what has become a familiar exchange on campus.

I spin the ball confidently in my hand and nonchalantly reveal, "I used to play volleyball in high school."

Momentarily taken aback, he pauses, then politely responds, "Uh, that's a soccer ball."

I raise my left eyebrow and look directly at him. "I know."

"Okay . . ." He doesn't seem quite sure what to say next.

I have to admit, he looks pretty darn cute standing there like that, a bit conflicted as to how to best respond to me. I help him out. "So where are you from, Kicker Jeremy?"

"I grew up in Sheridan, Wyoming," he shares.

"And you love football?" I offer.

"Uh, no. I love soccer," he corrects.

"I didn't start playing football until my junior year, when they needed a kicker."

"Ah, like *Necessary Roughness*," I state, "but you're not a girl."[30]

"Um . . ." He is rendered speechless yet again, which makes me smile.

We both turn our heads toward the end of the hallway when we hear the door slam. I grin widely and wrap my right arm around the entrant. "Hello, Shye!"

---

[30] *Necessary Roughness*, starring Scott Bakula, Sinbad, and Kathy Ireland, is a 1991 football movie that my brother and I used to watch frequently (IMDb, 2020).

My new teammate smiles politely and returns my hello. I have gotten to share some late-night meals with Shye, and our other new freshman teammates, at the sub after our pick-up games. Whenever I am with her I laugh a lot. I continue with a sidearm hug and guide her so that we both face Jeremy. "Jeremy Duprey, Rocky Mountain College kicker from Sheridan, Wyoming, this is Shyenicoleboggs, state champion and MVP of the Montana Class B 2001 state basketball tournament."[31]

Shye and Jeremy chuckle and nod politely at one another, and then both turn their attention to me. We find out Shye is heading back to her room after hanging out at her older sister's house,[32] and that she is ready for bed. Jeremy and I enthusiastically wave goodbye as Shye continues down the hallway.

I turn back to the cute skinny kicker and set the soccer ball to him, volleyball style. He quickly knots his fingers and inelegantly bumps it back; clearly he is a foot-sport guy. We continue back and forth like this for a while. I inquire, "So what do you guys do the night before a big game?"

Jeremy shrugs, cocks his head slightly to the side, sets the ball back to me, and answers. "Nothing special. Hang out, watch movies. I was just watching a movie in there." He motions toward room 123.

I peek in the entrance of the open door.

He follows my gaze, catches my eye, and invites, "You wanna watch with me?"

I snatch the ball, abruptly putting an end to our game, hold it out on my left hip and narrow my eyes slightly. I attempt to size up this nineteen-year-old college football player standing in front of me. He looks back innocently enough.

"Are you a player?" I ask pointedly.

"Well I told you I am a football player."

"You know what I mean." I insist a bit forcefully, "Are you a *player?*"

---

[31] This is how Shye referred to herself one time when we first met, and this continues to be my preferred way of addressing her.

[32] Shye's sister Misti lives in Billings, and we visited there frequently our freshmen year, sometimes for events like Mary Kay parties, sometimes just to hang out.

"Oh," he looks slightly taken aback. He recovers quickly. "No."

At first I assumed he was being sarcastic, but his eyes look so sincere. "Are you?" I lean in and continue to narrow my eyes, studying him.

The corners of his mouth turn up slightly, but he rearranges them quickly to respond looking as serious as possible. "No," he insists and leans in right back, staring me straight in the eyes. "I promise."

I consider his response. An image of Brent flashes through my brain. I bite the inside of my lip. Brent and I talked a lot about me going to college, meeting new people, what that might look like. This is all part of the experience, right? Part of the test? I was adamant that I enter college single. Well here I am, entered into college. Single. Meeting new people. Finally I break eye contact, look again toward the open door, shrug, and say "Sure," as casually as possible.

I follow this football-kicking soccer player down the entrance hall leading to the common area of the quad dorm room. It is just like Maci's room except mirrored. There are two bedrooms—one right after the other, tucked in just after entering—that each hold a set of bunk beds. There is a nice bathroom, like ours (but of course dirtier than ours—even though someone cleans their bathroom weekly as well—because boys are gross), as well as a common room that consists of a counter with a sink, microwave, and mini fridge. This room has a square table in the center, as well as a couch and a couple leather recliners that look like they were salvaged from a yard sale, or from someone's grandmother's basement. One recliner is unoccupied. Jeremy sits down and scoots over to the right. He raises his eyebrows and politely gestures to his left. I hook my right leg over the squishy armrest, resulting in one butt cheek pressed up against his, and the other angled upward on the padding.

I make a point to focus my attention on the movie. A burly man punches another burly man in the face; my eyes roll, and I feel my interest wane before it is even piqued. I turn cautiously to Jeremy, careful not to lean in too close. He turns to meet my eyes. I squint slightly and ask again, "Are you sure you're not a player?"

He smiles and chuckles a bit. "I am sure I am not a player," he states clearly.

I continue to search his eyes. They look pretty genuine. Or is he just really practiced at appearing genuine? Is that something college guys figure out how to do during their freshman year? Is there some secret class? I am a very trusting person, sometimes to a fault. I turn my attention back to the television. The camera zooms in on a bloody lip. Oh, for the love. Between the Boone's Farm and sharing this tight intimate space with this not-exactly-but-pretty-much-a-stranger-albeit-adorable sophomore football player, I find myself having difficulty staying focused. I turn back to Jeremy. He looks at me with slightly raised eyebrows. What is that look on his face? What is he thinking?

Suddenly I feel his lips on mine.

Whoa! How did this happen? Did he lean in first? Did I? Hmm, well while I am here, let's see. Soft lips. Gentle, not aggressive. Smells good, like sour cream and onion Pringles and possibly a faint mint and pine tree mixture. Seems sure of himself, but not like too sure. We separate after a few seconds, and I look forward again. I am extremely aware of the fact that I just kissed someone who is not Brent. I sneak a sideways glance and quickly look forward again.

Definitely not Brent.

"It's getting late." I use a line I have heard in several rom-coms that feels appropriate for this particular situation.

Jeremy kindly responds, "Let me walk you back to your room."

Well listen to us, all mature-movie sounding.

I roll sideways out of the chair, trying to land with good balance, so as not to look the fool in front of all these jocks. I wave sort of Forrest Gumpy at them, and only the John Belushi doppelgänger humors me with a two-fingered wave. Jeremy is standing just behind me, so I start walking toward the door. By the time we reach the hallway, his long fingers have danced gently into mine. Not a player, huh? But feeling his hand wrapped sweetly over mine sends up a slight pleasant spine shiver. I cannot help but smile.

We make our way down to Julio's room and announce to Kat it is time to go to bed. She grins happily at us, tells Julio goodnight, and wraps her long arm around my neck. "Hey, Jame," she greets as she rests her head on my shoulder.

"Hey, babe," I respond as I wrap my arm around her waist, supporting her tall frame. "Time for beddy-bye, birthday girl."

Kat continues to smile blissfully as Jeremy and I escort her back to our room. When we reach number 130 I peek in both beds, just in case. Peter takes frequent naps in our room these days, due to the fact that his room smells terrible because of his stinky yet unfortunately unaware roommate. Jeremy makes sure we are settled inside and asks if we need anything. I point to the mini fridge and explain the Mackenzie River leftovers we have waiting for us. "We're all set," I assure him.

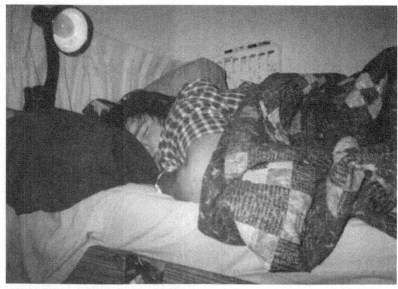

Peter napping in my bunk

"Okay," he says as he backs out the doorway, smiling. "Goodnight then."

I lock eyes and feel a tummy flip. My hand clumsily flicks the handle, eyes continue to study his with curiosity, and almost as an afterthought I respond, "Goodnight," just as the door slowly clicks closed.

Chapter 5

September 15, 2002, first home football game, Billings, Montana

Eyes still closed, I roll from my left side to my right and hear Kat rustle out of the bottom bunk. I struggle to open my eyes and focus them on the numbers shining bright on our alarm clock. It is too blurry, so I fumble around on the desk until my fingers find my glasses. When I get them over my nose I see it is already eleven o'clock. I lie back on my pillow and think through my day. Saturday, Saturday . . . Oh yeah, home football game! Northern is coming to town.[33] Chasi Lee is also coming to town! In fact, I better check my phone. It is going to be a great day. I can tell.

* * *

Chasi made it up from Sheridan right around twelve thirty, with her Swedish roommate Anna and a teammate named Kayla. Maci, Kat, and I met up with them and walked across campus to Herb Klindt Field. Now we stand in the aluminum stands in the blazing sun, listening to the band playing, "Buh, na na na na na!" and people shouting "Go, Rocky!" just before the one o'clock kickoff.

Speaking of kickoff. My eyes scan the field. They land on the green jersey sitting atop shiny tight green pants holding the tiny little tushy of number 34. After placing the ball on its tee, he takes two steps back then two steps sideways and holds out his left hand, possibly signaling to the referee that he is ready? Or perhaps that is how he finds his balance before a kick. Either way, it looks like he has quite a specific routine. Like getting ready to shoot a free throw.

---

[33] Northern Montana College is in Havre, Montana, up on Highway 2 (Montana State University-Northern. n.d.).

Jeremy kicking. Jeremy switched to jersey number 7 his senior year.

The whistle blows, and there he goes. One, two, three, kick! Head down, his long right leg extends as the ball ascends end-over-end high into the air. The kick is accompanied by a loud bang on the bass drum and one more messy blurt from the tuba. Before I can see the ball land my eyes settle back on the kicker. The kicker who played volleyball with me with a soccer ball in the hallway last night. The kicker who helped make sure my roommate and I made it home safely. The kicker who sweetly held my hand and swore he is not a player. A tiny tingle shoots through my body. Hmm, that feeling again. *What does it all mean, Basil?*[34] I wonder at the situation as a Rocky gunner sprints down the field and tackles the Northern kick receiver at the twenty. I shake my head before my thoughts threaten to get too deep and join the throng's excited cheers.

---

[34] IMDb. *Austin Powers: The Spy Who Shagged Me.* 2023.

Faithful fans

* * *

Just as I originally predicted, today has been a great day, for the most part. Aside from it being ninety degrees outside, causing me to sweat profusely, the game went well and we thank goodness beat Northern 45-6. We chilled around my dorm room for a while, and then Kat went with her parents somewhere. Later Maci, Chasi, and I got a ride to the mall with Kevin. Kevin and I slept on chairs in stores while those two shopped, like old men waiting for their wives. We met Chasi's friends at Olive Garden for dinner, and it took an hour and a half for us to finally get seated. Welcome to the big city! Of course it was worth it. I had chicken Alfredo and tons of breadsticks. I even had a little salad, so good for me. We got out of there around ten o'clock and came back here to the dorms.

Right now I am so tired I don't feel like doing anything cool. Pathetic. Plus, practically everyone is in flipping Hysham—seventy-five freaking miles away—for some party there.[35] Earlier we hung out in Maci's room, and Chas and I had a heart-to-heart.

---

[35] Hysham is a small agricultural community located on the Yellowstone River east of Billings. (Hysham, Montana, Chamber of Commerce, 2013). A couple Rocky football

Kevin, Maci, and Chasi

She is really not liking school or basketball right now and is really homesick. I feel so bad for her. So she went into my room to call Mike. Heidi Lynn called me a little after midnight, and she is doing kind of okay. Glad I am not in premed, but I am proud of her. Things seem to be going okay with Matt but could be better. I did not get the impression that she does anything besides study, go to class, and hang out with Matt. At one point she was telling me about a really hard science class she had. I had to bite my lip really hard so I didn't insensitively insert, "Chlorophyll? More like Borophyll!"[36]

Earlier today when Chasi and I were hanging out in my room after the football game, there was a knock on the door. I looked through the peephole. It was Jeremy. When I opened it up he asked me if he could have my cell number. Ballsy I tell ya. When he was leaving I told Chasi how much I like the name Jeremy. Little did I know he was walking right in front of our open window at that point, and Chas and I rolled onto the bed and busted up giggling. I told him we would just be hanging out in Maci's room tonight. Which is where I am now.

---

players were from Hysham, and in Montana seventy-five miles is not considered a long distance to drive on any given day.

[36] Fiduccia. *Billy Madison.* 2021.

40

I flush, wash my hands, and my mind scrolls through some images from today's football game. At one point, Jeremy was kneeling on his left leg on the sidelines, holding his gold helmet with his right arm. I swear he turned around to look for me. Perhaps he could feel my eyes boring a hole into the back of his head. He did call me from his friend Logan's (the one who reminds me of John Belushi) phone tonight around nine—while we were at Olive Garden—and asked what I was up to. But he was all the way in Hysham.

As if on cue, a light knock on the door interrupts my thoughts. It is after midnight. I peek through the peephole and experience some déjà vu. I take in a big breath, exhale, and open the door. "Hello, Jeremy."

The kicker who looks so cute in that shiny green Bears uniform looks at me, tilts his head slightly, and smiles. "Hello, Jamie."

"Uh, would you like to come in?" I invite.

"We're watching *Dirty Dancing*," I continue.

By the look on his face, I am guessing he has never seen this classic movie. I suppose that is okay. I think I can get past that. He follows me down the hallway to the living room area. Chas is lying on the black futon couch with her head on Maci's lap, and Mace is absentmindedly playing with Chasi's beautiful thick blonde hair. This causes a quick flashback to high school and makes me smile. Megan and Alex occupy the two other chairs in the room, so Jeremy and I sit down on the carpet just where the hall ends. I introduce my gentleman guest to my teammates. They all nod politely, but everyone looks pretty caught up in Jennifer Grey struggling to keep a straight face as Patrick Swayze runs his tantalizingly tickly fingers down her arm.[37]

Jeremy and I sit down and pull up our knees, arms draped loosely over our legs. Like last night, I notice how nice it is to feel his arm pressed up all tight next to mine. I try to whisper and fill him in on what has happened so far but finally sigh, because he really just needs to watch the best movie ever from the beginning. As if reading my mind, Mace looks our way and casually offers, "That first bunk's open."

---

[37] *Dirty Dancing* (1987), a drama, romance movie starring Patrick Swayze and Jennifer Grey (IMDb, 2023).

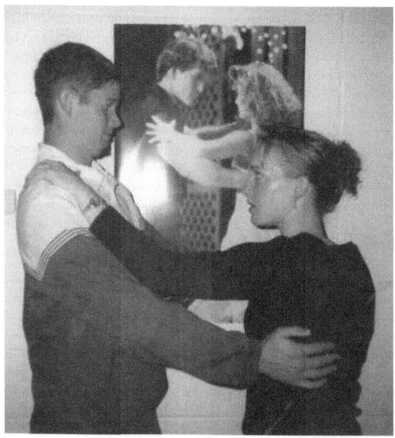

I made Jeremy watch Dirty Dancing.

I look to my right and see my thoughts mirrored in those big brown eyes. Wordlessly I lead Jeremy to the bunk cubby closest to the living room. I stop and consider the situation for a second, taking note of the streaming thoughts. Should we sit on the side of this bottom bunk? Well no, that would be awkward. We would be all crunched over or else hit our heads on the top bunk. It seems a little weird to lay on a bed with this guy I barely know, right? But there isn't a couch option. And the floor is too uncomfortable.

Well I guess that settles it. The bed is our best option.

I look toward the bed then look at Jeremy. Does he look nervous? Over eager? Uncomfortable? Comfortable? Too comfortable? Ah! So many thoughts. Shhh. Quiet down, brain.

I duck down and crawl on top of the covers toward the wall. As he crawls in it is suddenly blatantly apparent I am in a position where it would be difficult to make any sort of smooth or quick exit. Hopefully I will not need to do that. I think briefly about Richie's letter.

What is wrong with me?

Again our shoulders press together as we wiggle a bit and attempt to get comfortable in these tight quarters, now both lying on our backs. My eyes flit above me, flurrying from one wooden slat to another, in time with my thoughts. I become acutely aware of the rise and fall of the chest next to mine and wonder what he is thinking.

"What are you thinking?" Best to just get right to it.

He lets out a deep exhale, shrugs, and gives a quick giggle. "Lots of things."

"Me, too," I answer, wondering if our definitions for "lots" match. Because I am pretty sure I think more simultaneous thoughts than the average person. "So tell me more about yourself. I know you're from Sheridan, Wyoming, you're a sophomore, a football kicker who really loves soccer, in my psychology class . . . and that's it, so far."

"We-ell," he starts, with a little singsong scoop in the middle of the word, "I am also here on a partial choir scholarship."

Ah. That explains the singsong scoop.

"My dad is an Episcopal priest in Sheridan, and my mom lives in Cody and works for Senator Al Simpson."

His parents aren't together? I wonder what happened. None of my friends' parents are divorced, that I can think of. Well, that is not true. I guess Emily's, but that is just the way it has always been since I've known her. She would go to her dad's in Minnesota for part of the summer. We always sent letters back and forth, but we never wrote about our boring parents. Maybe I should have asked her more details about that situation. It just never occurred to me. I wonder how long it has been since Jeremy's parents split up. I wonder how he gets along with his parents.

"I have two younger sisters," he continues, snapping my forever-rabbit-hole-exploring attention back.

I work hard to focus on what he is saying and to not allow my automatic pop-up follow-up questions prevent me from hearing story details. He continues. "Alycia and Naomi. Alycia is a senior at Sheridan High School this year, and Naomi is in eighth grade. They are both very musical and very beautiful."

Well listen to this guy, I think, wondering how my brother describes me to new people he meets. I glance over sideways at him. His eyes are studying the slats, too, searching for more details to share.

"We have a cat named Issachar."

"Issachar?" I repeat.

"Yes," he confirms, tilting his head and smiling as he meets my gaze. "Issachar, named after the Bible character in Genesis. You know, like the tribe of Issachar?"

He poses this a bit rhetorically.

I bring my fingertips together to rest under my chin. Then I squint slightly, as if contemplating deep thoughts. "Ah yes, the tribe of Issachar," I answer fairly convincingly with a slight nod, trying to sound wise and reflective.

So this guy describes his sisters as "beautiful" and knows details about Issachar in the book of Genesis. Okay, he has my attention. Time for me to share again. How do I match that?

"We have a cat named *Sylvester*," I divulge dramatically.

He turns his head toward me, a look of amusement playing at his lips.

I continue with raised, expectant eyebrows. "You know?"

His eyes search mine, but nothing comes out of his mouth.

I go on to explain matter-of-factly, like he did when sharing about his cat. "Like the character from *Looney Tunes*?"

Nice, Jamie. Did you just compare the first book of the Bible to Saturday morning cartoons? See if he can resist that.

He lets out a laugh. "That's a good name."

He continues looking intently into my eyes. "Do you have any other pets?"

"Nope," I reply.

"I find it unlikely that my parents will ever have pets again. The only reason we had Sylvester is because my brother and I basically brought him home one day and begged if we could keep him. My parents keep our house extremely clean. Animal hair is not their favorite."[38]

Jeremy's close-lipped smile turns into an open-mouthed grin. "I see," he says, and he seems interested and amused.

"So you have a brother. Do you have other siblings?"

"Nope, just Jeffrey. He is two years older than me, but just one year in school. He plays basketball at Carroll. He played at Northern last year, but a lot of crazy stuff went down, so basically everyone transferred. He is redshirting this year. He is dating Jenny, a point guard on our basketball team."

I think for a second and add, "Jeff was the kicker in high school."

"Nice," Jeremy responds.

He really does seem genuinely interested in everything I am saying and seems to want to know more. I consider this observation and realize I really want to know more about him, too.

We are both quiet for a beat. Then we lean in together for a kiss. I think I could get used to this.

Next he asks me about my relationship with Jesus. Well either this guy is the player of all players, or legit the sweetest guy I have ever met. I talk about my church in Chester growing up, our youth group and mission trips, Pastor Pete and his wife Tonja, leading music with my friends during church services, Christmas pageants led by Cindy and Yvonne, belting out the national anthem with Michele on the church podium microphone and not realizing everyone downstairs at the potluck could hear us—and it was made very clear that some old ladies were very disapproving of our antics—and on and on.

He shares about his dad's church in Sheridan, exploring every nook and cranny of it, especially the basement, some crazy shenanigans with him and his friends Noah, Leif, Paul, Ryan, Dean, Ann. A story about this Leif fellow jumping off the balcony and managing to somehow not land on a pew and break his back. It is fun to hear him share about these friends of his. He talks about his youth pastor, Jake, and several crazy stories about their youth group van "The Blue Flame," music

---

[38] The VanDykes often had litters of kittens when we were growing up. It took us years to convince our parents to finally let us have one.

concerts and festivals, breaking an elevator in Las Vegas and getting lots of free stuff, or something, and on and on.

We continue to share stories back and forth. We begin to share even further back and go as far as birthplace and childhood stories. I find out he was born in Columbus, Ohio and is obsessed with the Ohio State University Buckeyes. And that his favorite Christmas present is a canister of cheese from Washington State University that his dad orders for him. He tells me about girlfriends in junior high and high school—Jessie, Hannah, Molly—and a couple girls he dated last year. Pretty casually, according to him. I share my "list" as well, but hesitate a second before mentioning Brent. He catches my hesitation and asks for more details. Does he really want to know all the details? He looks at me intently, completely alert. Locked in.

"Oka-ay," I begin, singsong scooping the syllables myself this time. I raise both eyebrows. "Do you have all night?"

"Why yes I do," he replies sincerely.

Chapter 6

September 18, 2002, preseason practice, first date, Billings, Montana

I hustle after my wayward ball gone astray after hitting the front iron. Rae Dawn, a junior teammate, stops my ball and tosses it over to me. She squares up, puts up a form shot and with a sly smile casually comments, "So we hear a freshman basketball player is dating Kicker."[39]

Kelley, who is also sharing our hoop to warm up, grins widely. "I told you I approve of him! Kicker is sooo sweet!"

"He is sooo nice," Rae Dawn agrees enthusiastically.

I shrug and smile as I continue putting up shots, considering their reactions. So two of my teammates that I look up to and respect most approve of Jeremy, do they? Hmm, that seems like a good sign. It is funny that Kelley was so specific about who I would be "allowed" to date, I think, recalling our time studying the football picture. Dating, huh? Did Jeremy say that? He must have. I did not know we were official. I think about this for a second and quickly realize I like it. Kicker's girlfriend. Yes, I think I can get on board with that.

The whistle blows, reminding me where I am. We jog to center court where Coach Hendo counts us off into groups of three. I find my two teammates, and we all flip our jerseys to green. These preseason "practices" are basically pickup games of three-on-three, four-on-four, and every once in a while, five-on-five. Apparently we are not allowed to start official practices until the first week of October. I am hoping those prove to be more intense. So far the atmosphere feels very different than with Coach VanDyke and Coach Schlepp. But it is fun to play, and interesting getting used to new teammates.

* * *

---

[39] Most students at Rocky referred to Jeremy simply as "Kicks" or "Kicker."

I hustle up the incessantly stinky tunnel that leads to the entrance of Fortin Center, tucking my shoes under my left arm while checking my indestructible Nokia. An alert in the corner of the screen shows I have two "urgent" messages. I fumble the phone briefly before managing to punch in the digits that unlock my answering machine feature.

The first one is from Jeff, short and sweet. "Jamie, call your brother."

The second one, also from Jeff, holds a few more details. "I hear you are dating the kicker."

Jeez, news travels fast. My brother knew before I did.

"So that means I am going to have to kill either him or you. The next time Rocky plays Carroll, I'm gonna have three of our football players run after him on the kickoff and break his legs. He can only date you if he beats me in a kickoff. Remember, I could have kicked for the Cats. Call me."

I roll my eyes but can't help a smile. I look up to find my bearings. Somehow I am already to the dorms. It's 9:39. Perfect, the movie is at ten.

Last night after practice I visited Jeremy in his room. I met his roommate Aaron and a couple other guys. I found out Aaron works for Pickle Barrel and sometimes brings home free sandwiches. Free Pickle Barrel sandwiches?! Yet another sign this relationship is a good idea. Then Jeremy walked me back to my room and asked if I wanted to go to "The Ghetto."[40] When I said yes of course he responded, all cute, "It will be our first date!"

Now I turn off the shower, shout, "Done!" hastily dry off and wrangle on my clean clothes.

I am even wearing jeans so, yeah, it is kind of a big deal. As I open the bathroom door to our living space, Kat checks the stopwatch on her phone. I check the microwave clock: 9:47.

"A new shower record!" Kat announces proudly.

A few water droplets from my clean hair trickle onto my sweatshirt as I pull it over my head. "Thanks, babe! See you in a couple hours."

---

[40] We referred to the discount theater (Cine 7) on Broadwater Street in Billings as "The Ghetto." I am not sure where it originated, but it was common lingo around campus when I arrived at Rocky.

"Have fun!!" Kat's voice follows me as I rush out the door and make it down my hallway, through the annex, down the lower floor Anderson hallway, and to Jeremy's door by 9:49.

Rocking my wet hair and clean sweatshirt, I attempt to catch my breath. Just always so sexy. Cannot help it. I rap on his door, and it opens almost immediately.

He looks as excited as I feel. "Ready?" I ask.

"Ready!" he echoes enthusiastically.

Our hands connect as if it is something they have done a thousand times. They swing freely as we make our way out to the parking lot. Jeremy leads us to the DK, or "Deer Killer," otherwise known as his 1984 gray Honda Civic. Its front bumper dons several deer dents, and one back light is completely covered by red duct tape, as it sounds like yet another deer took out the actual tail light cover. Classy. Between his uncanny classiness and my natural sexiness, we make quite the pair. Red carpet, here we come.

Jeremy gallantly opens the passenger door for me before taking his place behind the wheel. I watch as he turns on the CD player then easily shifts the clutch into first gear. Then I note a blue "Jars of Clay" case perched precariously on the front console. He seems completely at ease and genuinely excited to be with me. He confidently navigates through the busy Billings traffic. At a red light I am momentarily mesmerized by his rhythm and impressive drumming skills as his fingers follow the song's beat on the steering wheel. I look from his fingers to his face. He somehow does this thing where it appears as if his head is separate from his neck. He is white, but I do not know any other white guys with moves like that. This guy seems to be full of surprises. As we pull into the parking lot of the Cine 7 dollar theater, I feel a flutter of excitement flitter through my body, excited to continue discovering even more and more about him.

* * *

Morgan Freeman and Ben Affleck saved the world from nuclear disaster, thank goodness. The DK pulls into the quiet, dark, east Rocky parking lot just before midnight. As we weave through cars to the Anderson entry, I think about how I really should find Maci to study for our psych test. When we enter the commons area, though, we see Kat sitting at one of the computers. Seeing Kat makes me instantly feel hungry. She looks up from the screen and beams at us. Impulsively I state, "I'm starving." Then I suggest, "We should go to Perkins."

It takes about three seconds for Jeremy and Kat to nod in agreement, and I tell them I need to run to our room to grab my wallet. (I guess one could say I was being presumptuous not bringing my wallet to the theater, making Jeremy pay, but after all it was only two dollars in total.) As soon as I exit the commons area I see Peter in the Widenhouse hallway. "Hi, Peter! Wanna go to Perkins with us?"

Peter calmly considers my invitation, and for a second I wonder if this is what Jeremy pictured when inviting me on our first date. Before I can finish wondering, Peter accepts and says that he, too, needs to procure some purchasing power.

A few minutes later Jeremy and I continue on to the second part of our first date, this time with two friends joining us in the back seat. Hard to explain, but it seems like this unconventionality suits us.[41]

The meal is oh so enjoyable. The waiter keeps bringing us free stuff, because we are so charming I think, and we quote movie lines and laugh and laugh. When the waiter brings us our ticket, I look over at Peter and completely lose it. He pulls a giant white tube sock out of his red backpack and begins digging through the sock. After a few seconds of fumbling, he simply picks up the bottom of the tube sock and empties its contents onto the booth tabletop. Quarters tumble and bounce, colliding with our cups, cutlery, and plates.

Giggling ensues as we watch Peter. Jeremy and Kat can barely see for squinting so hard. Finally Peter looks up, impassive, and explains matter-of-factly, "For laundry."

Best first date ever.

---

[41] I found out later Jeremy was quite surprised when I came back with Peter. Up until that point, he thought Peter was "the smelly kid in choir." I was happy to straighten out that misunderstanding, and I still remind Jeremy and Peter who introduced them.

Jeremy, Kat, Peter, and I shared many meals together after that Perkins date.

Chapter 7

October 2002, Homecoming, Chester, Montana

Maci and I tried to do homework last night, but instead we ended up watching *Moulin Rouge*, doing the *People* magazine crossword puzzle, and packing for Chester. Whenever I go to Maci, Alex, Megan, and Shye's room I swear they are either watching *Moulin Rouge* or listening to that Kid Rock and Sheryl Crow duet. [42] Maybe I go there too much when I should be studying. Lately I just have not been caring about my classes very much. I mean, I do end up getting my homework done, and I do make it to (almost all of) my classes, but I could probably do more. Note to self: start caring.

Shye and me—not studying

Today we rode up here to the beautiful Hi-Line with Jenny and Tammy, and some guy named Bobby who was visiting his cousin at

---

[42] "Picture" was one of Maci and her roommates' favorite songs, as well as most any song by Toby Keith.

Rocky and supposedly wanted a ride as close to Canada as possible. The trip went by pretty quickly as Maci, Bobby, and I slept basically the whole time. I was alert from Fort Benton on. I could not believe how giddy I felt as I watched the many familiar curves in the road, and then essentially no curves at all for almost the last ten miles. I love seeing the Chester skyline and water tower for miles and miles before finally pulling into the "city"—I use this term loosely—limits. The nickname "Big Sky" really hit home as I looked across the acres of fields, sitting fallow for now, under the truly immense blue sky. Why didn't I ever realize before how really incredible the sky is out here?

Now we are dropping Maci off at her house after pulling into town. Memories flood my mind as I watch Mace hurry up the well-worn walk to her front door. How many movies did my friends and I watch together in that house? How many batches of Tang and Kool-Aid dessert did we down? My reminiscing is interrupted by the random guy in the car. Bobby scoots his way out of the back seat and assures us he has a plan from there. He thanks us profusely and starts walking north. We wave. Good luck, hitchhiker Bobby.

Jenny drives down Quincy Street, turns right, and pulls into the gravelly parking lot of the high school football field. She has no luck, swings back around to First Street West and finally tucks into a spot by the Sweet Grass Lodge.[43] We pile out of the white Plymouth Breeze, legs rusty from the tight quarters, and walk toward the inviting Friday night lights of the Chester Coyote gridiron. Jenny and Tammy head toward the visitor bleachers as Jeff signals them over. Don't get me wrong, I am excited to see my brother, but a tall blonde standing near the chain link fence catches my eye near the west end zone, and I walk that way first.

I jump and wrap my legs around my Heidi. Then I force Matt, Diemert, Cory, and Geoff to hug me, too. We chat briefly, and I decide I better make my way toward the home bleachers so I can let Mom know I made it safely. As I walk through the swarm of onlookers lined up against the chain-link fence lining the field's perimeter, it feels a little *Twilight Zoney*. Like everything is the same, but also nothing is the

---

[43] The Sweetgrass Lodge is an independent retirement facility in Chester built in 1979.

same. So weird. I hug a different person with every step I take. I do not see how I can possibly hug and catch up with every person here. What is the protocol for this? I suddenly feel unexpectedly unprepared.

My mind flashes back to last Homecoming: our basketball team dance-battling each other on the trailer at the bonfire, our class working on our Peter Pan float for the parade, dressing up silly for school every day of the week, preparing for the basketball and football games. How can all of that feel like it happened yesterday but somehow also feel like it happened a million years ago?!

* * *

"That wasn't weird at all, am I right?" Matt asks as he drives us east in his green 1996 Ford Taurus on Highway 2.

All of us passengers—Heidi, Cory, Diemert, Geoff and I—agree that it feels pretty weird being back home for the first time. Like we belong, but we do not know exactly where or how we belong anymore. We keep talking about how strange it feels being home as we order our Subway sandwiches then settle in a booth at Mike's IGA. Biting into my delicious Cold Cut Combo with Ranch dressing and extra pickles I think to myself, relieved, *At least this feels the same.*

* * *

"Did he say he'll have a kickoff with me? If he doesn't beat me, he doesn't get to date you."

I do not think my eyes can roll any higher as I listen to my brother go on and on about this supposed impending kickoff, and the fact that he is sure Jeremy is not good enough for me. We are sitting on a couch in the living room at the Mattson farm with several other Chester alumni that made it back for Homecoming. Jeff and I do not have a clear procedure when it comes to how we talk about serious topics. I know he means well, but unfortunately the ups and downs of my love life over the last few years have not exactly set us up for success in this area. Usually our attempts end with him offering an outrageous ultimatum and me sighing, exasperated.

I force myself to really focus on what he is saying. Same old stuff. But then he surprises me by sharing, "I just don't want you to get hurt anymore."

Aw, sibling bonding moment alert.

I look at him squarely. "Thanks, Jeffrey."

I smile. "I really do think you're going to like him."

* * *

Riding in the backseat of the Plymouth, bouncing along contentedly, I study the layers of clouds being propelled swiftly by the inevitable high plains winds and reflect on the weekend. I smile recalling seeing my cute mom, then running out on the field to hug Dad after he and his team made it through the "good game" line. I couldn't believe how excited I was to run to him for a hug. I think about how nice it was to hang out with my classmates, how it felt comfortable and familiar. It was fun hanging out with Isaac, Mitchy and the twins, and watching Savannah and Amanda play volleyball; it still feels strange that they are playing volleyball in the fall.[44] It was so nice spending time with Kaitlynn and Scottie and Brian and all those guys. And it was fun hanging out with Jeffrey. I also ran out to the Clarks' for about an hour this morning, and I stopped by for a chat with Rudy and Gail as well.[45]

Though I loved being in Chester—going to the football game, seeing all those people—I notice how excited I am to head back to Billings. I realize I miss Kat, Peter, my teammates, even though I have only known them a few weeks. And I miss Jeremy. I really miss him. So strange, feeling like I have one foot in one world and the other foot in another.

---

[44] Montana switched the seasons for girls basketball and volleyball that school year, 2002–2003.

[45] Rudy and Gail are Heidi Cicon's parents, and I made sure to stop by and visit them when I could, as Rudy always joked that I was his "real" daughter.

Chapter 8

Fall 2002, basketball season prep, Billings, Montana

I sit in a brown faux leather chair in Coach Henderson's office located in the lower level of the Fortin Center, just past the front desk. Coach Hendo sits behind his large wooden desk and Coach Gustin to his right. They both face me, expectantly. This is not an intimidating arrangement at all.

"How are things going?" Hendo opens.

"Good," I reply, nodding and trying to sound enthusiastic, hoping they can't hear the shakiness in my voice.

"That's good," Hendo continues.

"So the plan right now is to have you be a point guard for the JV.[46] That season finishes just after Thanksgiving, before the varsity season begins. There will be two varsity spots open, and you have a really good chance of filling one of them. That's not a promise, but just keep working hard."

"Okay," I say, continuing to nod.

Obviously I will continue working hard. Does this guy know me at all? I think briefly of Coach VanDyke and Coach Schlepp and feel a slight pang in my stomach.

"A lot of the older girls have said that they really like playing with you," Hendo adds.

That's nice to hear, I think, and smile. Coach Gustin joins in. "We already have a senior and junior point guard, but as far as we're concerned, you are the third one."[47]

---

[46] Some NAIA schools in the Frontier Conference have JV teams with game schedules in the fall, before the varsity regular seasons begin. We played some other JV teams as well as several junior colleges in Wyoming. An athlete could play both JV and varsity as long as the combined number of games did not exceed 50–55 total and occurred in a twenty-four-week period (National, 2021).

[47] Ashley Hammond—now Stuart, as she married Kremlin-Gilford's Jake Stuart—and Jenny Balgua.

They ask if I have any questions.

"Not right now, nope," I say, always so eloquent. "Thank you!" I offer a smile.

I feel excited as I stand up to exit the office and we say our goodbyes. It is nice to have an idea of what the plan moving forward might look like. It is a little odd to think about playing on a JV team, as I was lucky enough to get to start on varsity in high school from the time I was a freshman, but it is very helpful to have a specific goal to shoot for (ha, pun). Now I know where I am, and now I know where I want to go. Varsity, here I come.

Chapter 9

September–October 2002, tricky business, Billings, Montana

September 24, 2002. Man, days go by so flipping slow. We had psychology class this morning, and Jeremy made it and sat by me. He only got three hours of sleep last night after getting home on the bus from Dillon super late. He was exhausted. And they lost. Poor guy.

After class Jeremy went to take a nap, and Kat and I went to Walmart then the mall. I had to work on a group project at the library at ten thirty, and then I took a short nap from eleven thirty to one. Jeremy came in and woke me up. We have so much fun together. It's amazing, and I love it. I sang him some songs from the sweet burnt CD my high school teammates and I used to listen to for our Extreme Dance Parties. I pulled out my rendition of Britney Spears' "Lucky" and like to think he was speechless because my performance was so amazing, probably.[48] This kid is one of a kind, and I do not know why I got so lucky. Then he had to go watch film with his team, and I did homework from three o'clock until almost six.

I went to dinner with Shye. She makes me laugh so much. Then we had our last freshman seminar, thank goodness, and scrimmaged for an hour before partaking in step aerobics with the college fitness instructor. I felt very unathletic doing that. Jeremy left me a Pickle Barrel sandwich in our fridge. What a sweetie. He was so tired tonight, so I only woke him up for a quick sec to give him a goodnight kiss. Then I visited Kevin and Petrick for quite a while, and then Petey and I sat in the hall on a couch talking for a long time. It is past one o'clock in the morning. Why am I up so late? And why did I do no homework tonight?

September 29, 2002. It was a long week, but now it seems like it went by fast. That makes sense. Anyway, Wednesday I went to classes until two then did some homework and took a nap. Turns out naps are

---

[48] "Lucky," by Britney Spears, was a favorite of mine to lip-synch and dance to.

totally respected in college. If you say you can't do something because you are going to nap, people will never make fun of you. When I woke up, Kat and I got all showered and ready for basketball pictures for the media guide. We ate in the sub with Greg, Marshaun, and Tex. People kept asking us if we had a game since we were all dressed up. We passed some football players on the way to the gym and Jeremy was like, "Hello!" and whistled. That kid is so cool. Pictures took for freakin' ever. Practice was cake because by the time we got done scrimmaging it was so late and time to go. A few of us freshmen lifted and abbed.

That night we watched the first movie ever in our room after Tex plugged it in for us.[49] (Turns out we are idiots and weren't plugging in the right cord for the VCR to work.) Jeremy and Carlgoodtoseeyou watched it with us, too, *The Last of the Mohicans*.[50] After that, Jeremy and I had the longest talk. About old relationships and love and everything. He says he easily falls in love and gets attached to people quickly. It was a good talk, and we talked about how it seems like we have been together forever. He asked once what I was thinking, and I said I was wondering how I had gotten so lucky and got him. I asked the same question and he goes, "I was thinking about the stages of love."

Sigh.

Thursday was great because we had no classes! I got to sleep in for once. We scrimmaged for an hour, ate lunch, and then I did a bunch of stuff around the room: laundry, picked up, homework, then took a quick nap. Kat and I watched *Fight Club* in Jeremy and Aaron's room, and I did Kat's hair in cornrows. It is sweet.

Friday I was dragging, but I made it through my classes because it was almost the weekend. I slept through lunch but had to make it to math. Then I shot around, lifted, ran, and biked for two hours. Jenny was also shooting around, and we decided to go to her house for the night. After dinner Kat and I both took naps. Isaac called after eight, so we talked for a long time. Then Kat and I finally got out of our beds, picked up Megan, talked to Shye and her boyfriend, and eventually

---

[49] "Tex" Tanner, was a freshman redshirt that year and hung out with Kat and me a lot the beginning of that year. Guess what state he was from?

[50] When we greeted our friend Carl, it was always followed by, "Good to see you!" in reference to an Adam Sandler movie.

59

made it over to Jenny's. We played cards and did weird things like taped up our noses with Scotch tape, and it was such a fun night. Jeri and Maci came over after a while. We all laughed so flipping much. Curt May, Kristin, and a few other people came over, too, and we went to Perkins. Curt paid for the entire bill, crazy guy! So generous.

Hanging out at Jenny's house; Kat's hair in corn rows

Saturday morning Maci came down at quarter past eight and shut off our alarm that had apparently been going off for twenty minutes. Kat and I did not hear it at all, which is slightly concerning. Uncle Jay picked us up for Joshua's football game around eight thirty. Josh is such a little stud. They won 29–0. I took a long nap after the game, and Heidi Lynn got to town around sixish. Kat, Maci, Jeri, Jenny, Heidi, and I went to Olive Garden. Man do I love that place.[51] When we got back we watched *Dirty Dancing* in Maci's room, for a change.

Now I am going to try to read *My Antonia*, since I am only ninety pages behind on the assigned reading. Get with it, Jamie. Jeremy called at eleven. He has been gone visiting his family all weekend, and he's coming home tomorrow morning. Thank goodness.

October 7, 2002. Last weekend was very fun, but Sunday was really hard. Friday I was tired again, but I managed to make it through my classes. After class got over at two I went to the gym for a couple hours. Then for work-study Jeri and I had to hang up giant advertisement signs

---

[51] Any time people came from out of town to visit us and asked where we wanted to eat, Olive Garden was our go-to.

on the football field. When Terry Corey came out to check on us we found out—when we were almost done—that we were hanging them in all the wrong spots. Oh, for the love. By that time all the football players were on the field, and they just thought it was the funniest thing ever. They laughed and made fun of us, but did anyone offer to help us fix it? Stupid boys. I babysat Hendo's kids from seven to eleven. They are sweeties, but they are a little wild. When I got home I ate pizza with Kat and Tex. Jeremy came over, but he was really quiet. Something was definitely on his mind, but I don't know what. I still don't.

Saturday morning we had practice at eight bells, and it actually felt pretty good. The Ullmans were in town, so after we showered, Kat, Maci, and I met them at Chuck E. Cheese. My first time ever going to Chuck E. Cheese! It was seriously a blast. We ate pizza and breadsticks and played all the games. We got to the football game like ten minutes late, and we were already down 0-14. Adam got in for Benton and did a good job. Poor Jeremy didn't get to kick very much and did not do the best when he did. I waited for him after the game, and then he and his mom and her boyfriend, Greg, took us to eat at Red Lobster. I had chicken. Maybe someday I will like seafood. It was a very fun meal. They all laugh so much, and I love it. I was singing along to a song on the radio in the vehicle and Jer's mom said, "You are very . . . confident."

That was really funny to me.

That night we went to this place called The Underground. It is a club that lets in eighteen-year-olds but gives you a red X on your hand if you are underage. When we got there nobody was dancing but the music was blaring. I asked Jeremy if he wanted to dance, kind of jokingly, and was surprised when he said yes. It was always very difficult to get boys from Chester to dance. So Jeremy marched right out to the middle of the dance floor and started busting these sweet moves. I just stood there, staring at him. Then I about-faced and walked straight off the dance floor. Turns out Jeremy is an incredible dancer, and it really caught me off guard. I went downstairs, took a couple shots, then finally joined him, as he never stopped dancing, even when I left. Just another tally for that guy.

The other night Jeremy and I were playing ping-pong down in the rec room, and he was just whooping me. I was trying to hold it together, but then I saw what he was doing and shouted at him, "If you are going to beat me, beat me with your strong hand!" because he had apparently switched the paddle halfway through to his left hand, out of pity.

Sunday we ate at the sub around noon, and then Kat, Maci and I went to the mall for a long time. We are so "city" now, just hanging out at the mall randomly. I got back and started reading my book, again. Then I noticed I had missed a call and had a message on my phone. The second I started listening to it my heart jumped and my stomach tightened.

It was Brent.

Chapter 10

October 2002, complications, Billings, Montana

"Come in!" Jeremy's friendly voice invites, in response to my feeble knocks.

I enter his dorm room and see he is on the phone, with his dad no doubt.[52] He happily pats the seat next to him on their couch. His expression changes drastically when he looks at my face.

"Hey, Dad, I gotta go." Jer cuts the conversation abruptly.

After a few seconds of silence, as his dad prays with him, then, "Okay. Thanks, Dad. Uh-huh. Love you, too."

He hangs up and turns urgently to face me. A look of concern covers his face. Studying mine he asks, "Are you okay?"

I pull a breath in through my nose and sigh an exhale. "Brent called."

"Oh," Jeremy responds quietly, slumping slightly.

"How did it go? What did you talk about?"

My mind flits fleetingly through the conversation. After I listened to the message I called back, but there was no answer. Then I left a message and immediately felt like crying. I am not exactly sure why. Like I was nervous, maybe, or so surprised to hear from him. It really caught me off guard. It felt so overwhelming. Then I tried to focus on my reading assignment, but could not concentrate, so I listened to a CD Brent had made for me. I listened to "The Dance," "Here's to the Nights," "Somewhere in Between," "If You're Gone," and just cried. Then my phone rang.

The lyrics from one of the songs ring in my mind now, *I'm somewhere in between, what is real and just a dream.*

---

[52] Jeremy used his dorm room phone to talk to his parents every once in a while, using prepaid calling cards. Otherwise he used my cell phone now and then, sometimes to call people, but mostly to play the Snake game. He did not own his own cell phone until after he graduated.

"We talked for over an hour," I start to process out loud. "Just about pretty general stuff. Nothing really personal."

Jeremy nods intently, paying close attention to every word.

Suddenly I cannot remember any details of the conversation. Except one. "He will be home in six days."

Both of Jeremy's eyebrows raise in response. I look into his eyes for a few seconds, then lay my head on his chest and cry. And cry and cry.

Jeremy holds me. Save for sporadic sniffles, we are silent. Seconds go by, then minutes. At some point the realization that I am exhausted washes over me. I slowly sit up, look straight at Jeremy, and weakly attempt a reassuring smile. I give him a hug and peck on the cheek. "Good night."

I stand and walk slowly to the door, where I turn and offer one more small smile and tiny wave. I vaguely notice how distraught he looks, but it is hard to concentrate right now.

My walk down the hall and back to my room is a daze. It is like I cannot grasp on to one concrete thought but instead several thoughts swim, just out of reach. Now I am at the sink, facing the mirror. I pull a purple washcloth from its hook behind the faucet. After dousing the rag in cold water and wringing it out, I press the cold cloth over my tear-stained face. Somehow the cool wetness triggers more teeming tears. There is a quick knock at the door. Before I can respond Greg pokes his head in.

"Hi, Jamie," he greets.

When I look up at him he hesitates. "Um, I was just wondering if Tex is in here? Uh, but I see he's not."

Then, kindly, he asks, "Are you okay?"

"I'm fine." I lie and throw a fake half smile his way.

"Okay," Greg gently replies.

He offers a weak smile and doesn't press. "See you later then."

"Yeah, see ya."

Greg closes the door. I turn back to the sink and force myself to brush my teeth. Slowly I climb up onto my bunk. About two seconds later the phone rings. I know exactly who it is. Awkwardly I reach down and grab the receiver.

"Hi Maci," I lead, trying to sound strong.

"I just saw Greg. I'll be down in a minute," she offers.

"Thanks, Mace, but I really need to go to sleep. I am wiped."

"Are you sure?" she checks, like a good friend does.

"I'm sure. Promise."

"Okay," she relents hesitantly.

Then she adds, "Love you."

"Love you, too, Mace. Thanks for calling."

I drop the receiver back on its cradle and burrow under my sheets. I fade with exhaustion, all the while wondering why I cannot stop crying.

* * *

An anxious voice stops me on my way to the theater for acting class. "Jamie! Wait up!" I look over my shoulder and see Jeremy jogging toward me, Diamondbacks hat bobbing, books tucked tight by his right hip.

Still tired, I can't help but smile when I see him. "Hi."

I lean into his chest for a hug. "Hi," he says, with a note of nervousness in the syllable.

His eyes study mine as if searching for clues. "How are you?"

"I'm fine," I say.

I smile up at him. "Pretty tired, so I am going to take a nap instead of going to my one o'clock class."

We are just about to the entrance of Losekamp Hall.[53]

"Okay . . . have a good class . . . I'll stop by around two?" he half states, half asks.

Grinning, I say, "I would love that."

He looks relieved as I make one last glance back before the creaky wooden doors close.

* * *

I am faintly aware of a knock at the door as I struggle to open my eyes.

"Hey, J." Maci walks into our room.

---

[53] Legend has it that Losekamp Hall is haunted (Olp, 2015).

She sets a notebook on the desk near the window. "Here are the notes from class."

"Thanks," I manage, still feeling tired even after sleeping these last couple hours.

"I saw Jeremy at lunch today," she continues.

"He was sitting a few tables away and just kept looking at me with the most worried expression on his face."

"Aw, poor guy!" I prop up on my pillow, picturing the scene she is describing.

"So what are you going to do?" Her blunt question catches me off guard.

"Hmm," I start, thinking out loud. "Well I have just been crying and crying and not exactly sure why." I search. "Like Brent has just been part of my life for so long, and I have only known Jeremy a few weeks but, but . . ."—I feel frustrated that I cannot seem to articulate any of this—"but I don't know."

I look down and see Maci settled in on the red camping chair next to our bunk, listening carefully. I am having trouble explaining. "This might sound crazy, but honestly . . ."—I pause, trying to state a clear thought I have not been able to fully grasp yet—"honestly, I think I'm scared."

"What are you scared of?" Maci challenges.

I take a big breath and let it out, like untwisting the cap on a bike tire. "I think I'm scared of hurting—"

She looks up expectantly, eyebrows raised.

"—Brent," I finish.

It is quiet for a few seconds. I attempt to explain, "Everything has been happening so fast. And, like, I just didn't think it would end like this, you know?"

I try to collect my thoughts. "Or maybe I just didn't think it would ever *really* end?"

This last statement-question catches in my throat.

I open my mouth, only to close it right back up again. Swallowing down a lump, I look at my friend. We lock eyes and share an understanding look. I know she gets it, even if I do not even quite get it yet myself. She gives me her close-lipped, one-side-curled patented

"Maci" smile. It communicates more than any words could. I feel comforted in this exchange. It would take days to try to catch someone up on all the details and layers and complications that have led up to this point and time in my life. But with this friend that I have known since preschool, it is as simple as that. And she went through the same thing with my brother.

Another knock.

"Come in!" I call.

The door slowly slides open and Jer peeks his head in. "Hi."

Seeing Maci he confirms, "Are you busy? I can come back later."

His voice fades a little with that last word, like he would really rather not.

Maci breaks into a wide smile and stands up. "Absolutely not. I was just leaving."

"Thanks, babe," I say.

She emphasizes each word in response. "You. Are. Welcome."

Jeremy turns sideways to make room for Maci to leave and waves as she passes and pats his shoulder. We both watch the door close. Then Jeremy turns to me, his face a mixture of expressions. "Are you going to sleep some more?"

"No, I'm good," I say.

"You wanna come up?" I invite.

He is beside me a second later, back propped up on the pillow, looking hopeful and anxious all at the same time. I lay my head down against his chest. This feels so nice. So safe. Already so natural. I smile slightly and close my eyes. I notice his heart pounding and my eyes flip back open. "Are you okay?!" I ask.

"I'm scared, Jamie," he responds, brown eyes swimming with worry. "This morning I took a pregame pee."

Puzzled, I turn my face questioningly toward his.

"I only do that when I am really nervous," he explains.

"Oh!" I say, understanding.

I reach over and take his hands in mine. "I'm sorry. I have just been so tired. My mind has been racing with all kinds of thoughts."

"Care to share your thoughts with me?" he asks, still sounding nervous.

67

I hope he knows what he is getting himself into, asking a question like that.

I take a breath then launch into a narrative of my long and complicated history with Brent. I shared a lot that night in Maci's room, but there is more. More than I could share in that single night. We did grow up in a small town together, after all. That's the stuff soap operas are made of. After feeling like I have talked for ten minutes straight, I check to see how Jeremy is receiving all of this. I try to think of how to somehow summarize my feelings surrounding the relationship. "I have changed and grown stronger because of it," I say.

Jeremy, clearly trying to understand, asks carefully, "So you grew stronger from hurt?"

Hmm. I guess I have never thought of it like that before. For the first time in many minutes I don't know what to say.

I study Jeremy's deep caring brown eyes. He quietly tells me, "I want to make you stronger through love and joy and faith."

My shoulders relax, and my heart swells. I smile at him and again contentedly place my head back on his chest. My tired eyes close again. I feel Jeremy's heartbeat slowing down, steadying. I feel sure that this is exactly where I want to be.

* * *

"Thanks, Mom."

I am collecting addresses for a few more people this evening to call for our team's Free-throw-athon fundraiser. I study the notebook I am holding and look at the next name on the list. "What about the Hamels' box number?"

"Oh, I have a beep. Just a second." I hear a click as Mom puts me on hold.

A couple minutes pass, and I begin to wonder if she got lost in a conversation and forgot about me. Just as I debate whether or not to hang up and try back later, Mom comes back on the line. "That was Gary." She sounds shaken.

Her voice tells me something is not okay. It cracks as she says, "Grandpa Helmar had a stroke. He's in the ICU."

My already muddled mind struggles to process this information. It flashes back to when I was six years old. We lived in one of the small teacherages (yes, "teacherages" are a thing) a couple blocks down the street from the school. Dad was on the phone with Uncle Jay. Dad was not saying much, but he was listening intently. The tension felt tangible. I peeked my head around my door and looked down the narrow kitchen hallway, trying to pick up something from the conversation. Dad's head was down, one hand tightly clamped to the edge of the countertop, knuckles white. He said goodbye to his brother then slammed the yellow receiver down hard on the cradle.

Grandpa Jim with Jeff and me, a few years before his first stroke

I don't remember many details after that, just that the phone call was to let us know that Grandpa Jim had a stroke. Apparently he was checking the electrical box in the Civic Center during a basketball game and went down. So much changed after that. Grandpa Jim's entire left side was paralyzed, he was essentially confined to a wheelchair, and that big, powerful, independent man wasn't anymore. He lived for six more years—for which I am grateful—but I know it was hard for him. And hard for our whole family. I have always been sad that I do not have more memories of him before that stupid stroke.

Mom shares the details she knows, which aren't many, and I realize Shye has entered my room. I hastily swipe at some tears and look at the clock. "Oh, Mom!" I interrupt.

"I'm sorry, but I'm late! I gotta go eat, and then we have practice. Can you find out Grandpa's room number and if and when I can visit and leave me a message?" My shoulders slump when I finish my rushed string of sentences.

Mom tells me she will do that, and we say "I love you" and hang up.

Shye asks what's wrong. She gives me a big hug when I tell her. "Are you going to be okay to practice?" she asks, concerned.

"I think so." I produce a pathetic smile, and we start toward the sub.

* * *

I pull my covers up to my chin and take in a big breath. I exhale, roll over, and snuggle my stuffed bunny under my arm.[54] My body feels like lead. All I want to do is sleep. Instead, my mind insists on processing the last few hours.

Practice was a blur. As soon as it was over Jenny and Maci went with me to the hospital. I hate hospitals. The smells. Those beeps. I am glad I went, though, because it really helped seeing Grandpa Helmar. He held my hand in his and swung it back and forth. It was so cute. The doctor said his left side is pretty much paralyzed, just like Grandpa Jim's was, but there is a possibility he could regain some feeling. Grandma Barb seemed to be doing okay, considering the circumstances. Those Branaes somehow stay so calm all the time. I wish that trait had been passed down to me. I felt better after seeing Grandpa.

Jenny dropped off Maci and me at Rocky before eleven. Maci headed upstairs to her room, and I tiptoed to our room. Roomie Kat is very under the weather, and she was rustling around uncomfortably when I stepped inside. So I administered some cold medicine to her that was left over from when I was sick last week. Kat and I both agreed that it is terrible being sick at college because we just want our moms.

Now I give my bunny another squeeze. Kat's even breathing tells me she is finally sleeping peacefully. I hope she feels a lot better in the morning. Mom and Dad are driving down to Billings tomorrow. And not a moment too soon, because I really need my mommy!

---

[54] All through junior high and high school I slept with a favorite stuffed bunny my friend Amanda gave me for a birthday when I was young. Its fur was worn and was missing an ear by the time I was a senior, so Amanda gifted me another bunny for my eighteenth birthday, so I could take one to college.

Chapter 11

October 2002, fall break, Chester, Montana

There it is again, that big, beautiful sky. This time I sit in the driver's seat, Maci riding shotgun. My parents stayed in Billings—to be with Grandpa and Grandma—but Maci and I still came up north, our original plan for fall break. We switched drivers a couple times along the way so we could take turns napping. Maci is sleeping now. I look out the window and again find myself mesmerized by the endless fields, patched together under the large, blue expanse. Staring out at those rolling fields always triggers my mind to roll through life's recent events.

It is insane that I have only been at college for barely over two months. It is like I have a brand-new life. I try to recall the past week. Some highlights include me whipping Jeremy's butt when a bunch of us went bowling. But I left the seventh and tenth frames open and ended up with a 194. Should have had a 200, dang it! We went to the Ghetto several times. We watched *Sweet Home Alabama* there for Alex's birthday, which was really fun. One night we went to *FeardotCom*, and that was maybe the worst movie I have ever seen in my entire life. Good thing it was only a dollar. Our practices have not been that great. The intensity feels inconsistent; the expectations feel unclear. It is just crazy how different college basketball is compared to high school. Almost all of us come from unique high school cultures, and somehow we are supposed to blend together. I guess it will take some time. One night the "Mr. Rocky" contest happened while we were at practice. Apparently Jeremy did a lot of crazy stuff—he danced with skimpy clothing and ate weird things—and won. A lot of people were really excited to tell me about it the next day.

Jeremy, "Mr. Rocky," 2002

Thinking about my Mr. Rocky makes me smile. Things with Jeremy have been amazing. We love being together and laugh all the time. I am so glad he got to meet my grandparents, especially before Grandpa had that stroke. I took Jeremy to Big Timber the weekend right before the stroke, and we played cards with Grandpa and Grandma. I was dying because in the middle of explaining pinochle to Jeremy, Grandma Barb just stopped abruptly, took his cards out of his hand, and realigned the way he was holding them. She was like, "Oops. Oh, no, no."

Grandma insisted his cards were "backwards." He looked sort of stunned but mostly amused. Then Grandma just went right back on explaining the rules. It was so funny. We also got to eat with Grandma Joyce, and with Uncle Jay and Aunt Peg. Oh yeah, and Jeremy got to meet Jeff, too, when Carroll played at Rocky. Jeff told me he would be critiquing Jeremy's game. Nobody scored in the first half, but the third quarter killed us, and we lost 7–31. But even though we lost, Jeff seemed to approve—of his kicking anyway. I told Jeff thank goodness, and now

I will be able to sleep at night. Then Jeremy met Aunt Shirley, Shannon, and my parents when everyone came to Billings to see Grandpa in the hospital.

Jeremy, Grandpa Helmar, Grandma Barb, and me, 2002

Thursday we had practice for a couple hours in the morning, and then later Maci and I went to the gym to shoot our 200 free throws for the Free-throw-athon. I made 183 shots and need to collect all my pledges. When we left the gym we saw my dad walking across the campus. I was so excited to see him and ran and gave him a huge hug. Then I took him to my dorm room. Jeremy had apparently just been to our room looking for me. He left a cute scribbled note on the dry erase board hanging from our door and left our room dancing and singing down the hallway. When my dad and I turned the corner from the main hallway to my hallway, Jeremy literally ran smack dab into my dad. Jer stopped dead in his tracks. Then he gathered himself and shook Dad's hand, his face beet red. A pretty hilarious "meet the girlfriend's dad" scenario I would say.

Later that night, after Dad had left and I showered and everything, Jer and I went over to Gary and Linda's to meet everyone for dinner.

On the ride to their house I asked how he was doing. He goes, "I'm okay."

That response surprised me. I asked why he was just okay, and he said, "I met your dad today. He is big. And those stories you and Maci told did not help."

Hilarious.

Dinner that night with Jeremy and my family was really nice. He and Grandma Barb sat in the living room watching *Wheel of Fortune*. It was so sweet. We all went to the hospital right after dinner. Dad and Jeremy stood outside the door for quite a while, and I could hear them talking. Dad actually talked a lot about Grandpa Jim, and then he asked about how I had been during the week. Later that night, Jeremy told me he loved my family. He said, "I really like your mom."

I continue driving along and smile recalling all of the encounters between Jeremy and my family members. It is so nice that he feels comfortable around my relatives, is excited to be with them, and wants to get to know them more. Last night he and I talked about this weekend in Chester. Jeremy told me he does not want to compete with Brent. He said he understands we have a history and that I care about Brent, and that I always will. But then he went on to say—again—that he is still nervous, that he has never before felt this way about anyone. He also said he had never been in Brent's position, or mine, so he cannot tell me what to do. Then he encouraged me to pray for peace. And I have been trying to do that, really, but I have never been in this particular position before either, and also it is sometimes hard to know how to pray.

Today before Maci and I left Jeremy brought me a single red rose. I draped it over the car's rearview mirror. My eyes flicker to the flower and then focus on the familiar highway ahead. A slight wave of apprehension and expectation wiggles its way through my body as the car obediently slows down at the 45 mph sign. Maci stirs at the speed change. I turn right on to Quincy Street and park parallel to her parents' town house.[55] Maci stretches for a second, gathers herself, unlocks her

---

[55] The term "town house" here should not be mistaken with a "townhouse" with two housing units that share a wall. "Town houses" in rural places like Chester refer to houses that families with farms or ranches live in part-time in order not to have to drive constantly on gravel roads, especially through the winter and especially when kids are involved in extracurricular activities.

seatbelt, then begins to gather her stuff. "Kate said we can meet her at her house around six," I share as Maci heaves her duffel bag out of the back seat.

"Okay," Maci replies sleepily. "See you in a bit."

I wave then ease the car east down Quincy, pass Heidi's town house on the right, then Chasi's on the left. I take a left at Second Street West, then another right onto Monroe, now passing Emily's house. Seeing all these familiar houses settles my stomach. The car rolls through the alley and up through our open garage door. I maneuver the shifter (that's a word) into park and glance at the dashboard that tells me it is 5:34, confirming my prediction. When Brent called earlier today I told him I would be in Chester before six. I reach for the key but pause when the song from the CD player reaches my consciousness.

> *And now*
> *I'm glad I didn't know*
> *The way it all would end*
> *The way it all would go*
> *Our lives are better left to chance*
> *I could have missed the pain*
> *But I'd have had to miss*
> *The dance*[56]

You got that right, Garth. I listen for a minute more, then twist the key down. The car quiets. I sit quietly as well. My mind, however—as usual—stubbornly refuses to stay quiet and begins processing the phone conversation with Brent this morning. Brent said he was not sure what his family had planned for this evening, only that relatives would be visiting. I told him that was no problem, that Kaitlynn was coming to see me, and he and I could try to make a plan to connect sometime Saturday evening.

It felt equal parts normal and strange talking to him. What will it feel like seeing him? The last time we were together—over nine months ago—we were *together.* Nine months ago I was on Christmas break, just after our undefeated senior basketball season. It was the first time the

---

[56] "The Dance," written by Tony Arata, performed by Garth Brooks.

army let him come home. We spent every minute of his two-week leave together that we possibly could. Then, well, then he left again. We wrote lots of letters. We still do. But it felt like the odds were against us, or something. Like things ended up always feeling more complicated than they should. Like challenges from our past kept getting in the way. Then I graduated. Then it was time for me to head to college. Then I met Jeremy. Then everything changed.

How could everything have changed in just nine months?

My eyes close, and I massage the bridge of my nose with my thumb and forefinger. Then I click my seatbelt strap and exit the Taurus. Looking around my parents' comforts me. Jeff's Magic Johnson mini hoop hangs from the wooden storage loft. I walk through the garage door into the entryway, then I push into our living room, plowing the heavy door steadily across the thick, gray carpet. I close my eyes as I breathe in the familiar scent of our house, our family. It is so weird, I never noticed "our smell" when I lived here, but after being away and coming back it smells so distinctive. I of course leave my shoes at the door then tote my duffel through the living room and up the stairs to my room. My "old" room? How do I label things now? Mom has left a pile of items she thinks will interest me on the bed: a couple newspaper clippings with pictures of Amanda and Savannah playing volleyball, a program of the high school's fall concert, and a funny *Zits* cartoon clipped out of some Sunday paper. There is also the list of Free-throw-athon pledgers, a not-so-subtle reminder that I need to collect the rest of the money this weekend.

I grab the pledge list and skip down the stairs to the kitchen. Remembering my shoes, I skip down the second set of stairs, too, and then back up through the kitchen to the front room. I head out the front door, down the two concrete steps, and across the lawn to the Earls' house. Emma answers the door. I grin when I see her and remember pushing her on the swings at the school playground and watching *Blues Clues* with her in their basement. Isabelle appears from the hallway. I remember our many naps together, rocking her to sleep after our summer trips to the swimming pool. I give both of them—two of my past babysitting charges—big hugs. Their dad Brett gives me a hug, too, and he writes the check for our team's fundraiser. Dr. Earl is still working, but it looks like they are about to sit down for dinner. I tell them thank you and goodbye and turn to leave. As soon as I start to walk outside a familiar engine rumble stalls my steps.

Identifying car engines is not generally a talent of mine, but this one is unique. Sure enough, I look up to see the blue Oldsmobile Cutlass pull up alongside the curb in front of my house. There he is. What is wrong with my legs? Jello. In fact, my whole body feels wiggly. My heart is pounding. Why is this happening? Seriously, when is this reaction going to stop?

"Hey," Brent says, giving a little nervous wave as he walks toward me.

He looks really good. His hair is longer than it was when he came back for his visit after boot camp. It even has gel in it. Fancy. And clearly the gazillions of push-ups the army has been making him do have been effective. I wonder what is going through his mind. I attempt to look cool and collected, hoping he can't see through my farce. *I have a boyfriend!* a voice inside my head screams. But instead I call out, "Hi, Brenton!" maybe a little too high-pitched and overenthusiastically.

We are close enough to touch. What is the protocol for this? Why don't they teach you how to handle difficult situations and conversations in school instead of teaching you what iambic pentameter is? I do not think ten syllables eloquently strung together will help with the awkwardness of this particular situation: *Oh, I have a new boyfriend by the way.* No. No iambic pentameter now, Jamie. Focus!

I tilt my head to the right, and he tilts his to the left. Whoops. We both overcorrect. Whoops again. We smile nervously and finally manage a sort of awkward, dutiful hug. A whiff of green Extra mint gum, Irish Spring soap, and Old Spice deodorant sneaks in, causing unexpected flashes of memories. Can't he buy some cinnamon gum or something, for the love? How am I supposed to stop things like this from cropping up?! It feels like I have no control trying to suppress these memories. They simply manifest without warning.

We continue to look at each other, attempting to navigate what is supposed to come next. "I thought maybe you had a family dinner tonight?" I ask.

He looks down, both hands tucked in pockets, and sways a little side to side. "A lot of the family is at Grandpa and Grandma's. I was there for a while earlier."

Then he stops swaying and looks up, right into my eyes. "I wanted to see you."

Riiiight.

Looking at him now, scenes of so many experiences together swirl. First hand-hold. First kiss. First "I love yous." Laughing together. Watching movies. Crying. A lot of crying. Too much crying.

I press my lips into a smile, squint my eyes and shrug my shoulders up for a couple seconds. Before either of us has a chance to say anything else, a startling honk turns our attention. Kaitlynn sits on the horn of her white Cadillac Eldorado and parks behind Brent's Cutlass. I give a smile and a wave and skip toward the familiar carriage. Brent follows. Kaitlynn bops out of the driver's side and hooks me enthusiastically with her right arm, Brent with her left. Katy's presence magically resets the mood. I relax. "Hellllooo!" Kaitlynn sings in our ears.

We exchange pleasantries and soon hop into Brent's car, as he insists on driving, pick up Maci, and head to Subway. We all order our usuals and occupy a booth in the far corner of the dining area. Somehow this ritual transports us. Conversation and laughter flow easily. As I laugh, eat, and listen to stories shared by these people I have known for so many years, I think about and marvel at how many different seasons we have endured in our relationships. Our relationships one-on-one, our relationships in small groups, our relationships on teams, in classrooms. Relationships in so many settings and through so many seasons. Sometimes we have been the best of friends, sometimes we have wondered if we would ever speak to each other again. Sometimes we have felt so much love for another, and sometimes we have wanted to scream at another in anger, disappointment, frustration.

But always we have reconciled. Always we have somehow found a way to continue on in relationship with each other in some capacity. That is the way it is in small towns. You cannot lose your mind on someone and expect to simply wash your hands of that person. Because you *will* see them again. You will inevitably be connected in the future.

You will be on some shared project together. Or you will end up at a gathering with shared acquaintances. Or, if you are Maci, you will find out you are related. So you have to figure out how to handle the disagreements and the disappointments. You have to figure out how to forgive and move forward, how to bend, how to compromise. Because you will always be at least a small part of each other's lives.

"Right, Jame?" Maci asks, and all six eyes are on me, expectantly.

My mouth is hanging half-open, my sandwich held near the side of my jaw. My eyes quickly scan each person. Read the room, Jamie. Social cues. "Um, right!" I venture, feigning confidence.

Apparently satisfied with my response, they all chuckle and take another bite.

* * *

"It's already eleven!" Kaitlynn's surprised exclamation shakes me from my slumber.

I process her statement, quickly realizing our attempt to set a nine-thirty alarm clearly failed miserably. "Okay," I say, "you shower in my bathroom, and I will shower in my parents'. As long as we leave before noon we will be fine."

I quickly gather up my outfit for today—a pair of SilverTab jeans, a well-worn white Montana State Games T-shirt, my new soft, gray number 34 Rocky football hoodie from Jeremy, and of course the necessary undergarments—and hustle over to the bathroom connected to my mom and dad's bedroom. I close my eyes, face the spigot and welcome the warm water as it streams down my face and front.

My eyes feel tired, but I didn't cry too much last night, just a little when Kate and I stayed up and talked till four. Before that, we watched *Enough*, ate Doritos, and then chatted for a long time after. Maci went home around midnight, and Brent hung out with Kaitlynn and me for another hour or so. There was one point when Brent and I were sitting together in the living room, alone, while Katy went to brush her teeth and take out her contacts. We did not say too much; I could tell he was nervous. I noticed that I did not have the usual urge to be right next to him, to touch him or to kiss him. That was different. Affirming as far as Jeremy and me goes, but it made me sad for Brent. And it is so weird, because it is not like I do not love him anymore. I just love him . . . different? That feels confusing. How can that be?

I told Katy about all these thoughts. I told her how sad it makes me to think about Brent being sad and alone while I am happy with Jeremy. She told me that is not for me to worry about and that it is God's job to take care of Brent, not mine. That comforted me, but it does not mean I know what to do.

I asked Brent how it feels to be home for a break. He had a hard time answering. He said something about knowing he had to come home, knowing that he needed to see his mom, especially after not coming home over the summer. Then he said it is really hard because he does not want to go back. During that conversation I felt the same way I sometimes used to feel when we were in high school, like I wanted to make him happy, I wanted to be able to fix things for him, but I did not know how.

"Let's go, Graham!" Kaitlynn's command pierces my thoughts.

Oh, shoot. She is already done showering. I rinse the final suds out of my hair and wrench the silver handle around. I do not want to make us late for the game.

* * *

"Okay, let's go see him!" Katy tugs my arm wildly after the Rocky-Northern football game and pulls me down the bleacher stairs to the Blue Pony football field.

The game was not very pretty, but thankfully we pulled out a 35–34 win. [57] We navigate our way through the sweaty maroon-and-gold jerseys and come to the sweaty green-and-gold jerseys. It is easy to find our way to number 34, as my eyes are trained to keep that number in view. A wide grin spreads across Jeremy's face when he sees me. We hug tight, with no concern of sweat or smell. I finally pull away and gesture toward my companions. "Jeremy, this is Kaitlynn and Scottie."

Jeremy shakes Scott's hand, and before he can put out a hand for Kaitlynn she all but tackles him with a bearhug instead. Jeremy laughs

---

[57] Jeremy kicked three extra points in the game. A year later against Northern, Jeremy kicked the two farthest field goals of his career, one from 49 yards and the other from 50 (*Billings Gazette*, October 25, 2003).

and hugs her right back. We talk briefly about the game. Then Jer asks them a few questions about their campus and their classes. I watch him interact with one of my best friends and her boyfriend. He is so engaged. I can tell he already likes them and wants to get to know them more. I keep smiling. I notice I do have the urge to be right next to him, to touch him and to kiss him. He talks with them a little longer, then turns and faces me. Katy and Scott turn to talk to some of their football friends.

Jer faces me. "Hi."

"Hi." I smile back.

"Good win!"

"Yeah," he answers.

Then he asks, "Did you . . . see anybody yet?"

"Yeah," I reply, gently rubbing and cradling both his hands in mine, trying to express reassurance as I hold his intense gaze.

"Oh," he responds simply, clearly trying to stay calm.

He looks at me expectantly. "How was it?"

"It was fine," I tell him.

"He had dinner with Kate and Mace and me, and then we all watched a movie. Then Kate spent the night."

Jeremy nods intently.

"I'm not sure what we will do tonight," I continue, "but he said his family wants to see me."

"Sure." Jeremy nods slightly.

I imagine it is taking a lot of self-control to appear so calm and collected. I smile and lean my body against his chest. "I am so glad I got to see you today. I missed you."

He rubs my shoulders and hugs me tight. "I missed you, too."

We both look over at the slow stream of Rocky players lumbering toward the locker room. "I guess I better go." He sounds reluctant.

"Yeah, probably," I say, just as reluctantly.

"I will see you tomorrow, okay? I'll call Kat from the house and let her know when we leave."[58]

"Okay," he says, as he lets out a deep exhale.

---

[58] These were the days when there was spotty cell phone service—especially in small towns like Chester—as well as the dreaded roaming charges. So when I went to Chester or Big Timber, my phone was turned off the entire time.

I lean up on my tippy toes to reach him for a kiss and try to express comfort in my smile as we separate.

"See you tomorrow," he says, and looks back after a few steps toward the locker room.

"Can't wait!" I wave and watch him walk away.

* * *

This has worked out quite nicely, me having the entire house to myself, I think as I say goodbye to Amanda, Savannah, Miranda, Kacey, Mitchy, and Cory Decker. I had dinner with the whole Clark family earlier, after running into them when taking the movie back to the store. It was so nice to see everybody. We laughed a lot. Then I came back to my house and have been entertaining visitors ever since. People have been dying to see me, apparently.

Almost as soon as my high school friends head out, another car pulls up. I walk to the window and see Brent walking toward the front door, followed by his older cousin Amy and her husband. I open the door to greet them. Amy holds up a brown paper grocery bag and asks, "Mind if we hang out here for a while?"

"Come on in," I beckon.

We settle in on the stools around the kitchen peninsula, and I get out some glasses. Amy pours me some of that dangerous cinnamon bear–tasting potion that Roger brought to Kevin's room the other night. Uh-oh. I take a sip. Yep, still tastes like liquid candy cinnamon bears. Amy fills Brent's glass and offers a cheers. "To Brent," she starts.

"Thank you for your service, and we are so glad you are home!"

"Cheers!" we call and clink collectively.

A few minutes later we are joined by more visitors. "Hello!" a familiar voice calls, before I have time to react to the knock.

Diemert, Christopher John, and Chance join us in the kitchen a few seconds later. "Go ahead, let yourselves in," I tease.

"We heard Mr. Graham was gone, so we decided it was safe to enter," Chris explains. [59]

I laugh as I watch three of my former classmates greet Brent. Chris and Brent pair up to share army stories, and I chat with Diemert and Chance. Soon we all mix and mingle, the volume in the room gets louder and louder, and somehow my glass stays full no matter how many sips I take.

After lots of talking and laughing, I see Brent excuse himself to go up to the bathroom. I make a mental note to tease him when he comes back down, but a lurch in my stomach forces me to go upstairs to use the other bathroom. As I walk by the closed door, I swear I hear some sniffles. I pause, then continue on to my parents' bathroom. When I finish I walk back toward the hallway, expecting to join the crowd again downstairs. But the door is still closed, and I still hear those sounds. I gently rap on the wood. "Brent? Are you okay?"

I hear water running then a muffled mumble, "Yeah, I'm fine."

I hesitate. Then, "Are you sure?"

Silence.

"Can I come in?"

The handle turns and slowly opens. He looks at me and attempts a smile. I raise my eyebrows and open my mouth. No words come to mind, so I close it again. This triggers him. He bows his head and begins to cry. His shoulders shudder. Suddenly I am inundated with such intense emotion. The feeling builds up in my throat, my chin even. I try to keep my lips closed, but a whoosh of breath involuntarily pushes out, parting them, allowing a whimper to escape. There is no stopping it now. We both cry, unsuccessful in any vain attempt to hold it in. My knees are suddenly incapable of holding me up and crumple down to the cold tile floor. Brent's knees apparently experience the same issue. We sit across from each other, doing that whole desperate-cry-try-to-stop-but-can't thing.

---

[59] One time my senior year I went to open the door after hearing a knock. I was confused when there was no one on the front steps. Finally I saw a handful of boys from my class hiding behind a couple trees across the street. They claimed they panicked when they thought Mr. Graham might open the door, possibly shirtless, and they bolted.

After what feels like several minutes, but possibly it has only been seconds, we look up at each other.

"Those eyes"—he shakes his head—"they kill me."

He turns away again, then looks back. "Jamie, I miss you."

My breath has steadied some. Quietly I say, "I miss you, too."

My voice shakes, but I continue. "I don't know how to do this. I haven't seen you for almost a year. Sean told me you were hanging out with girls at parties . . ." My voice tapers off.

His eyes look down briefly, then up again. "My roommate Tommy likes you. He'll look at a picture of you in my locker and say, 'You really like that girl, don't you?' Jamie, I still love you. I know it's crazy. I know that."

We are both quiet again. "When Sean said there were other girls . . ." I try to find the words.

I continue slowly. "I kind of broke free a little bit, or something. I don't know."

I am having such a hard time explaining. Maybe because I don't understand it all myself. "I mean, I love you, too. I will love you forever, you know?"

His glistening blue eyes look so sad. "But?"

I pull in a centering breath but only manage a whisper, "But just not in the same way." I pause. "I know that doesn't make any sense." He keeps listening. So I continue on. "I met somebody." The words hang heavily in the air.

"You told me on the phone a couple weeks ago that all the guys at college are players," he challenges.

"Yeah, that might have been a little harsh," I explain.

"It seemed like that might be the case at that time. But"—I take another big breath, making an effort to communicate as clearly and gently as possible—"this guy is different."

After a pause Brent mumbles quietly, eyes down, "What's his name?"

"Jeremy."

The silence is loud. I do not hear any voices down in the kitchen anymore. Everyone must have left. What time is it? We sit here on the hard tile floor. I did not notice how cold it was at first. I feel tired, physically and emotionally. I push up on my hands and knees, then stand slowly. He stands, too. He offers a small smile that holds a shared understanding. "I still love you," he says calmly, quietly. "Always will."

I offer a weak smile, "Me, too."

Our shoulders relax as we lean forward and connect for a long hug. The hug expresses respect, trust, years of shared experiences. It expresses an understanding. An understanding that I cannot quite put into words.

"I'll grab you a pillow and blanket, and you can sleep on either couch," I offer, as we separate and shift back to our formal conversation registers (thank you, Psych 101).

I exit and retrieve said bedding items, then hand them to him in the hallway.

"Thanks," he offers.

I give the expected cordial response, "You're welcome."

I take my eyes from the couch and look up. He is looking directly back at me. My eyebrows raise involuntarily, lips purse, and tears pool and sting behind my eyes. I swear I can almost hear his thoughts racing. I cannot let him see me like this again tonight. We cannot keep going back. So I manage to turn up the corners of my mouth a bit and raise my hand in a weak wave. "Goodnight, Brenton."

I turn and start toward the stairs before I finish saying his name, determined to suppress my emotion, at least in front of him. Thanks to this, and the cinnamon bear potion, it takes all of my focus to stay steady on the stairs, and I only barely hear his reply.

"Good night, Jamie.

Brent and me, fall 2002

Chapter 12

October 2002, St. Vincent's hospital; RMC dorms, Billings, Montana

"Hi, Maci, I'm Jamie's Aunt Shirley." Maci shakes hands with my mom's sociable, sweet older sister. Petite, with short, reddish-gray hair, my aunt flew down from Fairbanks as soon as she heard about Grandpa. She continues to chat easily with Maci. ". . . and I am the black sheep of the family, you know, and Karen Elaine's the baby, the favorite."

I smile listening to my aunt give her comical introductory spiel.[60] Then she turns the conversation and asks Maci, "How was your guys's weekend? Was it nice going back to Chester?"

Maci's dialogue is drowned out by my own mental response to my aunt's questions. This morning we went to church, and it was so good to see the Ericksons, and everyone. We went to Maci's and had Doritos and Kool-Aid dessert, visited with Mitchy, Teresa, and Desi, and then headed out. We stopped at the Clarks' to say goodbye. I hugged the whole family. Then Brent got his camera so he could take a picture of us.[61] Then he gave me the beautiful purple glass rose he had gotten me for Christmas. Then we hugged for a really long time. I cried, surprise. I only cried a little bit in the car, and Maci and I talked about all the things.

---

[60] My Aunt Shirley had an entire bathroom decorated top to bottom with black sheep paraphernalia. She always (jokingly) lamented about being the middle child, the shortest, that my mom was the "favorite," etc. My mom and her two older siblings had loving and enviable relationships, with each other and with their parents. My aunt passed away on December 26, 2020, after a failed bone marrow transplant in an attempt to combat acute myeloid leukemia (AML).

[61] This was back in the day when you had to wait to get film developed to see pictures. The wait was tantalizing—such anticipation! Did the pictures turn out?! My own children will never understand.

When we got back to Billings, we headed straight here, to the hospital. I look up and see both Maci and Aunt Shirley are looking toward the nearest patient room. "How's he doing?" I ask my aunt.

"He's doing really good," Shirley says, nodding, arms crossed.

"He ate a little Jell-O and some mashed potatoes today, and he was sitting up in bed for a long time. He wanted Mom to find *The Lawrence Welk Show* reruns on TV."

We laugh at this comment. She points to Grandpa's room. "Karen Elaine took Mom to Gary's so she could get some rest. Jamie, you can quick go in and see him. There are still a few minutes left before visiting hours are over."

I walk into the impersonal white stark room, with its antiseptic smell and constant beeping. My stomach feels squeamish. I remember seeing Grandpa Jim lying in an identical bed twelve years ago. I remember him looking so small and helpless. I hated that then, and I hate this now. I make myself smile and approach Grandpa Helmar's bedside. His pale blue eyes are closed, but I can tell he is not asleep. Gently I reach out and hold the top of his spotted wrinkled hand, careful not to bump the IV. His hand is weathered and rough from handling farm equipment and taking care of sheep, from holding brushes while painting houses and buildings in Big Timber, from casting and reeling in rainbow trout again and again on the Yellowstone and Boulder rivers.[62] But at the same time his hand is soft and tender, from hugging and holding all his kids and grandkids, playing game after game of rummy and pinochle, making tall Root Beer floats, square-dancing with his bride of almost six decades.

I lean down toward his ear and gently announce my presence. "Hi, Grandpa. It's Jamie."

His eyes slowly open, and he looks my way with a tired smile. "I just got back to Billings after spending the weekend in Chester. Aunt Shirley said you had a good day today?"

---

[62] Grandpa raised cattle and sheep on a ranch five miles northeast of Big Timber, Montana, for twenty-eight years. They moved to town at the end of my mom's sophomore year (she attended a country school called Rapstad up until then), where Grandpa painted and then was the caretaker at the cemetery. He fished the rivers and creeks (pronounced "crick," just so ya know) as often as possible.

Grandpa nods slightly. "Barb went to Gary's," he manages.

My throat catches. He really wants Grandma to be here.

I attempt to steady my voice and sound as upbeat as possible. "Yeah, Mom took her to get a little rest. I am sure she will be back first thing tomorrow morning."

This seems to satisfy him. "I'm a little tired," he admits, words slurring.

"I bet you are. Do you need anything before I have to go? Visiting hours are almost over, and you need a good night's sleep so you can keep getting better."

"When's Barb coming back?" he asks.

Shirley joins me at his bedside. "Dad, Mom will be back after breakfast tomorrow morning, remember? The nurse is going to come in just a few minutes to help you get settled for the night. Jamie is going to head back to the college now."

I take my cue, lean over and kiss his cheek, and whisper, "Goodnight, Grandpa. I love you."

"Goodnight," Grandpa responds weakly. He closes his eyes. "Love you."

* * *

The salty oriental-flavored Ramen Noodles taste amazing. Thanks to my handy-dandy Sunbeam fast-boiling hot water kettle, I can have delicious Ramen Noodles in the comfort of my own dorm room any time I want.

I stopped by Uncle Gary's and Aunt Linda's on the way back from the hospital. They were all heading to bed. Grandma Barb was making sure Mom was going to sleep with her tonight. How would it feel to be separated from your spouse that you have shared a bed with for almost sixty years? I chew and swallow my current bite quickly when I hear a knock on the door. "Come in!"

There he is.

"Hi, Jamie."

"Hi!" My whole body perks up when I see Jeremy.

I hold up the bowl of Ramen. "I just checked my message and was gonna come down to the annex after I ate really quick. I was starving."

89

I set the bowl down and give him a big hug. The stress of the weekend melts away with the embrace. He sits on the camping chair. I stay at the computer chair and ask, "How was the rest of your weekend?"

"It wasn't the best," Jeremy immediately admits.

He sighs and continues. "I didn't even feel like playing on Saturday. That night I just watched a movie by myself, but I didn't even really watch it. I stared at the ceiling and thought forever. I went through every possible scenario of what you might say to me when you came back ..." His voice trails off, and he looks at me earnestly.

I smile at him and proceed to tell him everything that happened during my weekend. The feelings I had, and the ones I didn't. I tell him what Katy and I talked about, and what Brent and I talked about. And I tell him I could not wait to come back here, to see him.

Jeremy lets out a relieved sigh. "Where would you want to be, if you could be anywhere this second?"

It does not take me a second to respond. "Anywhere with you."

He smiles slightly, then holds out his arms. I clank my bowl into the sink and sit on his lap; he wraps his arms around my middle. "I got to go to Israel once. We hiked up Mount Sinai at two in the morning and made it to the top just in time for the sunrise. It was the most amazing, beautiful thing I had ever experienced."

His arms tighten around me, and I smile, picturing this image. Then he continues. "I get that same feeling when I'm with you, as I did when that sunlight first touched me."

I lean my head back on his shoulder. It feels like he wants to say something else, something more. But he is quiet now. I stand up, then he stands, and we hug for a long, long time. Then I say, "I am glad I am back here. Back with you."

"Me, too," he says.

"Goodnight, Jeremy."

"Goodnight, Jamie."

Chapter 13

October 21, 2002, powerful words, first game, hospital (again), Billings and Dillon, Montana

"Nice pass, Jame!" Kat jogs over for a high five after converting on a layup, courtesy my assist.

JD's whistle blows, and we gather at center court. "Nice finish," Coach Gustin compliments.

He addresses our huddle. "Remember no practice tomorrow, because the varsity girls are scrimmaging Sheridan at three thirty."

Maci and I look at each other and smile. It will be good to see Chas. I hope she is liking school and basketball better than the last time we talked.

"Then there is a home volleyball game here at seven, so make sure if you have work-study duties you know what you are supposed to be doing," Coach Gustin continues.

"Saturday we will practice from nine to ten, and then we will board the bus for Dillon at ten on Sunday. Make sure you have your away uniforms."

Coach Gustin lifts his arm, angled toward the center circle. My teammates and I follow suit.

"Bears on three," I prompt. "One, two, three—"

"Bears!" we chorus, then disperse.

A handful of us freshmen make our familiar trek to the sub, where we load our plates with food that is always available—apples, bananas, carrots, sandwich fixings—when students can't make it during normal dining hours. And of course we finish with bowls of Wilcoxson's ice cream. Montana Moose Tracks for me, thank you very much.

* * *

I'll be there for you, 'cause you're there for me, too!

Kat, Tex, Peter, Jer, and I turn our attention to the TV to watch the taped "The One With the Sharks" episode of *Friends*. I feel so happy tonight, so light. I laugh at Joey pretending he doesn't have a lot of experience asking people out. Jer laughs, too, then I look at him and go, "Tell me something."

"Anything?" Jeremy looks at me intently.

"Yes." I match his stare.

There is a sweet silence for several seconds. Then he leans over and kisses my shoulder, up my neck, then my ear. Ooh, tingly. He stops and whispers, "Anything?"

I turn and look at him again, but do not speak. He takes a big breath and looks at me with those sweet brown eyes. "I love you."

There it is.

I kiss his cheek and confirm, "I know."

He looks at me and pulls back a bit, a little surprised. I smile and assure, "I love you, too."

He smiles. "I wanted to say it before, but then I wanted to let you go home and get stuff figured out with Brent."

"I know." I lean in for a hug.

How did I get so lucky?

* * *

I alternate between looking out the window, dozing off, or chatting with Shye as our fifteen-passenger van bumps west to Dillon along Highway 212. I think about the late-night crisis conversations I had the last two nights that felt almost identical: one with Kaitlynn and one with Heidi. The calls consisted of me listening and trying to assure them everything would be okay, with my friends bawling about the huge fights they had just had with their boyfriends. It is not lost on me that the frustrations they shared sounded so similar to the frustrations I often had with Brent. Then I think about Jeremy, and how there has not been one instance even close to that. It feels like such a relief, like the way a healthy "adult" relationship is probably supposed to be. I am torn between feeling so bad for my friends' situations, yet so thankful for mine at the same time.

"There's the college." Shye's statement shifts my focus.

Mom, Dad, Jeff, and me in our Western and Rocky gear. The Graham family has strong connections to Western. Jeff transferred there his junior year.

I look up to see the entrance of the University of Montana Western.[63] This is the site where I will play my first college basketball game. Coach Gustin parks in the lot next to Straugh Gymnasium. As we walk into the building I look at the red, white, and black painting of the bulldog mascot. I feel familiarity and connectedness, likely because my dad frequently wears shirts and hats with the exact logo.[64]

An enthusiastic, helpful trainer leads us to our locker room. I plop my green duffel bag down on the warped, wooden bench. I unzip the bag to extract my shoes and uniform. I take out the shoes first and place them next to the bag. When I grab and pull out the dark green jersey, I hold it up in front of me. Green. This does not feel quite right. Ever since I can remember the jersey I have pulled out before a game has

---

[63] My parents still refer to it as "Western Montana College," and have a WMC license plate on their Ford Taurus.

[64] Both my parents, Uncle Jay, brother Jeff (eventually), and sister-in-law Megan went to the University of Montana Western; my dad and sister-in-law are in their sports hall of fame for football and basketball, respectively. My friend Amanda Schlepp also graduated from Western, as it is a school that was founded to train teachers.

been blue. Beautiful blue. Beautiful Columbia blue. So much prettier than green. I tilt my head to the side and consider this new uniform that represents the Rocky Mountain Battlin' Bears and not the Chester Coyotes. I guess bears are okay. Cooler than bulldogs, I decide. But this number: 14? I am number 12. I have always been number 12. Well, as of today I guess I am number 14, and I am a bear. That is a weird sentence. Is this what an identity crisis feels like?

* * *

Midnight. Well I think it is safe to say I will always remember my first college basketball experience. We played a doubleheader in Dillon.[65] It took a little while to get in a groove during warm-ups. Don't get me wrong, I love my new teammates, but it still feels weird. Once I had a turnover where I just chucked the ball a foot higher than any post on my team can jump and thought to myself, *Whoops*, then feeling slightly—and now I realize irrationally—annoyed I thought, *Michele would have caught that*.

Sunday we won 75-71. We were up ten with two minutes left, but I freakin' turned the ball over twice, and they got within two with seven seconds left. Then they fouled me, and thank goodness I made both the one-and-one free throws. I have learned that it is always a good idea to get the ball in Kat or Shye's hands, and it was of course nice having Maci on the court with me.

Maci. She is why I will always remember this experience. When we were shooting around before the game on Monday, she came up to me and said she had a really bad cramp that would not go away. Maci never complains, so I made her go with me to see the trainer. The trainer pushed on her belly. Mace just winced in pain every time she touched her right side. I couldn't help but think, well maybe stop pressing on her aching belly. The pain was supposedly higher than the appendix. Maci was crying, and she does not cry for pain. So I started crying

---

[65] Dillon, Montana, is located about an hour north of the Idaho border along Interstate 15, and is the county seat of Beaverhead County. Dillon houses the Beaverhead County Museum, with many outdoor exhibits. Visitors are often drawn to Dillon due to its convenient access to trout fishing rivers and scenic byway drives (BigSkyFishing.com, 2002-2021).

because it scared the crap out of me. They put some heat on it, and she came back for the last ten minutes of warm-ups and played the game.

We won by seventeen, so it was better than the day before. I flipping missed three free throws, though. We left right after the game and stopped in Whitehall to eat. I guess Maci's pain started coming back then. We got in the van again, and a little later Kat whispered to me that Maci was squeezing her hand so tight but did not want me to know. It was obvious Maci needed help, so I told Coach Gustin we needed to get to a hospital. We pulled into the ER in Bozeman, and they took Maci to a room. A nurse came and got me so I could sit with her. As soon as I entered her room and smelled that smell my stomach churned. Just like when visiting Grandpa.

Maci is always so strong. I hated how scared she looked. It dawned on me that I needed to be the strong one in the situation. I was not exactly sure just how to do that. I held her hand and rubbed her arm and tried to find something funny to watch on TV. They took a bunch of tests. I had to really work hard not to faint, what with all that needle poking. [66] I was slightly embarrassed when I had to ask for a Sprite for myself when they inserted her IV.

Aunt Kathy showed up because my parents let her know we were there, which was so nice. It was not appendicitis or kidney stones or the gallbladder, they didn't think, and the tests were all supposedly "normal." It sure did not seem like everything was normal. After two hours—and a lot of pain medication—they released us. We went back on our merry way, in a blinding blizzard, creeping along I-90 at 45 mph, and drove by a huge car and semi pileup on the opposite side of the interstate. It took us over an hour longer than it should have to get back home. Ah, winter travel in Montana.

* * *

I take another delicious bite of the Papa John's pizza Jer left for us in our room. I called his room when we left the hospital, and he left a note on the pizza boxes telling us congratulations on our first wins. So dang sweet.

"We'll take care of her," Megan says as she, Alex, and Shye start to walk Maci out of the room.

---

[66] I had several issues fainting after receiving shots growing up. Those needles really get me!

"Tell Jer thanks for the pizza," Alex adds.

"Okay, get some rest," Kat calls.

"Night, guys."

"Goodnights" are echoed all around. Then it is just Kat and me in the room. I sigh a big sigh. "Well that was eventful." I state the obvious.

"Yeah." Kat agrees.

"I am glad Maci is feeling better. That was pretty scary."

I nod in agreement. Glad we got that all taken care of.

* * *

What is going on? "Kat?" I ask into the darkness.

"Kat's asleep." I hear a strained whisper.

Who said that? What time is it? I struggle coming out of my hard sleep. Finally I sit up and lean over my bunk. It is blurry and dark, but there is a silhouette in our camping chair. I fumble and locate my glasses, then turn on the lamp clamped to the corner of my bedpost. I glance at the alarm clock. Five in the morning?! There are only two reasons anyone in this dorm room would be up at this insane hour, and there was no party last night. My eyes finally adjust, and I get a clear look at the camping chair occupant. "Maci Lea!" I exclaim with surprise, then worry.

My brain starts putting the pieces together. "Do we need to go to the hospital?!"

Maci, never wanting to be a bother, shrugs slightly and hesitantly confirms, "I think so."

I quickly switch gears and hop down to the floor. Gotta get my coat, my wallet, car keys. Should I call anyone? Not yet. Getting a call at five in the morning can really freak a person out. I scribble a quick note for Kat and stick it on the counter. I grab my coat hanging over the corner of my bed, wrap my arm around my friend's waist, and guide her out to the deserted parking lot. I punch in the five-digit code to open the car doors and help Maci into the passenger seat. The Taurus navigates slowly and cautiously onto Poly Drive toward the hospital, struggling against the ice and blowing snow.

As we walk in the ER entrance of St. Vincent's it dawns on me how ill-equipped I feel to handle something like this. The room is empty, save for a gray-haired worker behind a wooden desk in front of us. She gives Maci a once-over and immediately calls for an aide to escort her back to a room. I approach the desk and do my best to answer intimidating questions about symptoms, prior care, and insurance. After filling out a complicated form to the best of my ability I take a seat on a cold metal chair in the waiting area. I totally empathize with Joey on last week's episode of *Friends*, when he asked if Ross was short for "Rossel" or "Rostopher." Hospital forms are intimidating. Before I can begin to warm the seat, a nurse comes out and beckons me to follow her to yet another depressing patient room.

Maci is lying in a crisp, white-sheeted bed wearing a light-blue-and-white dotted dressing gown. The expression on her face suggests she is still extremely uncomfortable. "Did they give you anything for the pain?" I ask, feeling frustrated and worried.

"Yeah," she struggles, "they gave me some morphine."

Morphine. Jeez, I wonder why it does not look like it is helping. A nurse comes in and checks all the noisy machines. "How are you feeling now?" she asks.

Maci answers, "Not much different . . ."

"Okay." The nurse rubs Maci's shoulder and looks her over.

The nurse checks something on Maci's chart, then announces, "I will ask about another shot of morphine and maybe some Percocet."

I sit in a chair next to Maci's head and ask if I can get her anything, to which she responds with a quick headshake. So I do what I think someone in my family would do in a situation like this and turn on the television. I land on a *Seinfeld* rerun on TBS. Kramer abruptly enters Jerry's room. The nurse enters our room after a few minutes, not so abruptly, and adds more medicine to the IV drip. If two doses of morphine and that "set" medicine she mentioned do not work I do not know what in the world will. I watch my friend closely and finally see a wave of relief and relaxation wash over her face. I ask hopefully, "Feeling better, babe?"

Eyes closed, Maci smiles and contentedly tells me, "I see potatoes spinning around on a hardwood floor."

I take that as a yes.[67]

---

[67] Maci ended up being diagnosed with a couple extremely painful ruptured ovarian cysts and spent almost an entire week in bed on consistent pain meds.

Chapter 14

November–December 2002, first season highlights and lowlights, Billings, Montana

The season is going okay. We travel in a fifteen-passenger van through Wyoming a lot, usually in blizzards, and we eat a lot of Wendy's. I braid tons of hair, and it is really fun staying in hotels and getting to know each of my teammates better and better. Early in November we played Western Wyoming in a gym in Powell. They were pretty good. We were down three at half, and then we started off awesome in the second half and won by thirteen.[68]

Waking up Liz before a road game, 2002

The next day we played against Northwest College, and it did not go so well. At half we were down by eleven, and they came out in the

---

[68] Our college games consisted of two twenty-minute halves.

second and scored six points in a row. We were down by twenty-six at one point. I had never been down by that much in my life; it sucked. We got within seven twice, but could not get over that hump and lost by thirteen. I had four three-pointers and twenty-eight points, but unfortunately we did not play great as a team.

Classes are going fine. I am having to really make sure I have my poop in a group keeping up with reading, studying, and turning in assignments, since we are missing so much class for games. Good thing I am a genius. Kat, Jeremy, and I have gone to a couple church services. I really like the music, and I love being next to Jeremy and hearing him sing. Jeremy had a little bit of drama because turns out he broke his foot "tripping down the stairs when leaving one of his classes." (And by "tripping down the stairs" I mean playing a pickup basketball game with Peter and some other guys, which I believe is quite frowned upon, as he is in season.) Luckily it is his left foot, and the doctor cleared him to play, as long as it doesn't hurt too much. I told him my dad would say he should rub some dirt on it.

The next weekend in November we played Sheridan College. It was a blast. Isaac and Travis came with the Buffingtons; it was so good to have Chester people in the crowd! I popped a three to start off the game, and we pulled up by fourteen at one point. But in the last three minutes of the first half they got within three. The second half was close the whole time. With forty-five seconds left they tied it up for the first time. We got a shot up, and I crashed hard and somehow got the offensive board, put it up, made it, and was fouled. It was so cute because Jeremy jumped up, all excited, on that play (he and Petey drove my car to watch us; they are our groupies). I thought the game was over. But alas, Sheridan went down and did the exact same thing. We rushed back down to our end, and Tiff got up a shot that almost went in, they boarded it and got a shot that went in! Their crowd erupted, but the refs were all, "No good! No good!"

Overtime was five minutes. We started out with two steals and converted them to layups. It was ours after that. They had to foul Shye and me at the end, and we made all our free throws. Chasi Lee played really well, but it was weird playing against her, and I could tell it was really hard for her. After the final buzzer she ran off to the locker room with tears in her eyes. Jeremy's dad was there, too, and I got to meet Jer's adorable little sister, Naomi. They came down and talked to us for a minute after the game. Chasi Lee came out, and we hugged her and she cried. She does not like her coach very much and is not enjoying basketball. She said how much she misses us. I guess Maci and I are very lucky that we like it. So far anyway.

Let's see . . . where did we play after that? Oh yes! We went to Powell, Wyoming for a change! That time we played Southern Idaho. We played crappy and lost by eleven. At one point we were down by seventeen, but we went on a run with a couple minutes left in the first half. Jeri hit a short jumper, I drove, then hit four free throws, then popped a quick three. So we were only down nine at half. I came out and hit two threes right away in the second half, then Jeri made a layup and tied it with an and-one free throw. But we let it go in the end, and Coach Gustin was ticked.

Unfortunately the next game also sucked. The other team was really good, but still. I really do not want to talk about it.

Bonus, though, when we got home I discovered that our volleyball team was playing Northern, and Kaitlynn Rae was there! It was really blizzarding in Havre, so she got to spend the night in the dorms with us, which was so awesome. We watched our boys barely lose to Minot State. We were down eighteen with four minutes left, then Jake[69] hit five threes, a layup, but then missed a layup, and we lost by one. So close! And the crowd was going wild. It was really fun having Katy here, so she could see where I live and meet a bunch of my teammates.

On the thirteenth we had our first home game, against Powell. And we got crushed, 59–90. They could not miss, and we could. We were down by flipping twenty-two in the first half. The second half was a little better but too little, too late. The practice after that was, um, memorable. We ran a "16," which includes a lot of side-to-side sprints: 2, 4, 8, 16, 8, 4, 2, with ten sit-ups between each set. It made the seven-

---

[69] Jake Stuart transferred to Rocky after redshirting, then playing his freshman year at the University of Montana. While at Rocky, Stuart received NAIA all-America honors in 2004 and was a two-time all-Frontier-Conference performer. During his three-year Rocky career, Stuart helped lead the Battlin' Bears to two straight NAIA national tournament appearances and was a kind and humble teammate.

minute drill look reasonable. Then we played cutthroat one-on-one, three-on-three, then five-on-five, and we had to run if we lost, gave up an offensive board, didn't box out, etc. It was an intense practice, which I liked, and all of us girls thought it went well. But JD pretty much shot that theory down in the end, telling us (again) how we did not compete and play hard. Screw that. At one point he said we don't play with heart. That is such bull. We are lucky our team is supportive of one another and keeps each other positive. I called Coach VanDyke after practice, and she calmed me down. She gave me a coach's standpoint and told me to just keep working hard.

The next week was better. We beat Dillon at home by thirty-nine, and my parents brought my Amanda and Isaac. After that game my parents took Kat, Pete, Jeremy, Isaac, Amanda and me to my dad's favorite place: Tiny's Tavern. The Anglins met us there, too. Kat and Isaac had an eat-off. It was amazing. They each ate giant burgers with full plates of fries, onion rings, and all the random leftovers from everyone else's plates. The waitress scrounged up two ice cream cups from the bottom of the freezer, and we had to call it a tie. My dad was so happy; he loves feeding people.

Unfortunately we somehow lost to Dillon the next night by two points. Instead of talking in the locker room at halftime we ran sprints in the little gym because, "If we weren't going to hustle in the game, we'd do it now."

We probably deserved it.

I was benched almost as soon as the game started so that sucked. Same thing Monday night against Miles City. Watched a lot of the game from the pine and not sure why. Coach VanDyke and Coach Schlepp always talked to me and told me what they were thinking. Not sure how to handle the, um, different communication styles of my new coaches. Maci played well, so I was glad for that, but we lost in overtime by one. A girl tied regulation at the buzzer with a long three. I hate losing.

Thursday we headed to Casper for a three-day tournament. We left at ten, ate lunch in Buffalo, checked in to our hotel, and played Casper Alumni at six. I got pulled out early again, and I was so frustrated that whole night. We—surprise!—lost, by eleven or so. Then yesterday we ate breakfast, had shootaround, then chilled in our rooms. We played Utah at four. We actually played well, but they played better and beat us by twenty. I cannot believe I am saying this, but it wasn't as bad as it sounds. I played more, so I gained back a little confidence. It is really unsettling, though, having to wonder whether or not my coaches have confidence in me. It is a new feeling. I hate it.

That night we ate at Subway and went to the movie theater and watched *The Ring*. That movie is freaky. We were all super freaked out, and no one would do anything by themselves in the hotel. JD said he didn't get to sleep until three in the morning. It was a crazy night. Tomorrow is our last game before Thanksgiving break. I imagine it will be easier to give thanks if we win a game for a change. Hopefully we can pull one out tomorrow.

* * *

Good riddance, stupid Casper, Wyoming. We played the same team today that beat us in Cody. We played really well; we were even up two at half. But they honestly could not miss. I fouled out with nine seconds left, trying to take a charge. JD has been harping on us about taking charges. Shye was almost killed in practice the other day because she was not allowed to move when Liz was barreling in for a layup at full speed in a supposed charge drill. At least I got to play with Maci for a while tonight. My eyes are tired, especially because I could not hold it in and cried after losing, again. I am so sick of losing.

An announcement regarding hot McNuggets snaps my attention back to the present. Alexia hands me my brown to-go bag, and we all hustle from the nice warm McDonald's to our carriage. The wind is biting. The air smells like snow. I duck in the side door of our giant van and squeeze in beside Megan in the second to last seat. As we merge onto the interstate, I stretch my seatbelt way out in front of me and twist around in my spot. Maci holds out her flashlight so those of us in Jacquee Dundas's freshman English class can read *My Antonia*. I struggle to get through a couple pages and promise myself I can sleep when I finish the next chapter. I force myself to keep reading and try really hard to concentrate.

> *No, there was nothing but land—slightly undulating, I knew,*
> *because often our wheels ground against the brake as we went*

102

down into a hollow and lurched up again on the other side
(Penguin, 2021).

Speaking of lurch, what was that? An odd feeling moves through the vehicle. I look up at Alex. A look of fear seizes her face. Quietly she forebodingly announces, "We're going off."

I spin around quickly, press my back to the seat and feet to the floor, drop my book, then grab the seat ahead of me. I blink. Everything shifts to slow motion. I listen, but somehow cannot hear anything. I look, but right then my head crunches up against the ceiling. All I see is black. My neck jerks. I try to straighten up, but the momentum of the roll snaps me sideways. I again hit the ceiling and again, my neck jerks. Then, silence.

* * *

"We have to get everybody shoes! We have to cover everyone's heads!" I hear Megan give orders and feel a flurry of movement around me.

It takes a few seconds to find my bearings. I blink rapidly and rub my eyes with clenched fists. I am lying on my side. My eyes finally begin to focus. People are walking in and out of the door. Wait, that is not a door. No, it is the rear window. Kat crouches down next to me, concerned. "Are you okay, Jame?"

I look at her and blink a few more times. I do a quick self-scan and slowly reply, "Yeah I, I think so. Are you?"

It takes a few seconds to realize what has happened. With urgency now I ask, "Is everybody else?!"

She reaches for my hand and helps me sit up. "We aren't exactly sure. The people who were sitting in front are not looking so good." Her voice cracks. "Someone pulled over to help, and he's an EMT. Alexia called 911 right away."

We both go silent as we hear sirens coming closer and closer. Kat looks toward the ambulance, then turns her head to the front of the van. I follow her concerned eyes and see Tiffany.

Oh, no.

Maci and Becky are urging Tiffany to stay awake. Tiffany's face is bloody. Her ear is all cut up. It is hard to tell if blood is coming from somewhere else as well. Clearly Tiff is in a lot of pain. She is crying and moaning and struggling to keep her head up.

"The ambulance is almost here," I hear Maci explain to Tiffany.

Maci rubs Tiffany's hands gently. "Tiff, you just need to hang on for a few more minutes."

Kat looks back to me. "Here." She tosses me a duffel bag. "We gotta find everyone outside. People are out there without coats or shoes."

I rifle through the bag and pull out a sweatshirt, T-shirt, and a pair of basketball shoes. I press up onto all fours. A wave of nausea sweeps through me. I balance until I am pretty sure I will not throw up. It takes a minute to realize I am also in my stocking feet. I crawl cautiously across the van. Chaos. Coats, bags, books scattered around the sideways seats. The agitated winds shoo angry wet gusts through the broken glass, coating the interior with snow and dirt.

Somehow I manage to locate the strap of my bag and tug at it. Finally the bag dislodges. I grasp my *I love this game* keychain that is attached to the zipper, pull it back, and dunk my hand in through the contents. My hand gropes the clothes and runs across one tennis shoe. I pull it up, set it on my lap, then plunge in again. When I have both shoes I have sense enough to zip my bag back up and toss it to the corner near the broken window-turned-door. I shakily pull on my shoes but have trouble tying them. I carefully stand up and duck as I exit through the shattered back window.

The brutal frozen wind tears at my face. I gasp, blink, and try to make sense of the stormy scene. The angry swirling blizzard makes it difficult to see much past a foot in front of my face. As I trudge slowly away from the van, my burning quads tell me we are on a fairly steep embankment where the snow is deepening by the minute. I see Kat and Shye each holding on to a side of Liz, whose stunned gaze suggests shock. They walk toward me. Dazed, brow furrowed, Liz gestures to her neck area and slowly explains, "It really hurts right here."

A scene from *Tommy Boy* where Chris Farley describes his pain after David Spade whacks him with a wooden plank flashes briefly. I shoo it away. This is not the time, Jamie.

Disoriented, Liz asks, "Is that my bone?"

I swallow back the urge to gag when I spot Liz's collarbone protruding from her shirt.

"You are going to be fine," Shye assures Liz, then shares a concerned glance with Kat and me.

Shye's shaky voice threatens to give her away. "You just need to sit down and wait for the ambulance to get here."

"I'm gonna faint," Liz states as she sways to the right.

I rush behind her, and the three of us manage to get Liz propped up against the roof of the van. Jeri stumbles our way, coming from the other side of the van. She holds her head in her hands and crouches next to Liz. Alex carries two bags over to us, and one of them belongs to Liz. Alex rummages quickly through the bag and pulls out the tennis shoes. Kat and Alex awkwardly pull the shoes on Liz. Shye and I wrap a shirt around her head and ears, then one around Jeri's. "It's going to be okay," I hear my voice say.

Is it? I wonder to myself.

I look to the road. There are lots of headlights illuminating the disturbing scene. Alexia is standing close to the shoulder, talking loudly on her cell phone, motioning frantically with her arm. She looks so cold, and then I see she is not wearing any shoes either. I turn and trudge back to the van to find another bag, but instead find a pillow. I clumsily pull off its cover. Fighting the storm, which definitely seems to be winning, I put my head down and hike up to Alexia. I wrap the pillowcase around her head and encourage her to get inside one of the vehicles that has pulled over to help. As if on cue, a man jumps out of his Ford pickup and makes his way toward us. Alexia presses the end button on her phone and shoves it in her pocket. The man and I each wrap one of Alexia's arms around our shoulders and take her to his pickup. As he gets her inside I notice the blood. Her socks are red, and there are cuts in her pant legs. "Maybe she needs to go in the ambulance?" I manage, voice cracking.

The man assures me he will get her to the hospital and says I should get in the vehicle as well. A woman in the passenger seat nods, beckoning me. I look back down toward the van. I spot JD. He is walking around, holding his side, looking extremely disoriented and distraught. I look back up at the Good Samaritan. I tell the man, "I am going to do one more check, and then I will get a ride."

His expression is anxious. I attempt a reassuring smile. "Promise."

He looks at me, up at his pickup, then back at me. "Okay," he finally agrees.

"Everyone needs to get to the hospital," he adds, his voice taking a stern fatherly tone.

I picture my own dad and tear up again. Daddy, I need you.

I reach JD just as Megan does. Megan shouts, "Coach! You need to get in a vehicle."

JD winces in pain but keeps walking around frantically. "I need to find everybody. I need to find everybody."

Megan and I exchange a look, neither of us sure what to do. I look toward the road. The visibility is still terrible. I squint, trying to figure out what to do next. It looks like a lot of vehicles have pulled over. That looks like an ambulance about to park.[70] A few people dressed in rescuer garb break into view. My shoulders drop as I let out a relieved exhale.

Thank goodness.

* * *

My shaky finger punches in the familiar numbers automatically. Ring. Ring. Please be home. Ring. "Hello?"

"Hi, Dad." I barely get the words out before I break down crying.

"Hi, sweetheart. Mr. Corey called and told us you all slid off the road."

I am surprised at how calm my dad sounds. "Well, we didn't slide off the road. We flipped," I explain. Feeling slightly irritated I add, "Twice."

"Oh!" My mom joins the conversation on their other phone.

"We didn't think it sounded like it was a very big deal," she states.

"Well it was a big deal!" I snap.

Tears sting, and I am surprised at how angry I feel. I guess it is anger. A lot of emotions stir my insides.

---

[70] We heard later that something like fifty vehicles went off the road within a tenish-mile stretch due to the dangerous conditions brought on so quickly by the blizzard.

"Darn, sweetie. Well, are you okay??" Mom asks, this time sounding distressed.

I steady my breath and hold back the tears. No use worrying them more. I was just thrown off by how unconcerned they first sounded. "I think so," I reply.

I am not sure why I feel so upset that they are not more upset. I think for a second and share some details. "I hit my head a couple times, but I'm not bleeding anywhere, and I am walking fine. There have been so many accidents tonight that this hospital is packed. It's crazy. They are only seeing patients who are definitely hurt. Coach Gustin, Liz, Tiffany, Alexia, and Jeri are all getting checked out. They were all sitting in the front seats of the van." This makes me stop explaining. Picturing the scene brings on a fresh batch of hot tears. "But I think everybody is going to be okay, eventually," I add. It is silent for a few moments. Then I quietly say, "My phone is on roaming, so I better go." Why am I suddenly so anxious to get off the phone with them? Twenty seconds ago all I wanted was to hear their voices, to hear them tell me everything is going to be okay.

"Are you sure you have to go?" Mom asks.

The irritation immediately subsides. "Yes, but everything's okay," I say, giving them the reassurance I initially craved.

My defenses drop. I realize Mr. Corey probably found out no one was killed and did not want to have a bunch of freaked out helpless parents hundreds of miles away.

"Okay, babe, thanks for calling," Dad soothes. "Call us when you get back to Rocky. Love you."

"Love you," Mom adds.

"Love you guys, too."

I hang up and take a big breath. Then I dial the number I have scribbled on the back of my journal: Jeremy's home phone.

Before the phone completes a full ring, Jeremy's urgent voice answers, "Hello?!"

I smile and choke up all at the same time. "Hi," I squeak softly.

"Are you okay? Where are you? I knew something was wrong when my dad drove out to the interstate exit. I was waiting and waiting for your van"—he takes a breath and states the obvious, voice thick with frustration—"but it never came."

Hearing his voice triggers another surge of emotion. I wish I could be in his arms right this second. I was able to get a hold of his dad when waiting in the pickup. Luckily I grabbed my journal from my bag so I would have their phone number. In a shaky voice I manage to give Jeremy the details I reported to my parents. As I share out loud, I remember more.

I tell him about the nice couple that drove Kat, Alex, Megan, and me to the hospital. How a few people were taken in emergency vehicles, and how other people pulled over and took the rest of us to the hospital. How Thomas called three times before we finally answered Tiffany's phone. We thought we were protecting Thomas by not answering—we were trying not to worry him—but thank goodness we finally did answer because it turns out he had been on the phone with Tiff while we flipped. He heard screaming and all kinds of noises, and then silence. Then he heard people frantically calling out Tiffany's name right before the call was cut off. Tears fall down as I relay this story. We are waiting to find out if her neck is broken.

I do not want to stop talking to Jeremy, but I see someone beckoning us. "It looks like someone is here to take us to a hotel," I explain. "And my phone bill is going to be crazy with all this roaming. I will call you again if I can. Otherwise, we should somehow be home tomorrow."

"Okay," Jeremy concedes.

"Thanks for calling. I am so glad you are okay."

Then he says, "I love you."

Heart jump. Oh yeah, we are saying that now. Warmth and comfort rush through me when I hear him say those words. A smile even forms on my lips. "I love you, too."

I hang up and lock in to the conversations happening around me. Sounds like the owner of the Super 8 and his daughter are going to transport us freshmen (minus Jeri, who is still getting checked out in a patient room) to the hotel. That is so nice of them. Then they will bring everyone else back as they are hopefully released later tonight. Sounds like it might be another long night.[71]

* * *

"I'm not getting on that thing," Shye adamantly states in my ear, arms crossed defiantly, standing just over my shoulder.

We study the clunky white people-mover pulling up in front of the hotel. It looks like the vehicle my dad sometimes volunteers to drive when picking up all the old people who can't drive anymore and drops them off at the senior center or church. TC[72] emerges as the vehicle's clear doors split open. He greets us, tells us he is so glad everyone is okay, and beckons for us to board the shuttle. We stare and blink skeptically, arms crossed, unmoving. JD and TC chat for a few seconds. After some coaxing eventually—hesitantly—we finally board.

I tuck in to a back seat with Shye. I might as well be boarding a terrifying roller coaster at Cedar Point for how my body feels. We watch Alexia limp cautiously up the stairs, followed by a discombobulated-looking Jeri, then Liz, with her sling keeping her broken collarbone in place. Coach insists on "helping" Tiffany up the steps and to her seat, though with his broken ribs he cannot offer much support. Tiffany wears an intense-looking neck brace. The doctor said she was extremely lucky to not have broken her neck; she suffered a very bad strain. I wonder if Tiffany will ever be able to play basketball again. Or if she will want to. How can that be? That not even twenty-four hours ago she was out there on the court running, playing. Now she is lucky she can walk.

A picture of Annie[73] flickers in my mind. I think about that phone call telling us about her accident. Her being thrown from the vehicle.

---

[71] The hotel owners were incredibly hospitable and generous that night, providing us with free pizza and pop, free long distance, and free rooms. We freshmen settled into our rooms first, and our other team members trickled in over the next couple hours: Liz (broken collarbone), Alexia (feet went through the windshield, giving her many cuts, bruises, and a limp for a while after), and Coach Gustin (broken ribs) were brought back after our group. The hotel owners brought Jeri (concussion) and Tiffany (very strained neck) back last. We all talked in a couple rooms until two in the morning. Kat and I shared a room with Tiffany and fell asleep around four for a few hours.

[72] "TC" is how most of us addressed Terry Corey, Rocky's athletic director from 1999–2008.

[73] Annie Diemert was a high school teammate of mine who was killed in a single-vehicle accident in November 1999 (Graham Duprey, 2020).

The visit to the hospital. Her funeral. It takes me a second to realize tears are streaming, again. I pull my hoodie over my head and close my eyes as the driver shifts into gear and pulls away.

Every stop and turn feels dangerous. I hate how jumpy I feel. When we stop longer than it would ever take to wait for a red light, I poke my head out of my hood and chance a glance out the window. Heart racing, a wave of nausea sweeps across my stomach. We are in a garage, parked by the van that mercilessly tossed us around last night. The left side of the van is crumpled, windows shattered. Looking at the back window now, it feels insane that we were using that space as a door. Some of us plod off the shuttle and gather the bags and miscellaneous clothes and shoes piled haphazardly near the van. I realize I am shaking as I board again. This is going to be a long ride home.

* * *

"I've got everybody's orders," Jeremy announces.

I ride with Jeremy to Albertsons, then Wendy's, where we gather and purchase burgers, fries, and random grocery requests to deliver to my exhausted yet ravenous teammates. After we deliver everybody's orders, I make several phone calls in my dorm room. I call my parents, grandparents, the VanDykes, Amanda, and a few other people. When I hang up for the night I look at the clock: ten o'clock. I crawl slowly up to my bunk, where Jer is waiting for me. I lay my head on his chest. He said he wants to stay with me until I fall asleep. When I close my eyes, scenes of the wreck intrude my thoughts. Quickly I flip my eyes back open. So exhausted. I close my eyes again. Same thing. My shoulders shake first, before any noise comes out. I bawl and shudder, unable to stop the wreck from replaying in my mind. I wonder if any of my teammates are having the same issues. It might be a long night.

Chapter 15

November 27-31, 2002, Thanksgiving break, Big Timber, Montana

"Okay, babe," Grandma calls from the kitchen. "Dinner's ready."

I click the TV off and sit up on her scratchy yet surprisingly comfortable tan couch, careful to tuck the velvety red pillows back in place. Whoa. Little light-headed. I press both hands on the cushions and steady myself. I am so glad I am here. We had to go back to classes on Monday and Tuesday, after getting home from the accident. I could barely concentrate. I was so frustrated when Professor Dundas lost my intro paragraph and outline for my paper, and then the floppy disk I had saved it on would not work. Not only did Peter get a better grade than I did on our last paper for her—and I gave him ideas for the paper at midnight before it was due—but then this? I realize Peter is a brilliant wordsmith, but we worked together, so why did I get a B? I could not get off campus fast enough.

Never mind I was terrified the entire time driving here and could barely force myself to accelerate past sixty. Each twist and turn that used to soothe and comfort me had somehow transformed into potential danger. I kept picturing myself somehow swerving off at different places alongside the interstate, wondering what would happen if my car rolled into that guardrail, or near that embankment. When I finally pulled safely into Grandma's driveway it was all I could do to peel my hands off the steering wheel; I did not realize I was gripping it so tight.

At least I am here at Grandma's house now. After a few seconds I stand and start to walk across the tile toward the step up to the kitchen. Another wave of dizziness catches me off guard. I sway and cannot refocus my eyes. Dang it, I know this feeling, and I did not catch it early enough. I am going down. My eyes blur. It feels like my entire body is a swirling tornado. Such a helpless feeling, I think vaguely, as my arms remain stubbornly straight at my side. I hit the floor like a ton of bricks.

"Jamie?" Grandma's voice sounds far away.

It takes me a second to regain my balance. I sit up and wait for the swaying to stop. "Coming, Gram," I respond shakily. Slowly I rise to my knees, take a breath, then stand. My hand holds an end table while I ensure I have regained my equilibrium. Okay, I don't think I am going to faint again. Food willB help.

"Are you okay, honey?" Grandma enters the kitchen from the laundry room and walks my way. She rubs my shoulder and looks at me with concern as I settle onto a stool pulled out from the end of her long kitchen counter. She did not see me faint.

No reason to worry her. "Yes, I'm fine." I smile. "I just got up too fast and got a little dizzy. Had to sit down for a second." I change the subject: "Dinner looks good."

Grandma turns and beckons to my place setting. "Oh good. Have as much as you want."

I pick up my fork and press it into a few canned green beans—that have been cooked with cream, of course—and decide I will ask Grandma if she can tickle my back on the couch after we finish eating. We can turn on TV and maybe find a Hallmark movie to watch. Then I can lay over her lap and let her long red fingernails work their magic. No, I conclude decidedly, I will never be too old for Grandma's back tickles.

* * *

"Hey, sweetheart. Time to get up and get ready." Dad gently jostles me awake.

I blink blankly at him a few times then look around the room I am in. Oh yeah, we are in Big Timber for Thanksgiving.

"How are you feeling?" Dad asks, head tilted, and rubs my shoulder.

My shoulder is tender, but there is nothing Dad can do about that. "Okay," I say, yawning.

"Dinner at Barb and Helmar's is at noon, so you better get showered and dressed," Dad encourages.

On autopilot I shower, dry, change, and weakly attempt some primping. This includes swirling my wet permed hair against my head and fastening it with a brown plastic claw. Then I apply a light coat of mascara and—voilà. Maybe not quite voilà, but good enough.

I stroll slowly across the dark-blue and green swirled carpet in the back living room and enter the kitchen where Grandma is bustling around in her red-and-white striped apron. She pulls open a creaky drawer under the cookie jar—which holds noticeably fewer wafer cookies than it did yesterday—and pulls out a blue casserole dish cover. I watch her fuss with the zipper. She peels open the bag with her always dark-red fingernails. Then she pulls on a gray oven mitt and carefully tucks in the piping hot cornflake casserole. As she covers the delicious dish, she notices me. "Oh hi, babe."

Her eyes are filled with concern and care. "How are you feeling today?"

I take a couple steps toward her and lean in for a side hug. "I feel fine," I say, which is mostly true.

I ask, "Are you ready to go over?"

She kisses me on the forehead. "Yep, I'm ready."

Grandma hands me the casserole, unties her apron, and sets it on the counter. With my free hand I pop a handful of Skittles from the ever-present candy bowl on the opposite counter and follow her through the long narrow kitchen. We turn right at the tall windows that line the house's east wall. I spot a magpie snacking from a bird feeder, kept perpetually full by Grandma, hanging from a towering fir tree. Observing all the birds outside Grandma's windows is one of my favorite things to do when sitting at her breakfast table. I smile toward the magpie and gently set down the casserole on the entryway carpet. I retrieve and pull on my shoes from the entry room. Grandma already has on her white-yet-somehow-always-clean tennis shoes.

I grab the casserole again, pull open the screen door, and let Grandma lead. We descend the front steps and walk across her driveway and impeccable lawn.[74] We check briefly for cars, more out of habit than real concern that there might be traffic, and cross Stock Street. Then we follow the long sidewalk that leads right to Grandpa and Grandma Branae's little light-blue house. Dad is waiting with the door open, which sends a waft of sweet scents our way. It smells like hot

---

[74] Grandma's neighbor and friend Kenny Schott took meticulous care of Grandma's yard for decades.

roasted turkey, Grandma Barb's homemade dinner rolls, green bean casserole, and pumpkin pie. If comfort had a smell.

* * *

"You are cheating!" My Aunt Kathy's finger points accusingly at my new boyfriend, whose mouth is wide open, both hands held up in innocence.

Jeremy looks from Kathy to me, and then back to Kathy. He says nothing, though his facial expressions and body language suggest he is wondering whether or not she is serious. Kathy continues the allegation. She even pushes her chair back and stands. "He is looking at my cards through the reflection of the window!"

All eyes follow her finger to the window directly behind Jeremy's chair. It is around ten on this Friday night in November, so the sun has been down for hours. The light from the pendant lamp in the dining room creates an opportunity for some window reflection, I suppose, but it seems clear to all that my aunt's accusation will not hold up in court. Grandma Joyce's sturdy, rectangular dining table is occupied by Uncle Jay, Uncle Jimmy, Mom, Becca, Joshua, and Jeffrey. Dad stands behind Becca and Joshua, keeping an eye on their cards and helping when needed. Jeremy scans the room, deciding how to respond. He closes his lips together and unsuccessfully suppresses a grin. He then proceeds to pull the top of his long sleeve black T-shirt up and over his head, spreads both arms out to his side creating a T shape, and starts running and buzzing gloatingly around the room.

Everyone breaks into hysterics. Aunt Kathy manages to hold her hands on her hips for a few seconds, looking stern and indignant, before she breaks down and bends over, laughing. Jeremy completes several laps around the living room before returning back to the table. He sits down to rejoin the game, acting as if nothing out of the ordinary happened. Uncle Jay begins shuffling the cards, then starts dealing another round. Jay pauses for a second, takes a drink of his Busch Light, and then places his hand on Jeremy's shoulder. "You'll fit right in," he asserts.

Introduce boyfriend to family, check.

Receive family approval, check.

Chapter 16

December 4, 2002, last games of freshman year, Miles City and Glendive, Montana

The final buzzer sends us to our bench. I wipe a pool of sweat from my eyebrow as I jog sluggishly off the court.

Yesterday we braved a mild but steady snowstorm east on I-94 to Miles City.[75] The ride was stressful, as we were all pretty jumpy. That night we played the Miles Community College Pioneers. We were tired. We were all a step behind the entire game. It was a nine-point deficit at half, which didn't feel too bad, but then we got crushed by thirty. Not great for morale. We had a fun time swimming and hot tubbing at our hotel, though, so that was a bright spot. The hot tub felt so soothing on our many aching muscles.

Now we are in Glendive at Dawson Community College.[76] This game against the Buccaneers is the final one on our fast and furious schedule. I take a look at our pitiful bench: one exhausted substitute, five teammates in street clothes lining the second bleacher tier—adorned with scrapes, slings, and bandages—and a coach with a greenish-black eye and an arm also bound by a sling. Good thing this is our last game. We look pretty pathetic.

"Alright ladies," Coach Gustin addresses our awkward huddle.

---

[75] Miles City is a city of a little over eight thousand people located in the southeast corner of Montana, near the Yellowstone and Tongue rivers, and is the county seat of Custer County. Miles City was founded as a result of the Battle of the Little Bighorn on June 25, 1876. Livestock speculation brought thousands of cattle to the open ranges in the late 1880s, and the railroad was extended through the area (Miles Community College, 2021).

[76] Glendive, Montana, is the county seat of Dawson County and has a population of around five thousand. It was established by the Northern Pacific Railway. Like many Montana towns, Glendive is a hub for agriculture and ranching (Montana's Historic Landscapes, 2014).

I lean on my left knee, propped up on the bottom bleacher next to Alexia, in an attempt to adjoin us uniformed players and the injured bench dwellers. I lean in and focus on Coach. "Way to show some heart tonight. Way to fight through the pain and keep each other encouraged. This season has been one of ups and downs."

He pauses to look around the circle. He chokes up slightly as he studies his battered team. My throat tightens. I keep listening intently. After a steadying breath he continues. "I think we all learned a lot. Not only did you have to get used to playing with new teammates, but most of you had to work hard to figure out how to navigate your first college classes, live on your own for the first time, and all the other things that come with college life."

We nod silently.

Coach says, "Our record isn't what we hoped it would be—"

Understatement of the year, I think to myself. Six wins and sixteen losses. "Abysmal" is the first word that comes to my mind. I have never been on a team with a losing record. Thank goodness we won tonight, for the love.

"—but we had a lot of bright spots. Everyone improved, and we ended on a win—"

This statement triggers something in me. It transports me to gyms in Livingston, then Havre, Butte, and finally Belgrade. Hugging and high-fiving with Katy, Heidi, Michele, Chasi, Amanda, and Savannah. Crying with and consoling the same people. Feeling encouraged by Coach VanDyke and Coach Schlepp. Watching Carly and trying to understand her feelings of joy, and of disappointment. Instinctively I look across to the one face who was present with me in all those huddles. Maci looks up at the same time and our eyes lock. Then we both look around our current huddle. Similar, yet completely different.

"—so hold your heads up, and know that you are not only stronger basketball players after this season, but better people."

My arm lifts automatically to join my teammates' hands in the center.

* * *

"That's crap." My brother is dispensing sage advice after I tell him Jeri and Kat have been given the two open varsity spots.

116

"Jenny says you should be on varsity," Jeff continues.

"Well that's nice of her to say," I respond.

And I mean it. Jenny is a great point guard. Not only is she the quickest person I have ever played with, but she works her tail off 100 percent of the time and leads by example. And she is also backed up by a senior point guard, Ashley, who is the sweetest person on the planet.

"But we do have two point guards," I contend.

"You can be a two-guard. You're better than the two-guards they have now," Jeff counters.

I think on this for a minute. "Well, thanks, but I think Kat is the best two-guard we have, period. Plus, she has three inches on me. And they need Jeri for size, especially with Liz out of commission." I picture our entire team, varsity and JV. "And honestly, I would pick Shye after that. That girl is tough as nails. You tell her to stop their best player, she does it. You tell her to score, done."

"Yeah, you and Shye should both be on varsity," Jeff asserts.

"Well, there's nothing I can do about it now." I slump down in our super fancy camping chair.

"I will just have to work extra hard in the offseason."

"You can transfer." Jeff is clearly still irked by the situation.

I smile, touched by his protectiveness and passion. It surprises me how comforted it feels to know that even if my new coaches are not completely sure of me yet, my brother is. "I'll think about it." I lie, knowing this is the only way to tamp down his intensity. "Thanks, brother. I gotta get to class. Love ya."

"Love you, too," he replies, apparently satisfied for now.

I press end on my phone and set it on the edge of our desk. I reach back and pull out *My Antonia* from the stack of books piled haphazardly near my phone. My thumbs shuffle through the pages until they find the section I last read. A wave of nausea passes over me—something I am unfortunately becoming accustomed to—as I study the dirt-stained, snow-spattered pages. I was holding this book open when our van skidded off the slick road, and apparently it landed somewhere outside, or maybe near a window. I close my eyes and try to remember, but I can still only recall hearing Alex's warning, seeing her terrified expression, flipping around quickly in an attempt to brace myself,

117

feeling everything transition into slow motion, hitting my head and my neck being cranked once, twice, and that is it. That is all I can retrieve, until Kat started asking me questions.

I shake my head and blink a long blink, forcing myself to push the thoughts out of my mind. I try my best to focus on the text and begin to read.

> *No, there was nothing but land—slightly undulating, I knew, because often our wheels ground against the brake as we went down into a hollow and lurched up again on the other side* (Penguin, 2021).

After a minute or two, I realize I have read this paragraph at least ten times. Half-frustrated, half-resigned, I place the book face down on the desk. I lay my head back, cradled in the chair, and close my eyes. I replay my conversation with Jeff in my mind. To say I wasn't disappointed when Kat and Jeri told me they were on varsity would be inaccurate. Don't get me wrong, I am happy for my teammates and understand why they were chosen. They both told me they wish I could go with them. Was I a little disappointed that I heard it from them and not the coaches? Um, yep. But I guess I get that, too. They call you back when you get the job, not if you are the applicant who was not chosen.

Anyway, I truly am excited that now I get to go home for most of the month of December, and even a couple weeks in January, for Christmas break. Thinking about this gives me comfort. I am not too thrilled about being away from Jeremy, but hopefully we can work something out so we can connect when I am over in Big Timber. We also briefly talked about me going to Sheridan with him for a little while, right after finals are over. So we shall see. I would really prefer to know exactly what the plan is, but I am learning that maybe that is not the way things always work in "the real world."

Chapter 17

December 2002 – January 2003, Christmas break, Chester and Big Timber, Montana; Sheridan, Wyoming

Ah, wonderful Christmas break. Turns out college semesters are surprisingly short compared to high school. School starts later in the fall, and the semester is out the first week of December. Lovely.

Today is Christmas Eve, arguably my favorite day of the entire year. A day that has followed essentially the same schedule with the same traditions for as long as I can remember. I am currently following one of those traditions. I stand in front of Grandma and Grandpa Branae's bathroom mirror, primping and preening. Freshly showered, I don nice clothes—in lieu of the usual sweats—my hair is shiny and blow-dried, and I even dab on blush, apply mascara, and curl my hair. I am so fancy. This beauty routine is enjoyable, and the relaxation the routine brings allows my mind to review the events of past weeks.

Kat and I had a good talk before I left for the semester. Since she will continue on and play the varsity season—which she is glad about, of course—she had to stay on campus for almost the entire winter break. She and I talked about the pros and cons of that obligation. She said she was looking forward to focusing solely on basketball without any schoolwork, but the sacrifice meant barely any time to go home. You could tell it was bittersweet that I got to leave campus for so long and she had to stay. Kat also said it felt strange being not exactly on a "new" team, except it felt basically like a completely new team. Between bus rides and hotel stays and everything in between, our JV team had a lot of time to bond. And the accident took us all to a deeper level of connectedness. But we did not spend much time with the varsity players.

As I contemplate that conversation, I wonder how the last couple weeks were for Kat, and for Jeri. I wonder if they got homesick or lonely. I wonder about how tricky it can be to move from one team to another and try to find where you fit in. How tricky it can be figuring out a new role, or sometimes even multiple new roles. I wonder about the vulnerability it takes to connect quickly with and trust new people when joining a team. These thoughts feel overwhelming, since my teammates in Chester were basically the same since sixth grade. Also, in junior high and high school it felt like the focus was clearly all about "the team." In college there seems to be such focus on the individual player. Obviously individual development is always important in any sport, but the emphasis . . . I don't know . . . it feels different. It is hard to pinpoint.

I squeeze and let go of the lever connected to the handle of the iron, and the hot barrel releases a newly formed curl. I stare at my furrowed brow in the mirror and consider the complicated thoughts responsible for the brow-furrow. Maybe considering all that goes in to individual and team dynamics should be saved for another time.

I grab a new section of hair and shift my focus to my favorite topic. Jeremy Michael took me on a wonderful date Wednesday night. It was the first time we actually got dressed up for a date. Peter even gelled Jeremy's hair, so he looked extra cute. Jeremy was hanging out in my room just before we had planned to leave, but suddenly he rushed out to the hallway, closed the door, then knocked on the door seconds later because he wanted to officially pick me up for our date. Silly boy. Silly but oh-so sweet. Shye made us stop by her room so she, Liz, and Maci could take pictures. Everyone gets so excited when Jeremy and I are somewhere together. Lots of people already say we are going to get married. I do not think they are wrong. Is that completely crazy?!

So our friends took pictures of us, and then Jeremy and I went to Barnes and Noble, Olive Garden, and then he took me to Adam Sandler's new movie *8 Crazy Nights*. It definitely was crazy. We loved it. Then we headed back to Rocky. If only we had found some mistletoe to hang out under, it would have been the perfect date. Just kidding. We didn't need mistletoe.

Love to don our matching green 1980s garb any chance we get

121

Thursday morning I had my last final at a quarter to eight. All my finals went pretty well, I think, but frankly I do not want to think about them anymore. Jeremy and I scurried around all morning. We finally packed everything and picked up Robyn—the funny nontraditional student in my acting class who loves Jer and needed a ride to her parents' house in Sheridan—before hitting the road. It was such a great road trip. We dropped off Robyn and picked up Chasi Lee from the Sheridan College dorms. Then we followed David from the church [77] to the furniture store so he could buy his first new piece of furniture ever: a bed for Naomi for Christmas. Man, was he excited. He ended up buying not only the bed, but a mirror, bureau, and a little dresser. Apparently he goes crazy when it comes to buying gifts for people. Very sweet.

We hung out with Chasi for a while, and then we went to Naomi's orchestra concert. She plays the violin. These Duprey people name their cats after tribes of Israel and play in orchestras. Classy, I tell ya. Naomi went to stay with her mom at a hotel for the night, and then David made pork chops and creamed corn for Jeremy, Alycia, and me. Delicious. After dinner David showed us his new stereo system. He was so jacked that it had a remote control and the dial moved by itself when you changed the volume. It was so cute. That night we wrapped more presents in one night than I have maybe wrapped ever. They showed me a new level when it comes to Christmas presents. I loved it. Before we went to bed, Jeremy, David, Alycia, and I all held hands in a circle and prayed. I was thinking about what Richie wrote in her letter, about noticing traits in your partner's parents. I think Richie was on to something.

Friday consisted of us hanging out at the ranch house where Jeremy lived since he was in eighth grade. I braided Naomi's hair for her basketball games and junior high dance, and then Jer, Alycia, and I went to the movie theater and watched *Analyze That.* Saturday we went to this lady's house who they call "Grandma Dorothy." Dorothy was fabulous. After we left Dorothy's house we went to the fanciest restaurant I have ever been to, a place called Oliver's. The food was so fancy, and we had this potato pasta thing I did not even know how to

---

[77] David was the priest at the Episcopal church in Sheridan, Wyoming, for twenty years.

pronounce.[78] David made a toast to us since it was three months to the day that we had been dating. After dinner we picked up their friend Ann and went jackpot bowling. My bowling performance could have been better, but we had a lot of fun. That night Jer and Alycia showed me pictures from their trip to Israel. His family loves me, I think.

Sunday was bittersweet. I loved going to David's church. He is intense and passionate and inspiring. I said goodbye to him, and then we met Jer's mom for lunch. After lunch I had to leave my baby. I hate leaving him! But when I got to Chester that evening, my mom and dad were so excited to see me. Dad cooked me cheesy eggs and Mom made me grape Kool-Aid. Then I went to VanDykes' for a visit. Just like old times.

The next few days in Chester were so fun. Maci and I visited the school and saw Kathy and Mary in the office, all our old teachers, and Coach Schlepp and Billy Boy.[79] We watched elementary, junior high, and high school choir and band concerts and girls' and boys' basketball games. It is so weird the seasons for basketball are at the same time now. Maci and I also went to some girls' basketball practices. I felt a little out of shape! The girls seemed excited to have us there, and it was fun to practice with Amanda and Savannah again. And it was awesome to practice with Coach VanDyke and Coach Schlepp again.

It was wonderful being home. The house was cozy and warm and all decorated for Christmas. I spent some time wrapping presents and watching tapes of basketball games from last year. I am very grateful I got to hang out with so many people. We spent some time at the Tempels' house, and Chasi, Michele, Maci, Mari, Heidi, Kaitlynn, Kayla, Isaac, and I played board games at several random places. We all just wanted to play board games all the time. Who says you can't go home again? (Seriously, I have no idea who said that.)

Ouch! My reminiscing is rudely interrupted by a curling-iron-forehead-burn. My OCD would really like me to complete the reminiscing, so I snag another section of hair and vow to be more careful. Now where was I?

---

[78] "Gnocchi." How *do* you pronounce that?

[79] I called Amanda's dad "Billy Boy" when we were not in school, and in settings when he was not my track coach and principal.

Oh yes, it was so much fun being in Chester for a few days. On Friday I caravanned with my parents to Big Timber, where we still are. Saturday morning a bunch of our family went to the high school gym. It was a blast going with all the cousins. It was ridiculously windy on our two-block walk, of course, but warm and fun when we got inside. I noticed an extra special feeling being in that gym. A feeling of contentedness. Of peace. I think because of how much time Grandpa Jim spent there over the decades. We played in the gym for a long time, and by the time we got back to Grandma Graham's house, my baby boy had made it to Big Timber! I saw his car in Grandma Joyce's driveway and got so excited. He was sitting in the living room. When I walked in he greeted me with an enthusiastic, "Hi, Jamie!"

I love the way he says that.

Grandma fed us lunch, then we watched football, napped, snacked, and ate dinner. We were lazy. Then we headed back to the gym because Aunt Peg was running an open gym for Big Timber's high school basketball players. Leif Stephens[80] and his brother Todd were both there, and we talked to them for a long time. Then we went bowling with Joshua and Becca. Uncle Jimmy, Aunt Kathy, and Mom and Dad came to the bowling alley after a while as well. Then everyone headed back to where they were staying for the night.[81]

Jeremy and I were the only ones staying at Grandma Joyce's house. She went to bed around ten, and Jeremy and I put in a movie. I didn't want Grandma Joyce to be kept awake by the movie, so I slid shut the door between the upper room—where her bedroom is—and the kitchen and lower living room where we were. We lay on the couch, but we only watched each other and not the movie. All of a sudden that door slid open and Grandma sternly commanded, "Get to your own beds!"

Poor Jeremy practically flew down the stairs.

---

[80] Jeremy loves to tell the story about Leif always wearing gym shorts underneath his pants—including his choir tux pants—because he always wanted to be ready in case there might be an impromptu pickup basketball game.

[81] My Uncle Jimmy Ullman's dad is from Big Timber as well, and so the Ullmans would sometimes stay at his house. My parents alternated each time they were in Big Timber, staying either at Grandma Joyce's or across the street at Grandma Barb's.

Then Grandma said pointedly to me, "I don't approve of what you are doing."

That really fired me up, so I said, "What are we doing?!"

And then she said, "You, crawling into bed with him!"

I raised my voice at her. "We were watching a movie and talking! On the couch, not a bed! Don't you trust me?!"

She said something like, "Well I hope I can—"

"Then do it!" I screamed. "We weren't doing anything! I can't believe you don't trust me!"

Details blur after that, but we yelled back and forth, and I yelled something last and slammed the bedroom door. I was shaking forever. I do not remember the last time I was that furious.

The next morning I had to go to the bathroom for like two hours but refused to get up because Grandma was in the bathroom getting ready for church. I got up finally after she left and peed a Jimmy Dugan from *A League of Their Own* pee.[82] Then I went downstairs and woke up Jeremy. He felt so bad. I was still super mad at her, but he said, "Well, my jeans were at the top of the stairs, because I changed in the laundry room into my sweats. Maybe that's why she got so mad."

After that we took showers, ate, and packed. Jeremy had to go to Cody with his sisters, but before he left he wrote a nice thank you letter to Grandma and left it on the counter. I did not write her a thank you letter. I hastily packed my bags and toted them over to the house across the street. My parents, Becca, and I went to Billings to meet Jeff and Jenny, and we shopped around all day. We had dinner at Jay and Peggy's that night, and I did not even talk to or make eye contact with Grandma Joyce all night. And she did not try to talk to me. I fell asleep on the couch for a while, and by the time I woke up, Grandma was gone. Dad told me she talked to him today and said she feels horrible. Apparently she did see the jeans, but she said to Dad, "I'm sure he had something else on. I shouldn't have said anything. I shouldn't have said anything."

Dad said she was crushed. So then I felt kind of bad, but she is the adult and she can come talk to me. I guess I am technically an adult, too . . . but still.

---

[82] Zachary, 2018.

"Time to head to church," Dad announces, and I shake my focus back to the present.

I twist in one more curl, set the curling iron down, then unplug its cord. I take one last look in the mirror. It will have to do. I walk out of the bathroom, through the laundry room, and check the clock on the microwave: 4:25. Christmas Eve service is at Grandma Joyce's church at five. So why are we leaving over a half-hour early? Because Grandma says so, that's why.

Last night we had dinner again at Jay and Peg's, and Grandma still had not said a word to me. I saw her sitting on the couch by herself, and my heart softened for that sweet but stubborn old lady. So I cuddled up next to her on the couch. Neither of us said anything, but we held hands, and she was clearly giddy and relieved. So if Grandma wants to be at church thirty minutes before it starts—and since she and I are on speaking terms again—I see no need to flip over the apple cart, or whatever that saying is.

I zip up my puffy, purple, down coat, slip on my black shoes, and brace myself. The frigid night air hits as soon as I step out the back door. Luckily Dad parked close, so Mom and I scurry in the car as quickly as possible. Dad reverses down the long driveway, pulls out onto Stock Street, and chauffeurs us to the Big Timber United Church of Christ, just past the grade school. Dad parks behind Uncle Jay, and we hurry toward the light, warm sanctuary.

Grandma wants to secure the front two pews for our family, hence arriving a half-hour early. This is one of the only times I get to experience what it feels like to be early for any event. It is nice, I will admit, sitting here in this peaceful little church, pleasant and cozy with the pretty snow and frost sparkling outside. Candles lit, piano music playing softly, families packed tightly together. This service is my favorite.

The lights dim, and a gentle hush ensues. The pastor starts reading the Christmas story. I close my eyes to listen. After I picture the Wise Men following the star and finding the baby, we pull out thick green hymnals from the wooden shelves lining the backs of the pews in front of us.

We start the first verse of "The First Noel." I am excited for when we will head back to Grandma's house for our traditional barbecued steak dinner—no matter the snow accumulation or temperature—with plates of steaming spaghetti and buttered French bread perched in the middle of the pushed-together tables, chairs from all different parts of the house tucked in tight so that everyone has a spot.[83] We will eat and eat, and the little cousins will start making the individual piles of presents, trying their best to be patient while the adults finish eating and doing all the dishes before *finally* getting to open the colorful packages they have been studying and wondering about for the past few days.

Now I tilt my short white candle to the right, where my wick catches a flame from Grandma's just-lit candle. I then hold my own up, and Rebecca lights hers. When everyone in the church holds their lights upright, we begin to sing. A feeling of calm and serenity moves through and overwhelms me. The piano slows as it plinks out the final celestial notes: *Sleep in heavenly pe-eace, / Sle-eep in heavenly peace.*

"Heavenly peace" feels almost tangible tonight, and I am thankful.

---

[83] The tradition at the Graham house was for the uncles to brush the snow off the barbecue and cook up a bunch of steaks, regardless of the temperature outside.

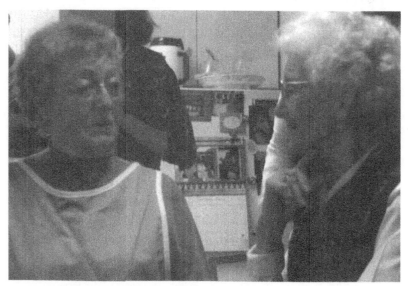

Grandmas Joyce and Barb chatting in the kitchen, Christmas Eve 2005

Christmas in Big Timber, 2005. We spent Christmas in Big Timber until both of my grandmas died—within six months of each other—in 2014.

Chapter 18

January 2003, second semester, freshman year, Billings, Montana

January 1, 2003

Happy New Year 2003. I had a very fun New Year's Eve. First of all, my Jeremy showed up at Chester yesterday. I was so happy when I saw him that I could not stop smiling. We left for Medicine Hat[84] after noon. Jeremy drove Michele and me, and Maci drove the van with Mari, Kayla, and Brekke. We stopped in Havre and picked up Alex on the way. Emily got the flu and couldn't come. We got to the Comfort Inn around four and just chilled. Then we went to the Medicine Hat Lodge and sat in a bar and ordered drinks. It was so fun because we could just order drinks and it was legal. If Brent and Chris can be shipped overseas to fight wars when they are eighteen, shouldn't we be able to legally drink beer?

January 3, 2003

My baby boy came and woke me up this morning, and I absolutely love having his arms around me. I went to work at the fitness center for a few hours and almost died doing the elliptical for thirteen minutes. Yes, thirteen. Embarrassing. Matthew Klay joined us at my parents' house for a Mac and Cheese lunch, and then after school Isaac and a bunch of other high school boys came over. We played Scattergories and Catchphrase, and they kept telling me how much Jeremy looks like Jim Carrey. Tell me something I don't know. The boys had to get to the bus for their basketball games against KG[85] and then we had pizza

---

[84] Medicine Hat is in Alberta, Canada, and is about three hours north of Chester. Places in Canada are closer to Chester than many Montana towns, so we often took weekend vacations across the border.

[85] The Hi-Line towns Kremlin and Gilford consolidated to become the KG School District in 1972. Then KG and Blue Sky consolidated into North Star in 2005, the same year Joplin-Inverness and Chester joined forces to become CJI.

with Mom and Amanda for dinner. I asked Jeremy if he was ready to go to KG to the games, and he just looked at me, sort of speechless and maybe a little stunned. Finally I realized he did not want to necessarily tell me no, but Ohio State was playing Miami for the NCAA football national championship that night. I laughed, and Mom and I went to the games without him.

The games were good, and when we got home Jeremy was standing in front of the TV with his giant Ohio State blanket wrapped around his body, chewing his nails, and swaying back and forth. Ohio State won in double overtime and my baby was so happy. My brother, however, was not. I called my brother's cell phone, made Jeremy say hi, and Jeff hung up. Sore loser.

January 4, 2003

Right before I woke up this morning I guess Richie called for Jeremy. She asked for his last name then told him she worked at the clinic and that she needed a urine sample, blood sample, and erection test from him.[86] Oh, Lordy. At the boys' game that night, our boys were down five with fifty-one seconds left. John Tranberg canned a three, and Travis scored. So it went into overtime. Then we were down one with five seconds left. Coach Schlepp had the boys run "Griz," Mitchy missed a layup, but Stubbs tipped it in right at the buzzer. It was so sweet. Carly brought some friends home from Carroll and Michele, Mari, Maci, Emily, and I stood by them and led all the cheers all night. Good times, great win. That night we—surprise—played board games at VanDykes'. Chelers and I talked, and she is struggling. Makes me sad.[87]

January 7, 2003

Today was the first day of classes for my second college semester. On Mondays I have English and math and a philosophy and religious thought class. On Tuesdays and Thursdays I have human development and history of civilization. Oh, and yoga. So that is sweet. Brent called me today and told me he leaves somewhere on the tenth. He doesn't

---

[86] The only true thing about Richie's phone call to Jeremy was the fact that she was a lab technician at the Chester clinic.

[87] Michele redshirted at UofM her first year out of high school. During the winter of her freshman year she found out there would not be a scholarship for her the next season, and she decided to transfer to Montana State University-Northern up in Havre.

know where but maybe Turkey or something like that. That doesn't make my stomach feel very good. After I hung up with Brenton, Jeremy crawled up to my bed with me. I stared at him in silence for a long time, and then I noticed his heart was pounding. I asked what was wrong and he goes, "Baby, say something. Tell me something," in this worried, anxious tone. Then he said, "I don't like that long silence after you talk to him. It's like you're not here. I know you're thinking about the past and stuff, and it's sad."

He was genuinely concerned, not jealous or angry. I told him I was thinking a little about Brent and and a little about the past, but that I was completely wrapped up with him.

January 29, 2003

Today I went to English, skipped math so I could take a nap, and went to my philosophy class at two. I played cell phone games for a while, but then I answered one question and the professor would not stop talking to me after that. What have I done?! I went to the gym after that and played shooting games with Maci, Alex, and Shye. We went to the Pickle Barrel for dinner, where I successfully plugged the toilet. The whole restaurant was laughing, and I plunged it myself. Shye, Maci and Alex were laughing so hard they just went out to the car. Such helpful, supportive friends.

Tonight we played four-on-four at the Billings Athletic Club. It was good to play other people and get up and down a court. It was weird having such a short basketball season. Now we freshmen girls do practice some days with JD, and then we work out and play a lot on our own. I also do quite a bit of work-study at the gym. The other night Brent called and said he might be going home to Chester in a couple weeks. I asked, "Then are you going somewhere?" He said yes, he has to go somewhere around or in Iraq. I hate this. I hate the world situation. I am so scared for him. He asked how "my boy situation" was going.

February 2, 2003

Happy birthday to my baby boy! Jeremy is twenty years old today. Wow, that sounds so old to me. Jeffrey called and asked if I would get Jenny something for Valentine's Day, so I went to the mall with Kat and Jeri and picked out a beautiful silver heart necklace. Jeff was like, "Yeah, so could you give that to her on Valentine's Day or something?" So

131

romantic. Then Liz, Jeremy, and I met David, Alycia, and Naomi at Olive Garden to celebrate tonight. We ate a lot of breadsticks and laughed a lot. Jeremy opened presents and we took a few pictures. I got him a cute shirt from A&E and a wallet, with a picture of me and a picture of Kat in it. Then we said goodbye to his fam. It was a very good day.

Jeremy's twentieth birthday, February 2, 2003

February 15, 2003

Last weekend we left for Helena, because Rocky was playing Carroll, but the weather and roads were not so good. We ended up staying in Big Timber with Grandpa and Grandma, and it turned out to be a great and relaxing weekend. We visited a lot with Grandma Joyce, and we borrowed movies from Becca and Joshua. Sunday we went to church with Grandpa and Grandma. I really liked their church a lot. It had been forever since I went to the Lutheran church there.[88] Then we went to a potluck dinner at Grandma Joyce's church. At one we ate yet again, because Grandma Barb made us chicken. Then we played pinochle and that was so awesome. I am very glad we stayed there because Grandpa has been pretty down lately, since his stroke. Mom said they just put him on Ritalin because that is supposed to help older people be happier. Sweet Gramps.

---

[88] Jeremy and I had no idea how important that church would be in our lives seven years later.

132

School was okay this past week, but I have been having to read a lot. Maci said Christopher John called her and he also got his orders to go overseas.[89] This war stuff is so insane and so terrifying.

Well I am super lucky, though, because I got to get ready to go with Jeremy on our five-month anniversary date. He came to my door right at seven and was holding five red roses, one for each month, a heart-shaped candy box, and an adorable Mickey and Minnie Mouse kissing doll thing. He took me to the movie *Chicago*. The place was packed and at one point Jeremy goes, "How many people do you think are here with us?" I just looked at him and he said, "None." He makes me feel so special. I can't get enough of him. We ate a very nice dinner at a restaurant downtown called Jake's. It was a perfect night. We also had to hit Walmart real quick, so that was romantic.

This morning I was still sleeping at eleven when Kevin came in and wanted to go somewhere to skip rocks. He just really wanted to skip rocks. So Jeremy, Pat, Emily, Peter, Kevin and I found a half-frozen river, and we threw rocks. TC had me work concessions all night and both men's and women's teams won. Yay. Peter, Jer, and I watched *My Big Fat Greek Wedding* tonight. And here is the letter Jeremy gave me for Valentine's Day:

Jamie

> I was walking across campus the other night, thinking about my life. I thought about college and the great people that surround me. But mostly I thought about you, and how happy you make me. There is a different kind of energy that boils up inside of me even when I think about you. As I was walking I wished everyone that I care about could feel this good at some time in their lives, because it is one of the greatest feelings I have ever experienced. You do this to me. You bring so much joy to my life, and I want to thank you for that. I

---

[89] Chris Decker graduated with me and entered the army the summer after we graduated. He visited Maci and me several times over the years at Rocky.

want to thank your parents for helping to mold you into the most beautiful person I know. Mostly, I want to thank God for bringing us both to this place and making our paths cross at the perfect time. (The bottle of Boone's Farm deserves some credit for our first night.)

I got you these five roses to begin showing you how much I love you, and to thank you for the last five months and how you have affected my life. When I think about the time I have been able to spend with you, I smile. When I get to a low place in my life, I will be able to look back at our experience of falling in love with one another, and I will instantly be cheered up.

Seeing you is the highlight of my days, and I would not pass up the opportunity to just spend one more minute with you. You treat me so well, and that makes me want to treat other people better. I have seen you do this with so many people, and this is one of your greatest qualities. You are a fun and loving person, and that is why I never want to leave your side. I am falling deeper and deeper in love with you every day, and I am going to do this forever. You are my perfect love.

Happy Valentine's Day
Jeremy

March 17, 2003

Hooray for spring break. Our women's team played Carroll for the playoffs and won. It was exciting as a Rocky fan, but it ended up being Carly's last game. Ever. The truth is that most seasons for most teams at most levels end with losses. Somehow that has never been the case for me in basketball in seven seasons (counting two in junior high), so that is crazy. I cried with Carly. Once a teammate, always a teammate. The VanDykes were all there, and I caravanned home with them on Saturday. The roads were horrid, and it took us forever to get to

Chester. It was a nice, relaxing week. I lifted and ran with the track team a couple times and did a lot of shooting. Mitchy took me snowmobiling, and I went to soup supper and Lent service at church on Wednesday and got to see Pete, Tonja, and sweet baby Emma. I also hung out with Heidi, Maci, Kayla and Isaac. It was a good week.

Friday I drove to Sheridan and got to the Dupreys' house just before they got back from skiing. Jeremy ran inside and was holding tulips for our sixth-month anniversary. I did Naomi's hair for a dance, and Jeremy and I watched Alycia play Sandy in *Grease* on both Friday and Saturday. She did so awesome. We also met Ann and Greg for lunch before the play Saturday, and Jeremy's grandparents (David's mom and stepdad) just moved to Sheridan, so that was pretty cool.

Yesterday we went to church; I love David's sermons. We got back to the dorms around four, took a nap, and Jeremy decided to take me to Olive Garden. I loved it. Then we cuddled and told each other how much we love each other, forever.

April 5, 2003

Thursday I came back from borathon (aka history of civilization) at two thirty, and Jeremy was waiting in my room, looking anxious. He told me my parents had called about Gram Joyce. Apparently Wednesday night she stayed overnight in the Big Timber clinic, due to some chest and arm pains. Then they took her to Billings where she was supposed to have an angioplasty (no idea what that is, or how to spell it) and be released that night. Jeremy and I went right to the hospital—for a change—and waited with Jay, Kathy, and Jimmy. Why not visit another flipping hospital? Turns out things are much worse than they first thought. Before we knew it, the doctor was saying an open-heart surgery needed to be scheduled.

Yesterday I was back at the hospital, and all the aunts and uncles and Mom and Dad soon showed up. We stayed with Gram until eleven thirty, and then they took her into surgery. She wrote us a letter. It basically said she was very thankful and she had a good life, and if this was her time then this was her time. That she was thankful for her beautiful family, for all of us. So we did what anyone would do in a situation like that, we bawled for a while and then went to eat. The quadruple bypass ended up going great.

Grandma got out of the hospital today and went straight to Mitchell's baseball game. Tough old bird. Tonight Jeremy and I went and watched Peter in Rocky's production of *Grease*. He did so great. I wish I could be in a play, but I of course can't because basketball rules my life.

April 8, 2003

The last couple weeks have been a blur. I have been so busy. Maci, Shye, and I have been going to some "optional practices." I want to play ball so badly next year. I don't think I can stand another season finishing in December. I talked to my parents about my basketball situation a lot on the phone tonight. Dad told me if I want to transfer they will support it. He said I need to get things figured out quickly so we can start reaching out to other coaches. That really surprised me. I was expecting more of a "Well let's stick with it and see what happens."

I was walking around the lawn just outside our dorms when I was on the phone with them. When Dad brought up transferring, I stopped in my tracks. I looked up and took in the stone buildings, the beautiful trees, and the people contentedly strolling across campus on the maze of cement pathways. I thought about Kat and Maci, all my teammates and coaches. I thought about Peter, about my classmates and professors. And of course I thought about Jeremy. It was so weird, and hard to explain, but at that very second I was struck by this intense moment of clarity. Even though I love basketball, and I have always been all about basketball, it is not basketball that keeps me going. It is the people, the relationships. I guess I knew that—I know that—but it really hit me in the gut right then. I felt super peaceful and knew I would not leave Rocky. It is my home right now. So I am going to stay. I will work hard and be encouraging, like always, and try to remind myself that this whole experience is not about basketball. Not really.

Rocky is my home now. Jeremy modeling the Rocky sweater.

May 8, 2003

Freshman year of college, done. How can that be? The third week of April was "Dead Week," where everyone just worked on final papers and projects and lived in the library. Maci and I went to Helena for their softball weekend, and that was completely insane. Maci hit it off with

137

this guy named Ryan, so it was a good weekend. Then it was finals week, aka the longest week of my life. We played ball with a recruit on Monday, and aside from some ultimate Frisbee on Thursday, that was the extent of my physical activity. The days seemed like weeks. I studied, watched movies, studied, ate junk, studied, and slept. Finals went well, so that was a plus. I got all As for the semester, except for one B, in writing. We won't even go into that.

Speaking of sleep . . .

Jeremy and Liz, post-crash

May 9, 2003

So I thought I was going to get to bed early last night, but that did not end up being the case. Kat, Megan, Erin, Kevin, Logan, Peter, Jeremy, and I went over to Mike Elliott's apartment. We played an epic game of Slaps. [90] Then we went bowling, and we ended up back in the dorms where Mike and Logan played guitars, and we all sang. Then the craziest thing happened. Peter, Kevin, and Megan left at some point during the singing, and they called us a while later. They told us we

---

[90] Slaps was a favorite game of Rocky students. The rules were very strict, and if you could not fully focus and commit, you would be kicked out of the circle.

should come swimming at the Fortin Center pool. Nobody believed that they were really there, until they called again and insisted. Sure enough, somehow Peter and Co. found a way through a bunch of doors and used a random key, apparently somehow a key to Ashley Hammond's house opened the lock. So we had a wild pool party in Fortin Center in the middle of the night. For real. Against the rules? Perhaps. But no one will ever know. . . .

Chapter 19

July 2003, summer before sophomore year, Chester, Montana; Sheridan, Wyoming; Tyler, Texas

"I miss you so much. It is killing me being away from you this long." I smile and look down at the picture of him he sent me last week. He smiles under his Diamondback baseball cap, his face extra tan from time spent in pools and boating and tubing on Lake Tyler.[91] I take note of the actual physical ache in my body. "I miss you so, so, so much!"

Jeremy and I have been apart for fifty-three days, but it might as well be an eternity. He is interning this summer at a church in Tyler, Texas. Jeremy's youth pastor from high school, Jake, now lives in Texas and works at a giant Methodist church. After spending last summer doing backbreaking work mending fences, irrigating, and shoveling junk at a ranch near Sheridan, Jeremy jumped at the chance of a job in an air-conditioned church with promises of lots of poolside Bible studies and various mission trips.[92]

But that was before he met me.

"I can't believe we decided it was going to be okay for us to be apart for this long," Jeremy continues.

I smile and tilt my head to the side. "I know! And next week I won't even be able to talk to you because you will be in Mexico![93]

---

[91] Lake Tyler (or Lake Tyler West) and Lake Tyler East are located adjacent to each other, connected via a canal. Situated just east of Tyler, Texas, these are the largest lakes in the area in addition to Lake Palestine (Lake Tyler, 2021).

[92] One day while Jeremy was working at his summer ranch help job he stepped without looking, and a long rusty nail went right through his thick leather boot, piercing his foot. He remembers this experience as a time where he confirmed his hunch that he would really prefer a desk job.

[93] Jeremy worked that summer at a large church with a vibrant youth group and substantial youth budget. He was able to experience and serve on week-long mission trips in Mexico, Oklahoma, and Kentucky.

Jeremy in Mexico—during his summer in Texas—donning his Arizona Diamondbacks hat, 2003

"Maybe I should just tell Jake I can't finish out the summer. I can't stand being away from you. I need to hold you! I'm sure I can get a job at the IGA in Chester." Jeremy considers his options. "Maybe I can work at Subway."

141

I giggle and play along. "Right. And I'm sure my dad would be happy to put you up here at our house."

The line goes silent. As if someone splashed cold water on his face, Jeremy quietly accepts reality. "I guess we will just have to wait."

I still smile and sigh dramatically. "I guess so."

"But now it's only thirty-three more days until we see each other!" I offer my familiar reminder in an attempt to cheer him up, and think excitedly to myself, *But really it's only nineteen more days!*

"Right. But that is still a really long time!" Jeremy laments. Then he adds, for what must be the hundredth time, "And it will be the last time we are ever away from each other this long. Right?"

Without hesitation I echo, "Right."

* * *

"Well hello, darlin'. I was a little worried when I didn't get a message on my phone. Glad you made it okay."

David wraps his arm around my shoulder and pulls me in for a hug.

"Oh!" I say, surprised. "I thought we made eye contact during the service, so I thought you knew I was here."

"I didn't see you during the service. I am just glad you are here safely. I didn't worry about check-ins like this until I met you!" He says this in a sort of teasing, mostly serious way.

I am touched by David's care and concern for me. I sit back down at my place at the round guest table and take another sip of my Sprite. As the toasts begin, I pick at my plate of typical wedding buffet food. I pop a delicious tiny hot dog in my mouth and listen to the father of the bride address the room. My eyes tear up as the father hugs his daughter and we all clink glasses in an enthusiastic "cheers!"

The father up front materializes into my own dad. Dad dons a sharp black tux and, misty eyes, kisses my forehead. Then I close my eyes and nuzzle into his chest. I separate from my dad and look over at my groom. He smiles adoringly and pulls my hands into his. I look up to double check and make sure my groom is who I think he is. Before I can get a clear picture of his face, the intro of "Butterfly Kisses" breaks in and dissolves my daydream. The real bride and her dad spin around on the dance floor, all eyes on them.[94]

* * *

"Let's watch *You've Got Mail*[95] next," I suggest, pulling out the DVD case with Tom Hanks and Meg Ryan from our ridiculously large collection stacked in the corner of the trunk, pressing against four stuffed duffel bags. Every time I see this movie now I think of my experience walking into my dorm room last semester and the look on Peter's face when I walked in. Clearly he was not expecting anyone, and we simply stared at each other for a few silent seconds. He looked guilty or embarrassed, or maybe both, and I narrowed my eyes at him suspiciously before turning toward the television. Sure enough, he was watching *You've Got Mail.* I smiled and looked back at him. After a few more moments of sizing each other up he quietly said, "It's my favorite movie. Don't tell," and I promptly sat down next to him to watch.

I climb back into the passenger seat and pull David's computer up on my lap. I snap my seatbelt and situate our makeshift movie theater, adjusting the blanket hanging from the "oh sh*t" handle located above the window. The blanket is vital to our operation as it keeps away the sun's glare and creates the ideal movie-watching atmosphere. When I slide the DVD in the computer drive I gently place the computer at my feet and look out the front window.

We already brushed by the Oklahoma Panhandle and took a bathroom break slash DVD change at a rest stop near Hartley County, TX.[96] I know this because I am the official map checker, automatic duty of the shotgun rider. I confirm with David that we are about an hour north of Amarillo, so we have about nine more hours left on our twenty-hour trek. David's eyes are on the road, so I fold and slide my map in the door pocket and then start the movie.

As we pull into the Amarillo (by afternoon for us, not morning) city limits, the orange light on the Civic dash blinks its warning. David signals

---

[94] The wedding I attended that evening was for Jessie Story—a good friend of Jeremy's growing up—and Aaron Odom.

[95] Tait, 2019.

[96] Hartley, 2022

toward a Maverik gas station. Just to the right of the gas station is a—surprise!—Dairy Queen. We have only been in this state for like a minute, and I have already seen a gazillion signs for DQ.[97]

David glances out a side window. "Would you girls like to stop for some ice cream?"

Silly man. As if he has to ask.

It has been super fun road-tripping with Jeremy's dad and sisters so far. One thing I have learned about them is that they love snacks. Especially ice cream. David drops us near the sidewalk leading to the many choices of hot eats and cool treats. I turn to him and ask what he would like. His eyes are laser focused. I have seen this look a few times. I am not exactly sure what it means yet, but it does seem like he may or may not be processing my question very clearly at the moment. "Just pick something," he replies distractedly and hands me a twenty as we hop out, then he continues across the parking lot heading for gas.

Alycia, Naomi, and I stand side by side facing the giant menu behind the counter. We instinctively cross our arms and rub our shoulders because turns out people crank up their air conditioners to unnecessarily frigid levels in the summer in the South. This is baffling to me because it seems like a big fat waste of energy and money. If you set the thermostat even to eighty-five degrees it would feel amazing and refreshing compared to the sauna outside. But nobody asked me.

"So what does your dad like?" I ask the girls, studying the frozen treat options.

"Well, he likes dipped cones," offers Naomi.

Alycia nods her head in agreement, and we approach the counter to put in our order. The three of us order our usual blizzards, and I add, "And a large chocolate-dipped cone, please."

"Will that be all, ma'am?"

My head snaps up. What did he just say? That kid looks maybe five minutes younger than me. Why in the world did he refer to me as "ma'am"?

---

[97] "A gazillion" is slight hyperbole, but Texas does have more Dairy Queens than the next two most DQ-populated states—Illinois and Minnesota—combined, as there are around six hundred restaurants in the Lone Star State.

"Yes . . . that will be all . . . ," I slowly respond, then with a curious, rumpled brow add, "siiir."

Naomi and Alycia snicker as the server punches the button for a cone. A few minutes later we head back out the door and see the sleek, green Accord waiting for us near the side of the store. Naomi and Alycia each proceed to a door in the back as I approach the driver's side window. It takes a second, and then the front window whirs and slowly lowers. I make eye contact briefly with David, and then observe that he is intensely studying the giant dipped cone I offer. I smile slightly. *You are welcome*, I think, giving myself a mental tally in the "Impress Boyfriend's Dad" column.

He still has not spoken. Now the silence is starting to make me uncomfortable. I push the cone an inch closer to him. Then, as enthusiastically as I can muster I say, "Here you go!" Still no response. I glance behind David to the girls, now buckling in their seats in the back. Their eyes are wide. Am I missing something here?

Finally, David speaks. Slowly and quietly. "It is one hundred and four degrees out here."

One hundred *four*, I think to myself, but decide this might not be the best time for a grammar lesson on decimals.

"And you thought it would be a good idea to get me an ice cream cone?"

Is this a rhetorical question? I flit my eyes to the back, hoping to get some cue on what to do from the girls. Too late. In the second it takes for me to look at the shrinking passengers in the back seat, David takes the cone from me. I straighten up and stumble a few slow steps backward, watching and wondering what in the world he is doing. Again his eyes are laser focused. He strides away from the car. It takes him about four giant steps to cover the twenty feet from here to the dirty, dark-gray garbage standing in the middle of the baking cement. What is he . . . ? Oh I get it now. He dumps the dripping cone face first into the can.

Then he turns back towards us. I scamper around the front of the car, open the door, and hop into my seat. I fumble with the buckle, and it finally connects, just as the driver's door opens. I lean my elbow just below the window and rest my chin in my hand, mouth pressed against my fingertips. Soon we are pulling out of the parking lot and back

145

toward the interstate. I concentrate really hard on looking like I am enthralled with the fascinating scenery out my window. I take a peek at my rearview mirror and see that Alycia and Naomi are sitting stock-still and only holding their blizzards, not making a peep. I look back out the window.

But I cannot help it.

My shoulders are the first to give me away. They shake uncontrollably up and down, up and down. Now I am really pressing my knuckles against my lips, trying to suppress it. But it is no use. A giggle is pushed straight from my stomach through my throat and out my mouth; there is no stopping it. The noise surprises David, and his head turns my way. It is hard to tell whether my attempt at suppression is making things better or worse. Either way, I am somehow giggling through my nose, sound coming from the back of my throat, as I keep squeezing my lips tightly together. My shoulders bounce, and I risk a look. Our eyes meet. He looks back at the road, then stops at the red light just before the freeway entrance. He looks over again, studying me perhaps. I meet his inquisitive gaze and continue to giggle. I look back at the girls. They give each other a glance that seems to say, "What is going on here? What is he doing? What is *she* doing?"

David looks forward again, then back at me one last time. The expression on his face suggests he is simultaneously feeling and thinking many things. Then, slowly, he smiles. And lets out a single pleased-yet-possibly-perplexed chuckle. As he turns onto the ramp, I scoop a big bite of blizzard into my mouth. The girls follow suit, David presses the AUX button, and we continue on our merry way.

* * *

"Here," Alycia urges in a loud whisper.

She tosses a blanket up to the front seat. "Put this over your head."

From my squatted position beneath the passenger seat—tucked under the jockey box on the floorboard—I reach out and pull the covering over me.

Aside from the whole DQ incident we had a pleasant drive, with movie-watching and song-singing and a few more food and snack stops. When I saw a sign telling me Tyler was only sixty-three miles away, that

146

is when I felt like I was going to completely lose my mind. For the last hour I have not known what to do with myself. Excitement, anticipation, and sheer giddiness has been coursing through my body like . . . like dry ditches suddenly being flooded with gushing water! (This must be what people feel like when they write love poetry.) It is hard to even explain. Like my skin really is crawling, but in a good way, in an exciting way. In *the* most exciting way. I guess it is kind of how I felt before playing in the state championship game.

But even that does not compare.

I absolutely cannot wait to see Jeremy. To touch him, to hug him. To breathe him in. When I think about it I can barely contain my excitement. I really do not think I can wait another minute. Three car doors slam. From my hiding spot I hear muffled voices outside.

Jake's friendly southern drawl greets, "Hey, y'all! Y'all made it!"

David, Alycia, and Naomi respond simultaneously, though I am not able to make out their exact sentiments. I strain to hear Jeremy, but nothing yet. Jake comments on how beautiful the girls look and asks about the trip. Again it is hard to understand all the dialogue being exchanged. Plus, now that we are this close it is as if my body literally senses that Jeremy is in the same vicinity. My gosh, I have made it all these hours—all these weeks—but it feels like I may not be able to control myself any longer. Plus now with the vehicle and its lifesaving air-conditioning off, I can feel sweat threatening. Oh come on!

"Jer Bear!" I hear Alycia squeal.

I freeze.

"Hi, brother!"

My ear stretches toward the door. Then I hear him.

"Hi, guys!" His enthusiasm sounds sincere, yet slightly forced.[98]

That is it. I cannot handle this anymore. I wrench the jacket off, flinging it wildly over the stick shift. I overeagerly pop up from my cramped position and nail my head on the flipping visor. Bleepity-bleep! I rub the top of my head with one hand and reach for the silver

---

[98] Jeremy was a little slow coming out of the house that evening because he had been leaving a message from the house phone to my cell phone. I told him I was in Canada for a few days with my friends and had to keep my phone off due to roaming charges. He was feeling frustrated that he had not been able to talk to me for a couple days.

handle with the other. My hand is shaking. David's voice gives me brief pause. "Hey Jer, we gotta unpack. There's something for you in the front seat."

I know Jeremy will be here in moments, but even a few moments is too long. I grip the handle and pull, then push and hurl the passenger door wide open. Jeremy is turned sideways, standing in a small circle with his family and Jake.

I sprint.

Cue up "Kiss Me" from *She's All That*, people.

Jeremy catches my movement and looks up. Everything switches to slow motion. I see the gleeful expressions on the faces of David, Alycia, and Naomi. Jake throws his head back in a happy guffaw. I take Jeremy in, with his super tan skin, blue-and-gray athletic shorts, stocking feet, and unkempt hair that likely hasn't had a trim since he came here to Texas. First his expression is confused, and then the confusion is quickly replaced by one of surprise, then elation.

Finally fifteen feet away, but it is taking a year to get to him! I reach both arms out and jump at him. He catches me and swings me around and around and around. We pull in for a tight hug, and then he pushes me back out—locking his elbows like we are at a junior high dance—to get a good look at me. As if he cannot believe I am real. Cannot believe I am here.

"I can't believe you're here!"

See?

We hug and spin and spin and hug. My body relaxes, and I could not suppress this grin if my life depended on it. All is right in the world.

Chapter 20

August 2003, summer before sophomore year, Chester, Montana

"Well that's it. Now I am going to go home and cry because we couldn't find him." Matt solemnly navigates his 1996 green Ford Taurus down Jackson Avenue and stops in front of the VanDykes' house.

I look over my left shoulder, eye Michele then Chasi, and attempt to hold an expression that matches Matt's somber tone. Michele and Chasi appear to be trying to do the same. We are unsuccessful. We all burst out in giggles and reach for our door handles. I look over at Matt one more time. He remains stone-faced, staring forward. "Thanks for trying, Matthew," I offer. No response. "Have a good semester. We'll see you when we see you."

Matt, unflinching and still looking forward, mechanically responds, "Yes. Goodbye then," and pulls away the second our car doors slam.

I shake my head in amusement and watch my former classmate of thirteen years—jeez, that makes me feel old—drive off toward his family farm. For the last hour we drove around looking for Cory to tell him goodbye. Sadly we could not find him. Finally we had to give up. We just dropped off Heidi—because she works crazy hours at the clinic and had to get ready for work—and now I am going to hang out with Chasi and Michele just a little longer, since I will head back to college tomorrow.

Matt's Taurus turns south toward the wheat fields, and I turn and follow Chasi and Michele. They walk ahead of me up the steps of the front door entrance, chatting and laughing. Before I can take a step up, the stars twinkle and insist I stop and give them some attention. I obey and tip up my chin. This sky. Wow. Hundreds of millions of billions of stars. A few times in Billings I looked up at the stars. It was hard to really get a good look, with all the streetlights in the way. Presently I see only one cozy house light and a distant streetlight whose shine cannot compete with this incredible celestial display.

"Coming, Jamers?" Michele's voice pulls my eyes down.

"I'll be right there, babe," I respond.

Michele nods and lets the screen door close behind her. I look back up. I take an inhale of the fresh August Montana air and note how different that hot, heavy, humid Texas air tasted. Thinking of Texas produces an instant grin. My mind immediately conjures that magical scene of Jeremy and me swinging around and hugging in Jake's backyard. My grin widens at the memory. I take a seat on the bottom stoop and continue to watch the stars as I reminisce.

Jeremy and I latched on to each other and hugged and kissed and spun and cried. I am not sure how long we just stood there in each others' arms, but we finally broke free to unpack and tour Jake's house. After the tour, Jake took us to his landlords' "house" (note: "landlords' house" = mansion) next door. His neighbors were on vacation for the week, and they graciously let us stay in their beautiful home. The next morning I seriously did not remember any of the rooms in either house because I was in an absolute daze the night before and could not stop looking at my baby boy. We could have slept in a shack for all I cared, as long as he was close to me.

The house had a huge pool in the backyard so Jer, Alycia, Naomi and I all went swimming that very night. Never mind that it was ten o'clock (where in Montana means no way are you swimming outside, unless you want to freeze your chi chis off), because it was so hot outside and the water felt glorious. Jeremy and I could not keep away from each other. We had to be holding hands or hugging or touching at all times. How we made it two months without seeing each other is beyond me. After our swim we started a movie called *Kate and Leopold.*[99] Love stories are fun to watch, but they are more fun to live.

The skin on my arms prickles pleasantly with the memories. I cross my arms and rub my triceps (my ripped triceps these days, mind you, thanks largely to Coach VanDyke's summer classes, as well as Mitchy's crazy arm-muscle-failure workouts) and give myself a little hug. It felt like the perfect night in Texas then, and reliving it feels almost just as good. I turn my neck and look toward the VanDykes' front door, but remain seated, not yet quite ready to click off the memory reel.

---

[99] Ebert, 2001.

The rest of our time in Texas was a blast. We ate at fun restaurants, including this barbecue place where there was a giant sheet of paper covering the long wooden tables. People were served long loaves of white bread and slabs of brisket on waxed paper. They just served everything right on top of the tables, with no utensils or plates. The next day we got to take a trip with the middle school youth group to this colossal waterpark near San Antonio called Schlitterbahn, apparently the largest waterpark in the nation.[100] It was nice to be in the water on such a boiling-hot day. We stayed in a church in this town called New Braunfels and had a really cool Bible study that night. I love how Jake teaches. It was really nice to get to know him better.[101]

We toured Marvin United Methodist Church, which is the most massive, beautiful church I have ever set foot in.[102] We attended a service on Sunday morning, and I wore one of my best outfits: a plain, black, short-sleeved, V-neck shirt and white capris. When I walked in the church it felt like I was wearing sweats and a T-shirt compared to those Texan churchgoers. No matter. Jesus loves me regardless of what I wear. Right?

We took our sweet time driving back to Montana. I like to think of it as my first family trip with the Dupreys. We drove to Arlington and watched the Texas Rangers play the Cleveland Indians. I was slightly disappointed we didn't hear the song "Wild Thing," [103] but we did get to see four home runs. And yes, Alex Rodríguez, "A-Rod," is as good-looking as it seems on TV.[104] We also saw a cousin of David's, Ruthie,[105] and went with her family to Six Flags.

The crazy Dupreys are crazy for roller coasters. I am not. I was a trooper for the most part, but I offered to hold everybody's stuff on the

---

[100] Schlitterbahn, 2022.

[101] Jake had worked for Jeremy's dad as a youth worker at St. John's Episcopal Church in Sheridan, Wyoming, and since then he has played a special role in Jeremy's life. He is the godfather of all three of our children: Jordan, Justin, and Jackson.

[102] Marvin, 2021.

[103] Tallent, 2019.

[104] Baseball, 2022.

[105] David's cousin, Ruth Cheatham, was a beloved English teacher in North Texas who fearlessly fought cancer for over ten years. The Ruth Cheatham Foundation was established in 2016 to give support and a voice to teens with cancer.

really big rides. It was also a bazillion degrees out, so I shed a lot of sexy sweat. Jer and I went back to Ruthie's house around four, and wild-riders David and Naomi didn't get home until a quarter to eleven that night! I am pretty sure Jeremy secretly wanted to stay and ride more rides, but not as much as he wanted to be with me.

Alycia flew back to Sheridan on Monday, and we kept driving on up to New Mexico, my first time in that state. David has a godson who lives in New Mexico, and we watched him in his high school marching band. I have seen marching bands on TV, but I do not know any small schools in Montana with them. It was impressive.

Then we drove to Phoenix to see Jer's cousin Monet and her family. David planned it out so he could baptize Monet and her siblings while we were there. We also got to see my cousin Shane. Shane is the best! He took me to a bookstore and bought me *The Hobbit.* We got to hang out with Shane's cute kids, Emma and Elliot, and swim at their building's pool. I decided if you live in Phoenix, you better have a pool nearby. Jer and I also got to hang out with Curtis and Heather and Colt and Jamie![106] They took us to dinner at this fun restaurant called Bobby McGee's, where the waiters were all dressed as different characters and sang to people. Then we went neon bowling. It was a blast. I told Curtis it felt just like old times at K-Lanes in Rudyard.[107] They all said they were doing pretty well but were a little homesick. I know I would be homesick, living that far away from Montana.

We did not stop as much after Phoenix, but we did make a quick decision to detour slightly to the Grand Canyon. It was definitely grand! We got there at ten thirty at night, so we cautiously walked up to a lookout point. When we got to the point where we could see out it scared the crap out of me, what with its beyond immense vastness. (That might be redundant; my point is that it was impressive.)

---

[106] Curtis Keith and Colt Frederickson graduated with me from good old Chester High. They lived and went to DeVry University in Phoenix during that time, and Heather attended massage school. We had so much fun visiting them that summer. Jamie Sparks graduated from Chester the year after I did.

[107] Curtis and I bowled in a league for years at the bowling alley in Rudyard, Montana. Several other kids from Chester bowled, too, and all our parents took turns carpooling those Sunday afternoons. I liked the bowling, but the vending machine with the Jolly Joes was arguably the best part.

The next morning we drove and drove and drove some more. We had a fun stop in Big Piney, Wyoming.[108] This was the tiny town where David used to be the priest until Jer was in third grade.[109] We stayed with these sweet people that were good friends of the Dupreys. It was fun to see where Jeremy lived for a few years as a little boy.

We finally got back to Sheridan on the eighth of August. We had a nice dinner and hung out at the ranch. Jer and I took a walk and watched the sunset. We had a little talk about Brent. I told Jeremy that I miss Brent sometimes. I told him I miss my friend. Jeremy admitted he gets scared for when Brent comes home next. He said he knows I will want to spend time with him. I told Jeremy I am scared, too. Scared of how Brent will be after being so lonely and scared and at war all this time. I want to be there for him while at the same time I do not want him to receive any mixed messages.

I sit up and shake my head. I cannot even think about all that. It is too crazy. Jeremy is so incredibly understanding. I stand slowly and take one last look at the stars. Even though these thoughts sometimes jumble up and make me feel crazy and frustrated, I really do feel like Jeremy is my perfect love. With that comforting thought, I walk up the steps to the door to find out what movie Chasi and Michele are watching. Tomorrow I leave to start my sophomore year of college. Ready or not.

---

[108] Big Piney, 2022.
[109] Vickrey, 1997.

SECOND QUARTER

"Therefore, if anyone is in Christ, the new creation has come: The old has gone, the new is here!"

—2 Corinthians 5:17

2003–2004 RMC Battlin' Bears

Chapter 21

September 2003, sophomore year, back to school, Billings, Montana

"How many swipes do you have on your Rocky sub swipe card?" asks Peter, linking his arm with mine as we stroll down the stone walk near the library.

"Plenty," I respond happily, "and I'm feeling generous."

"My lucky day."

We continue our sprightly walk down the path and nearly run into Takuto, arms barely swinging by his side, looking characteristically nonplussed. Peter and I simultaneously split and link an arm through each of Takuto's. Our impromptu hookup takes Takuto off guard, and I swear he hovers briefly as we pull him up to our pace.[110] Now if the Cowardly Lion joins us from the other direction, we will be all set. "Are you heading to the sub, Takuto?" I ask, though our pace and connection hardly leave him a choice.

"Uh, I do not have a meal plan," he answers.

"Jamie has lots of swipes," Peter graciously offers.

Takuto looks my way, and I nod enthusiastically. We remain linked as we ascend the sub stairs, turn right at the mailbox/bookstore junction, hang a left, and enter the cafeteria. I pull my green lanyard out from underneath my shirt collar and swipe my Battlin' Bear card once, twice, three times a lady.

"Thank you, Jamie Marie," Peter says with a slight bow.

"Thank you, Jay-may," Takuto echoes kindly.

"You are very welcome, gentlemen."

---

[110] Never in a hurry, Takuto was one of my favorite classmates to see on campus. An exchange student from Japan, Takuto enjoyed his time at Rocky almost as much as he seemed to enjoy his naps (just like me). When Takuto entered the gym for a sporting event, it was common to hear an enthusiastic, collective call from the student body: "Ta-ku-to!"

We proceed to the short line of students ahead of us and each pull a green plastic tray from the tall stack. I pull two plates from another stack, as well as an indestructible cup for my chocolate milk. We have a new chef this year named Sam, and he offers fresh cooked-in-front-of-your-face Asian delicacies. I opt for his delicious chicken stir-fry today. When my plates are full and my cup all but runneth over I choose a table near the north wall. As I wait for my lunch mates I take a bite of my crunchy apple and look outside a window toward the Rims.

How have we already been back in school for a month?! It has been nice to be back, save for those pesky classes that get in the way. Kat worked on the Rocky grounds crew over the summer and used that "in" to procure us an apartment in Jorgensen Hall. With the unprecedented numbers of incoming freshmen this school year, the Anderson and Widenhouse dorms could not hold all of the freshmen and sophomores. So some lucky sophomores—including us—got a crack at Jorg a year early.[111] Not only that, we were assigned apartment number 209, right next door to room 211, where one Jeremy Michael Duprey was randomly assigned. Ah yes, all the stars aligned.

My seventeen credits are so far manageable. I had an online History of Jazz class, but those online classes stress me out, and I dropped it. I finally have my first class with Ron/Dr. Cochran.[112] He teaches sociology, and unlike a couple classes last year, there is no threat of me falling asleep while he is teaching. My other classes all relate to teaching, and so far those also keep me awake. All good signs.

The Rocky football team had its opening football game again this year in Miles City, against the University of Mary Marauders.[113] I have no idea what a Marauder is, but evidently Marauders are good at beating

---

[111] Jorgensen Hall is designated to be available to students with a junior or senior class standing, graduate students, students with families, or students twenty-one years of age or older (Rocky, n.d.).

[112] Gazette, 2017. Ron/Dr. Cochran was arguably Jeremy, Logan and Peter's favorite professor. He taught sociology and anthropology—and apparently flint knapping—for over thirty years. Some days he would come to class as "Ron" and others as "Dr. Cochran." He often brought his blow-up sheep Dolly with him and certainly made you look at the world with new perspectives.

[113] Rocky's quarterback, Adam Sanchez, graduated high school from Miles City, so this was a fun venue for the fans.

Bears in football. Our chances looked good at first, until they didn't. My poor baby missed a field goal and an extra point. I rode to the game in my Taurus with Kat and four giant boys. Ken drove, Luke sat shotgun—with me squished between—and Kat sat in the back between Peter and Brett.[114] We lost 9-34, but at least the road trip company was entertaining. That night when we got back to campus, Luke gave me a ride all the way to Logan and Kevin's new house on Illinois Street on the giant handlebars of his giant bike. We rode back to Jorg just in time to see the football bus pulling back on campus. Just in time for me to greet my cute little kicker.

We started scrimmaging for basketball a couple weeks ago. There are ten new freshmen for some crazy total of something like twenty-five players. Jenny and Rae Dawn are redshirting, so everything feels completely different this year. Last week our official preseason conditioning started. We did all these jumping and running and shooting stations, and then we lifted with this new weights regimen. Normally all of that would make me super sore, but since I was a workout beast over the summer, it did not. Impressive, I know.

"How is it?" Takuto's voice turns my head back to the table, and I see he has settled in his chair.

I promptly pop in a first bite of noodles, chew, and announce, "Delicious."

"Where's Logan?" Takuto asks me, "and Jeremy?"

"I think they have an anthropology class right now," I reply.

Peter is still waiting in line, so I turn my full attention to Takuto. "So Takuto," I ask, "what is your major?"

Takuto looks at me skeptically. Clearly he has been asked this question before. "It is a little difficult to explain."

"Try me." I challenge.

With a big inhale, Takuto proceeds to explain all kinds of things to me regarding computers and business and management. He continues patiently explaining, and I knit my brow in concentration. After what feels like several minutes I nod and feel like I have a good handle on

---

[114] Luke Kunkel, a 6'7" center for our men's basketball team, from Carlsbad, New Mexico, drove. Ken Waldo was a 6'5" forward from Bremerton, Washington, and Brett Wilson was a 6'2" guard from Big Timber, Montana.

what he is saying. Just then, Peter takes a seat next to us. Peter asks, "What are you guys talking about?"

"Takuto was just telling me about what he does here for school," I inform Peter.

"Oh nice," Peter says—with genuine interest—turning to our friend, "so, Takuto, what do you do?"

Takuto's head flops back in exasperation, and his eyes close. After a second of him hanging over his chair in this position, he sits up and slowly exhales, "Faaaaaaaaaawk."

Chapter 22

October 2003, sophomore year, preseason games, Wyoming, Montana

"That was the worst performance I have ever seen since being associated with Rocky Mountain College."

I flinch at Coach Henderson's summation of our scrimmage against the Sheridan Generals. Might that be a bit of an overstatement? This is only his second year as coach after all, I think to myself. He is clearly not thinking rationally. But I am sensing he does not want my input at the moment.

He continues. "If you had plans for the weekend, change 'em. We have practice tomorrow at ten."

Coach leaves the locker room in a huff. Well I feel a little huffy myself, after that last unexpected announcement. There are no classes tomorrow, so I had planned to go visit Jer's family with him in Sheridan. Realizing my plans have now been foiled by basketball really grinds my gears.

We silently go through the motions of packing away our basketball shoes, pulling on our travel gear, and exiting as quickly as possible. I walk toward the people mover with my teammates and take a quick underarm sniff. Should have applied a few coats of deodorant. Since I am a sophomore, I decided it would be best to simply follow suit. The upperclassmen did not shower, so I did not shower.

I squeeze in the fourth row of the vehicle, close to the window, and Kelley sits beside me. For the first twenty minutes it is dead silent. Then it turns to merely awkwardly silent. Then Amber whispers something to Kelley, Kelley whispers back, and Amber lets out a quiet giggle. I glance up front at Coach Hendo. He is looking out his window. I cannot tell if he is still super angry, but he does not turn to look back at Kelley and Amber. Is that a small flicker of a smile he is trying to suppress? I decide it is safe to join in their conversation.

"And I will probably run into his new girlfriend at Safeway or something. I will be walking quickly by the produce section, and she will be shopping for a variety of health foods," Kelley says.

I smile as I listen to Kelley lament about her irrational and unlikely—but ridiculously hilarious—awkward interaction with some girl who may or may not exist. My understanding is that she and Logan dated last year, and that everyone thought they were such a great couple. But then Logan acted like an idiot, and they broke up. I think they got back together at least one more time, but recently she called it off for good. Now she is sharing some of her fears about what might happen if she runs into a new girlfriend of his.

Amber continues to laugh, and I cannot contain myself. I know the mood is supposed to be somber after our loss tonight. I know Kelley is sharing about a touchy topic, and maybe I should be trying to console her, but the image her words conjure up in my mind is just so absurd and hysterical.

Kelley goes on. "She will be wearing some fancy, black lingerie number, daintily placing a fresh sensible orange in her basket. And I will have a six-pack of Busch Light in my basket with my greasy hair—uncombed—wearing grungy, baggy sweats . . ."

* * *

Crunch. Crunch. Crunch.

I chew my usual breakfast, a bowl of Honey Nut Cheerios, but I am not feeling so great. Maybe it is because we have our first regular season game this afternoon. My stomach does do crazy dances before games, but this unfortunately feels different. I take a bite of the Cheerios' best friend, banana, to see how that tastes.

Chew. Chew. Chew.

Uh-oh. Not again. Dang it. Yes, again. I push my chair back from our small wooden table in the middle of our apartment's kitchen floor and rush to the bathroom.

Ever since the van accident I have been having trouble. Trouble in the form of a lot of nausea and struggling to keep food down. Especially breakfast. We tried on our uniforms the other day, and I swim in even the smallest size. I stepped on the scale in the training room the other day. I did a double take. It says I only weigh 122 pounds. That is ten pounds under what I have weighed since my sophomore year in high school. I felt weird asking Hendo what to do about gaining weight. He asked the trainer and some of her interns (or assistants or something) what I should do. They looked at me like I was a real weirdo. Then Suzette[115] told me to try drinking Ensure. Ensure, like what my grandpa has to drink for extra calories.

Sometimes I think I should have seen a doctor that night in Casper. But it was so chaotic in the hospital, and they were saying to only check in if you were for sure hurt. And Coach Gustin and Alexia and Tiff and Liz and Jeri were so clearly hurt that it did not seem to make sense for me to take up any extra time or space. I was conscious and not bleeding, after all. But I get dizzy a lot. This nausea has gotten worse since I was blindsided by a screen at a preseason scrimmage. The impact of that screen caused a squiggly fissure from my neck down through my shoulder. Or maybe that fissure was formed when my head slammed twice against the van ceiling. Either way, now every time I am screened without warning, I feel that same painful sensation. That is why we need to call out screens, people![116]

I flush. Then I wash my hands, wet a rag, and wipe my mouth at the sink. I look in the mirror and take a deep breath. I stand up straight and check my nausea level. Manageable. I turn into the kitchen, where the clock tells me I better get a move on if I am going to make my next class. Hopefully lunch goes better than breakfast did.

* * *

You! Shook me allll niiiight long! I sing along in my head as I rebound Jeri's layup during warm-ups. First home game of the season. The usual combination of excited-nervous jitters circulates through my body. I flick the ball toward the outlet position, into Ashley's outstretched hands. Then I replace Ashley near the baseline and turn to receive Kelley's pass. I toss the ball up to Maci and jog to the green midline. I

---

[115] Suzette (Hackl) Nynas was Rocky's trainer while we attended Rocky.

[116] "Calling out" a screen is important for a teammate to do when they see that the person they are guarding is running to screen their teammate, who is usually guarding the ball and cannot see what is happening behind them.

study the giant Battlin' Bear head that designates half-court. This Quality Inn Tournament kicks off our home season. The floor is recently waxed, sparkling in invitation for our squeaky tennis shoes to tread on it. I breathe in deeply through my nose, taking in that lacquer smell. That scent is the same, regardless of the gym or what mascot sits at center court.

We shoot around for a minute or so, after completing warm-up drills, then gather at the bench. Coach Hendo reminds us of our match-ups and reminds us to enjoy this first game of the season experience. I briefly marvel at the strangeness-yet-normalcy of this situation: Coach VanDyke and Coach Schlepp were my basketball coaches for all of high school; they gave me instruction, and I knew what their goals and expectations were. Last year I was listening to Coach Gustin. This year I heed instruction from Coach Henderson. Not only that, but Coach Gustin is not even on the Rocky bench this year. He took the head coaching job at Westminster, got married, and bid farewell to RMC.[117] Now we have a new assistant coach, Chris Mouat.[118] All I really know about him so far is that generally when asked how he is doing on any given day, he responds with, "About 62 percent," or something like that. So many things felt the same for so long, and now Change is just taking over without permission. What a bully.

Time for tipoff. I jog away from the huddle and toward center court with Ashley, Amber, Mandy, and Stacey. Since Jenny tore her ACL at Northern near the end of last season, I moved up the bench quicker than anticipated. This year I am starting at the point guard position. I think my coaches do probably believe in me, even though they would obviously prefer to have Jenny at the helm. I know this is all normal—I have watched *Love and Basketball*[119] eight hundred times, so I obviously completely understand how things work—but it does not stop that feeling of insecurity from creeping in. My new enemy-now-friend Amy

---

[117] Westminster, 2022.

[118] Coach Mouat soon became a favorite. He worked at RMC for two years as the women's JV coach, assistant women's varsity coach, and assistant AD. Then he took the head women's basketball position at Northern Montana College—now Montana State University-Northern—where he still coaches today (Anderson, 2018).

[119] Liggons, 2020.

will also be playing point guard. It took us a little while to get used to each other at first, as there was definitely competitive tension during those first practices.[120] But now we are "Jamers and Amers," official teammates.

Last year I was at first disappointed that I did not get to be on the varsity roster. I liked practicing some with varsity, though, and then continuing to work out and play consistently with my fellow freshmen teammates. Also I loved the freedom of playing and staying in shape while not having the rigorous commitment of the full-time varsity schedule.

Mostly I loved all the time I got to spend with Jeremy. Aww, Jeremy. I smile as I picture him hugging me when I saw him after class earlier today.

Jamie, this is not the time to think about Jeremy! I snap back into the present. Amber takes her spot to face off for opening tip. The Rocky pep band offers up its last encouraging chord before the referee blasts her whistle to indicate the start of the game. Flip flop. My stomach gives its usual signal that something significant is starting. With the whistle blow my eyes instinctively follow the spinning orb. I press my hip against the hip of my counterpart, like a partial box out, and after a bit of tipping here and there the prize lands in my hands.

Oh, bleep. Now what?

My mind goes blank. Why in the world did my mind go blank? Why do I feel dizzy? What is happening with my legs? They are blobs. For the love! Get a flipping grip. *You have played in literally hundreds of basketball games, Jamie. You got this.*

Who said that? Oh, man. I really am going bonkers.

"Motion!" An urgent command comes screaming from the direction of our bench.

My head jerks to the left, pulling me out of my conversation with . . . myself. Coach Hendo shouting the reminder that it is a good idea to go ahead and start running our offense resets my equilibrium. I blink a

---

[120] Amy joined the RMC Battlin' Bears Women's Basketball team as a freshman in 2003. She graduated from West High School, in Billings, where her team won the State AA championship her senior year. She and I have remained friends since and were both part of each other's weddings.

few blinks, let out a long exhale, and study my surroundings. There are four other white-jerseyed Battlin' Bears taking their spots around our basket. There are five orange-jerseyed Jimmies from Jamestown, North Dakota.[121] Ashley pops to a wing after a down screen and thank goodness, instinct takes over. My nerves leave my body with the ball, as it flies toward my teammate.

Coach Hendo addressing us on the bench

* * *

"Not a bad first half." Coach Hendo addresses us in our locker room after the first twenty minutes have ticked off the clock.[122]

We are up 30–29 in this so far evenly matched contest.

"We need to get more inside touches, and then guards, make sure you relocate after an entry pass," Coach continues. "Then everyone needs to do a better job crashing the offensive boards."

I nod and keep my eyes locked on my coach. He offers a few more pointers then exits, stage left.

---

[121] University, n.d.

[122] When we played, the games consisted of two twenty-minute halves. Now they are split into four ten-minute quarters (Sportsfanfocus, 2022).

We stand and huddle, and Amber addresses us. "Alright, let's stay focused. Let's get this first home win and start the season off on the right foot. 'Bears' on three. One, two, three—"

"Bears!" we chorus then file out of the locker room.

This time when I step on the court I do not feel the nerves I did before. So that is good. Just play. I just gotta play.

* * *

"Nice job, Jamer!" Jeremy wraps his arms around my sweat-drenched, jersey-covered top half.

I smile and snuggle into his excited embrace. We stayed composed in the second half, despite a late run by the Jimmies, and won our home opener 63-58. Amber led us with sixteen points, steady at the line with an impressive 10-10.[123] "Thanks!" I say. "I couldn't believe how nervous I was!"

"You didn't look nervous!" Jer replies. "You looked like a pro."

He kisses the top of my head, a loving and comforting gesture that I have received from my dad ever since I can remember. My smile broadens as I connect Jeremy and my dad in this way. Jeremy gives me one more squeeze before releasing, and I am even more convinced of his deep care for me. "I better go shower," I tell him.

"I will be at your apartment," Jeremy responds.

He adds, "Then we can get some dinner."

"Okay, see you in a sec!" I wave and start jogging toward the locker room. Then I add, "I love you!"

He smiles and shouts, unashamedly, "I love you, too, Jamie!"

My heart and legs skip around the corner, toward the showers.

---

[123] The rest of the scoring was super balanced that game, a good sign for a season opener: me 11, Ashley 8, Mandy 8, Kelley 6, Stacey 5, Maci 4, and Kat 2.

In Oct 2003 Jeremy played football while I played b-ball. My green-clad kicker made
field goals of 49 and 50 yards against MSU-Northern.
(*Gazette* photo by John Warner)

Chapter 23

October–November 2003, sophomore year, more preseason games, Billings, Montana

"What's that?" Jeremy points to the envelopes I hold in my hands.

The two envelopes are today's mailroom treasures. Getting mail makes me feel really loved. The top envelope is from Grandma Joyce, and the second bulging envelope is from my mom. I take the bulging envelope, tear open a corner, rip across the back of the envelope and pull out a folded note, protecting several newspaper clippings, a yellow sticky note hanging from its back. I read the sticky note to myself: *Good free throw shooting! Love you, Mom.* Then I pull out the small clippings and lay them out across the table. "It's from Mom," I explain to Jer.

He takes a seat next to me. I turn my attention to Grandma's letter while Jeremy starts scanning articles.

11/4/03

Hi —

> *Not sure if you had a chance to see this article in the Gazette.*

I unfold the article and see it is one of the same ones Mom sent, about the Black Hills State game. I continue reading her letter, of course typed on her typewriter.

> *The weather has closed in on us. Dug my path to the garage this morning and we must have 6 inches. . . . Sun is out this afternoon and melting snow on the ice we had — so the streets are miserable. Today is our big annual church dinner. I've been down at the Legion (where we hold the dinner) working all morning. Home for a break — and a nap! — and*

*will go back down in a couple of hrs till we close up this
evening. . . . It's a long day, but we do have a great time
putting on the dinner. The whole county shows up.*

*How's your neck? Hope it's much better. Take this $, get
to a drug store and get yourself some ASPERCREME. Rub
on the neck and then use your warm rice bag. It will really
help take some of the soreness out and it's not greasy nor
does it smell!!!! Listen to your grandma — and do this, please.
. . . I use it on my hands when they really get to hurting, and
they do hurt in weather like this.*

*Good luck against Minot tomorrow. Wish we
could all be there. We'll be thinking about you. No more
hurts. . . . . . .*

All for now. Take care.

Love you,
Gram G

I tuck Grandma's letter back in its envelope and beginning reading
articles with Jeremy.

LADY BEARS OFF TO 2-0 START

Senior Amber Griffith scored 16 points and
pulled down eight rebounds as Rocky Mountain
College defeated Black Hills State 61-55 in the
Quality Inn Tournament Saturday night at Rocky's
Fortin Center. Griffith led four Lady Bears in
double figures, including Jamie Graham, Ashley
Griffith, and Mandy Norby, all of whom had ten
points. Rocky outscored Black Hills State 32-22 in
the second half to erase the four-point halftime
deficit. "Black Hills controlled the tempo for the
majority of the game," said Rocky coach Brian
Henderson. "Our girls did a nice job of not
letting things get out of control."

Rocky made 28-of-37 from the free throw line,
while the Yellowjackets made just 10-of-21. Joni

Lunney led Black Hills State with 11 points.
Teammate Becca Waters chipped in 10 off the bench.

I cringe when I remember the four-point halftime deficit. We came out insanely slow, and I swear it felt like we should have been down by twenty. I sat for like fifteen minutes in the second half because I had four fouls. Jeremy got back from Tech that night around halftime, and he got to see my dad's entire side of the family because they all came for the game. I redeemed myself when I went six for six from the line down the stretch, eight for eight on the night.

I look up and flip through other scenes from the game that night. I giggle recalling an intense moment near the end when Ashley was shooting a free throw. I sprinted across the floor until I was standing face-to-face with Coach Hendo. He gave me a questioning look. I asked him why he called me over. He said he had not called me over. Well at that point I was committed. So I told him to just tell me anything and nodded a lot and acted like it was the best advice any coach had ever given me.

That was also the night I also found out that Brent had received leave to visit Chester. I called Mary—after Brent called me—and figured she would be over the moon excited. Well, she was not. She told me that the morning before two helicopters carrying soldiers heading home to America were bombed. Sixteen soldiers died. She told me, "Well, we didn't get a call, so I guess that is good."

This world has gone crazy. It really feels like The End is actually near. Is that because things are really crazier now than ever before? Or is it because I am finally sort of a grown-up and things are affecting me in new ways? Either way, it feels freaking bonkers. My mind just sometimes feels like it legit cannot even handle considering "all the thoughts."

Anyway, potential world-ending signs aside, we had a lot of fun that weekend when all of my family was here. Mom and Dad took Kat, Jeremy, and me grocery shopping, we ate at Gary and Linda's, and then we hit up Walmart. When my parents left, Jer and I went to Hastings and then took a long nap. Then I went and ate at the sub with Peter.

Jeremy hands me another newspaper clipping.

ROCKY HOSTS MINOT STATE TONIGHT

ROCKY MOUNTAIN COLLEGE AND MINOT (N.D.)-State
will engage in a women's basketball game tonight
at 7 p.m. in Rocky's Fortin Center. Rocky will
enter the non-league game with a 2-0 record, while
Minot State is 1-0. The Lady Bears posted home-
court victories over Jamestown (N.D.) College 63-
58 and Black Hills (S.D.) State 61-55 last
weekend, while the Beavers opened their season
last week with an 87-62 win over visiting Montana
Tech.

I look up for a second, trying to recall details about that game.
Hmm. I do not remember much. All I remember is that it was close,
and we won, so that was good. I think the trip to Jamestown was where
I sat with Kelley, and she was asking me all about my history with Brent.
She wanted to know all the details. Goodness knows we had plenty of
time on the trip. Maybe there is some clause that states 90 percent of
our preseason games must be (a) out of state, and (b) no fewer than
three hundred miles away.

I remember Kelley's most intense reaction to a recent conversation
I had with Brent. She closed her eyes, looked up to the ceiling of the
people mover, and pounded her right palm over her heart. Then she
opened her eyes, tilted her head, looked back at me and said, "That is
the saddest thing I have ever heard."

She thought it was so sad that Brent told me he listens to "While
You Loved Me" by Rascal Flatts every evening when he gets off duty. I
suppose that is a little heartbreaking.

I turn my attention to the next article.

ROCKY WOMEN FALL TO DICKINSON

DICKINSON, N.D. — Jessica Campbell scored 22
points and Sara Berglund added 17 to lead Dickinson
State to an 80-63 women's basketball victory over
Rocky Mountain College on Tuesday. Campbell and
Berglund went a combined 6-for-10 from behind the
3-point arc, with Berglund hitting five. The Blue

Hawks shot 8-for-18 from long distance in the game.
Rocky was led by Amber Griffith's 25 points and 10
rebounds. Katherine Bitz was the only other Bear to
reach double figures, notching 11 points off the
bench. Rocky is now 3-1 on the season, and
Dickinson State is 4-0.

After that loss I went home to see Brent. I hung out with Amanda, Mitchy, and Isaac when I first got back on Friday. Love those guys so much. Then Mary called and told me Brent's flight had changed and would not be getting in until ten o'clock on Saturday night. That was seriously disappointing. I needed to leave at a reasonable time Sunday, and they were going to spend the night in a hotel in Great Falls, with a flight that late. Which meant I would not even be able to see him. Not gonna lie, I cried a little bit. Surprising, I know. Sometimes I swear something is wrong with me, for all the crying I do.

Anyway, Saturday morning Mary called back. She said Brent figured out a way to change his flight. He was going to fly into Great Falls four hours earlier, at six. So the plan turned into me riding with the Clarks to the airport. I still do not know for sure if Brent knew I was going to be at the airport. I hung way back when he arrived at the gate, so all of his family members could get right in and love on him. The whole Clark clan was there. There were grandparents, cousins, aunts, and uncles. After he hugged his parents and brothers, he glanced up and caught my eye. That was when I could not tell whether or not he knew I was coming. He continued with the hug line, but then he glanced at me every two seconds, maybe like he could not quite believe I was really there. He eventually got to me. We hugged, but with his entire family watching—and with all things considered—it somehow oddly had this feeling of brotherly love. Like Philadelphia.

When we got out of the airport it was decided we would go eat at the Golden Corral buffet. You cannot go wrong with Golden Corral. Something for everyone, I tell ya. And that chocolate pudding. Mmm. "The Corral" (that is what I have just now decided to call it) is my dad's favorite place to take a bus full of hungry track kids. The dinner was nice. Mostly I chatted and laughed with the twins. Then I rode home in the van with all five Clarks. I ended up doing most of the talking, surprise. Those Clarks, they have never been accused of being too talkative.

Brent and I spent some time in his family's sweet new pool table room area above the garage. I sat on the floor way over on one side of the room, and he sat on a couch on the other side. We talked some, but just on-the-surface stuff. Then he drove me home. We ended up driving around town a while first. We talked about the stars. About how we both missed Chester's night sky, that it feels like maybe no other night sky will ever quite compare. We took a drive and parked out by the grain bins behind the IGA. Then we sat on the hood of the car. A burnt CD took the place of any more conversation, and we both teared up when 3 Doors Down crooned "Here Without You."

Jeremy hands me another newspaper clipping, and the scene fades in a swirl. I sneak a quick kiss on Jer's cheek and focus again on the next article.

ROCKY HOOPS TEAMS HIT THE ROAD

The men's and women's basketball teams from Rocky Mountain College will be spending this weekend on the road. The Rocky men, 1-2 on the young season, will be playing at Minot (N.D.) State University tonight at 7 and the University of Mary at 6:30 Saturday in Bismarck, N.D. The Rocky women, 3-1, will be participating tonight and Saturday at the South Dakota Tech Tournament in Rapid City. The Lady Bears will be playing S.D. Tech at 7 tonight and Black Hills State at 2 on Saturday.

ROCKY WOMEN FALL AT S.D. TECH

RAPID CITY, S.D. — Miaken Zeigler had 23 points, and Megan Barnes added 22 to lead South Dakota Tech to an 88-67 victory over Rocky Mountain College in women's basketball Friday. Tech led 43-21 at half. Katherine Bitz led Rocky with 25 points. Rocky plays today at 2 p.m. against Black Hills State at South Dakota Tech.

We just drive to South Dakota or North Dakota every week, turns out. On the way to Dickinson that Tuesday the trip was pretty sweet because we rigged up a TV and got to watch three movies. I have always wanted to watch movies while riding in a vehicle. However, we played crappy and lost, so that was no good. On the way home we could not watch TV because the alternator was messed up, and then it went out altogether leaving us stranded in Wibaux, Montana.[124] Amber and Ashley's parents saved the day by picking us up and driving us to Miles City. There, we were picked up by another shuttle. Two hours later we made it back to Billings. Four thirty in the morning. Who knew college basketball travel would be so glamorous and luxurious? Just another unexpected perk.

I was a zombie during classes that Wednesday. Thankfully Hendo canceled practice. Friday I took a seven forty-five sociology test before boarding yet another people mover and heading to Rapid City. Good thing, because I was really starting to miss the Dakotas. It not only sucked because we lost the first night by seventeen—thankfully we won the next day by seven—but Maci's grandma died that Thursday, and she went straight home to Chester, missing the games.

Maci was an absolute wreck.[125] When we got back from South Dakota Jer and I drove right up to Chester for the funeral. Michele and Chasi were there, too, and it was good to spend time with them. We also got to have our traditional Chester breakfast of donuts and chocolate milk with Isaac at the store. The funeral service was nice. Pastor Pete did such a good job. But it was a really sad weekend.

I refocus on the articles once again.

LADY BEARS REGISTER 69-57 WIN

RAPID CITY, S.D. — Senior Amber Griffith connected for 22 points Saturday afternoon as Rocky Mountain College downed Black Hills State 69-57 at the South Dakota Tech Tournament. Stacey

---

[124] Located in eastern Montana, with a blend of badlands and rolling hills, Wibaux always had extremely competitive football teams when I was in high school. Jer had a couple Wibaux boys on his football team at Rocky.

[125] Maci's grandmother, Shirley "Nan" Lybeck, was a loving presence in the Chester-Joplin area for decades.

Nevrivy added 17 points, while Ashley Griffith notched 10 points and nine rebounds for the Lady Bears. Jamie Graham was credited with four assists and three steals. Rocky, which jumped ahead 13-0, improved to 4-2 on the season. The Lady Bears shot 56 percent from the 3-point range. "It was a good performance," said Rocky coach Brian Henderson. "Everybody that came in had some good minutes and contributed.

Joni Lunney notched 13 points for Black Hills State, followed by Becca Waters with 12. Melissa Bruns contributed seven rebounds. Rocky will play Dickinson State at home on Wednesday.

RMC WOMEN BEAT JAMESTOWN

JAMESTOWN, N.D. — Jamie Graham scored 19 points, handed out seven assists, and came up with five steals to lead the Rocky Mountain College women to a 75-70 victory over Jamestown College Friday night. Amber Griffith led the Lady Bears with 21 points, Mandy Norby had 13, and Stacey Nevrivy added 12. Griffith was the Bears' leading rebounder, grabbing six. Rocky was badly beaten on the boards, as Jamestown gained a 42-26 advantage. "It was a very good team effort. The girls did a good job of holding their composure and taking care of the ball," said RMC coach Brian Henderson. "I'm happy we kept our turnovers (17) down tonight. The rebounding remains a concern for us."

Rocky is now 5-3 on the season. The Lady Bears face Valley City State University (ND) in Jamestown at 2 p.m. MDT today.

LADY BEARS TRIUMPH IN OT GAME

JAMESTOWN, N.D. — The women's basketball team at Rocky Mountain College improved to 6-3 on the season with a 95-94 overtime victory against

Valley City State Saturday afternoon at Jamestown College. The Lady Bears forced the overtime session when sophomore Katherine Bitz nailed a 3-pointer in the final second to tie the game at 88-all. Bitz finished the game with 26 points, shooting 4 of 7 from 3-point range. Freshman Mandy Norby added 19 points and 10 rebounds. Jamie Graham finished with 18 points, two steals, and five assists, while Amber Griffith tallied 17 points and seven rebounds. Janae Larson had 28 points for the North Dakota school. Loni Hall added 17. Rocky hit on 25 of 28 free throws and was 8 of 15 shooting from behind the arc. "Down the stretch the girls just showed a lot of poise," said coach Brian Henderson. "They hit some big shots and started getting some big rebounds."

The Lady Bears led 95-91 in OT, but Valley City hit a 3-pointer and had other shots at securing the victory. Norby blocked a last-second shot by Valley City State, Henderson said. Rocky will play at South Dakota Tech Friday afternoon in Rapid City.

I finish the last article and smile up at Jeremy. Reading about those last two games was fun, recalling the overtime win. A scene from *Major League 2* plays through my head, where Lou is slowly enunciating while carefully, sarcastically explaining to his motley crew: "We won a game yesterday. If we win one today, that's *two in a row*. If we win one tomorrow, that's called a *winning streak*. It has happened before."

I stack the articles up and slip them back in the envelope. "My mom and grandma are so cute," I state matter-of-factly.

"That makes sense," he says, smiling sweetly at me, then adds, "cutie," and reaches out and kisses the top of my hand.

I feign an eye roll and tease, "All this smooth talk, and you claimed to not be a player? You really got me good."

Chapter 24

December 2003, sophomore year finals, LA, Disneyland, Christmas, Big Timber, Montana

The first week of December in college equals Dead Week. *Dun, dun, duhhhh* (cue foreboding, vamping, organ music). I believe "Dead" is used as an adjective in this situation to describe the expected stopping of activity so that students can study? Perhaps it also describes how exhausted we feel? Or maybe the reference means, "I better finish my final projects and study for exams, or I will be 'dead'"?

Whatever the original labeler of this week had in mind, it seems aptly named.

I sit here in my home away from home—the cozy computer lab—staring at the screen. My finger clicks on the Hotmail tab. Should checking email take precedence over writing a final paper? Well, there could be an important message. Yes, that justifies it. When the screen refreshes, I do feel justified in my decision. Sure enough, a bold heading announces a new email, from Brent. I have not heard from him since Kat and I saw him off at the airport in Great Falls a couple months back. My stomach automatically clenches, bracing for what the message might reveal.

Tue 12/2/2003 11:38 AM

hi,

> *well im back in that bad place.[126] :(it was crazy cuz when i first stepped off the plane it was all muddy and i had to stand in the rain for what seemed like forever which was horrid, but what can ya do. it really sux that i had to come back to this filthy place. enough of this. how is bball comin along and school and anything else that u would like to tell me about. it's*

---

[126] Iraq

*kina cool havin this email tent and phones so close to where i
am so maybe i'll b able to stay in contact with people better
than i have been. i found out today that im gonna b fired or as
the army likes to put it replaced. it's really not the first one cuz
my time is up in the position that im in but i like to think of it
as being fired. the lady that i work for is goin crazy and in turn
it is makin me more crazy. it was really good to see u the
couple times that i did. i pry shouldn't be tellin u this and i
don't know why but everytime that i've seen u these past
couple of years i get so nervous and scared and sick all at the
same time it's crazy. ohh it was crazy at the airport right before
i left i went to the bathroom for quite a little while right before
i gave u all hugs, i was puking my guts out and i couldn't stop
for the life of me i've never done that before. ohhh tell ur
friend that came to the airport with u that im sorry that i
wasn't more polite i.e. shake her hand or say hi at all i felt
kina bad about that. ahh i've been so confused and out of it
ever since i came back which isn't entirely a good thing but i
guess im just lost. i really hate comin home for such a short
time i mean it's really good to see people, but saying good bye
to them really gets to me. i just wanna come home forever and
start my life ya know and two years seems so far away when
really it's not. i just don't want to wait that long i feel like im
missing out on so much. what im missing out on i have no
idea but i know im missing out on something and it really kina
bothers me. well time for me to go to bed. so email me back
whenever u get a chance. i luv u and miss ya.*

luv brent

*ps if u don't mind telling me about that engagement thing i
would really like to hear about it, but if u don't want to talk
about it that's cool too. i've just been thinkin about it alot
lately. I know i shouldn't b but i am.*

*pps im sorry if im messin with ur emotions i just have so
many questions, but if u don't want to answer them then tell*

me to back off and i most certainly will. i just don't know what im doin anymore.

I read through the letter one more time. A sigh escapes. Of course he referred to "that engagement thing" again. The last time we talked on the phone he told me Kali said she heard Jeremy and I were going to get engaged. I know she did not think anything of it, and she was not trying to hurt him, but I don't think people maybe quite understand how close Brent and I are. Were? Kali probably thought she was making casual conversation about a shared schoolmate. Anyway, I know it really caught Brent off guard. My brain does not feel equipped to think more about this right now. I will respond later. I need to get back to this paper. Time to focus, for crying out loud. Again I concentrate on the blinking line.

That blankety-blank blinking line is always mocking me.

The blinking line: *Oh, it's you again, Jamie. How long is it going to take you to get me to move this time?*

Me: *Why must you mock me so, you sassy blinking line? Can't you see I am already stressed out enough?*

Am I having a conversation with the computer's blinking line? That cannot be what it is actually called, can it? I open a new window on my screen and type in "google search." Turns out "googling" things is pretty stinking convenient; I have only recently learned about this fancy new tool. I scroll through the "hits" (that is what you call the results) and learn the technical term is "cursor."

Cursor? Curse you.

I have got to focus! What time is it? I look to the top corner of the screen: 10:14. Have I been here that long? The breakfast! Flip. I almost completely forgot. I save my progress on my floppy disk—had to learn that the hard way, that one must save every single time—pop the disk out and toss it in my backpack, sling the backpack over my left shoulder, and hustle out the lab door.

The succulent smell of French toast, pancakes, and bacon—mmm, bacon—greets me as I pull open the door to the sub. I make my way up the stairs and through the hallway to the eating area. It takes only seconds to spot some of my favorite people. I smile and proceed to load up a plate. There is a tradition here at Rocky where staff members cook up a delicious breakfast feast for students and serve it at ten the first night of Dead Week. One of my favorite professors piles some sausage on my plate. I smile. "Thanks, Professor Swain." [127]

"Hi, Jamer!" My favorite greeting.

"Hi, Jer," I respond sweetly and take the open seat next to my baby boy.

I look around and smile at Kelley, Logan, and Peter. "Hi, guys."

"Hello, Jamie Marie." Peter offers me his usual greeting in his deep baritone.

"What are you talking about?" I ask, realizing full well what I may be getting myself into with that question.

"Dolly," Logan replies plainly, the name of Ron/Dr. Cochran's blow-up sheep.

This makes me chuckle. Oh, Lordy. Here we go again.

* * *

Okay, my stomach is full, I laughed a lot, and I got to see Jeremy. I should be all ready to finish this paper. Yes, that should be the case. In theory. But I am so tired. Slow blink (my eyes, not the cursor). I close my eyes tightly and shake my head. Come on. You got this. I force myself to focus on the screen and scan through what I last wrote for my final summary of Hurston's *Their Eyes Were Watching God.*[128]

> *Janie still doesn't care what others think. She only wants to be happy, and Tea Cake makes her happy. Janie is not stupid, but she takes a risk and follows her heart. Her heart is right. Finally Janie leads the life she has always desired. She does what she wants to do. Tea Cake puts her on a pedestal. Better yet, he treats her as a friend and an equal.*
>
> *Tea Cake dies, but Janie doesn't have any regrets. Even if she was only happy for a while, at least she was once truly happy. She resists the world's common laws and breaks free from the traditional and unfair bonds that accompany black womanhood. Janie Woods is born with a good head and a*

---

[127] Rocky, 2018.
[128] Danticat, 2021.

> *strong heart, and she defies the long-established rules written*
> *for black females.*

Janie is such a bada**. I cannot imagine how insanely hard it must have been to have gone against the cultural norms like that. To pave her own path, instead of trying to please everyone around her and trying to meet everyone else's expectations. Instead of trying to be the "good girl," trying to follow all the rules, worrying about the judgment of other people. On second thought, maybe I can imagine that . . .

I reread part of my opening paragraph:

> *Janie is examined through a microscope her entire life*
> *because people can tell that she is different than most black*
> *females at that time; she doesn't like being told what to do,*
> *how to act, or how to live. It is obvious Janie has a mind of*
> *her own, and in the time period in which she lives, females—*
> *especially colored females—are not supposed to think for*
> *themselves. The author places much emphasis on the fact that*
> *Janie's peers keep a constant watch over her. Hurston makes*
> *it clear that Janie is on trial by her community for challenging*
> *gender roles in a time where roles are accepted by everyone*
> *and literally written in black and white.*

The cursor blinks at me a few more times, but this time the blinking feels patient. I place my fingers back on the home row and attempt a final line:

> *Janie is put on the stand by almost everyone she crosses, but*
> *in the end she is set free, and the awestricken, admiring*
> *prosecution rests.*

* * *

"But I really want to see Minnie." Amers shares her reasoning behind prioritizing Main Street USA as we nail down specifics for our day's itinerary.

We are in sunny California to play a couple games but mostly, I think, to have some bonding time and fun together as a team. We got to LA Thursday night. My roommates are Jeri, Ashley, and Stacey, and we have an adjoining room with Kat, Amy, Kelley, and Amber. The hotel is pretty swanky. Friday we played Vanguard University, ranked third in the nation. How would I summarize that game? Oh yes, they spanked us. By forty. We played on this tiny junior high-like court. It was hotter than blazes. All the better to crush us in, my dears.

Yesterday after our shootaround we went to a huge shopping complex with a Niketown. Pretty big time for small-town Montana girls. We ate at a Rainforest Cafe, which was very cool. We then went to another random gym and played against Biola. We played much better but still lost. Sigh. We are going to have to figure out how to "play to win" before conference starts. Even though we lost, the coaches still gave us a great surprise by taking us to the Staples Center to watch the Clippers beat the Suns. Glad going to the game was not contingent upon our personal team performance. Even though we were in the nosebleeds it was way cool. I had not been to an NBA game since first grade when I got to see Kevin McHale play with Larry Bird in what ended up being Larry's last game. I bawled my brains out because Larry lost, and I really thought he should win his last game.[129]

And today we are at . . . Disneyland!

We had a team vote about how we would spend this last day. SeaWorld or Universal Studios would have also been cool, but I was crossing my fingers for Disney. Some of my teammates had never been here before today, and I am a firm believer that everyone should experience Disney at least once.[130] Plus, now everything here is decorated for Christmas, so it is extra magical.

I turn and reach my arms up high, like a toddler. Without hesitation, Bills reaches down and pulls me up to rest on her hip.[131]

"Let's go on the Indiana Jones ride, and we can decide after that," I suggest.

No one seems to have any objections as we walk toward Adventureland.

---

[129] We were able to attend that game because of the Elks Hoop Shoot. My brother competed at nationals in Indianapolis, Indiana in 1991, and we watched the Celtics play the Pacers.

[130] My mom has historically been quite lucky when it comes to winning random raffles and sweepstakes. When I was in sixth grade, she won a Liberty County Hospital Trip of the Month and presented Disney tickets to my brother and me at Christmas. We had also gone to Disney when I was in first grade.

[131] Sarah Bills, a 6'4" center from Utah joined our team her junior year. After a few weeks practicing together, I confessed to her I sometimes had a desire to ask if she would carry me around like a baby. She did not even balk at my request.

"I thought that boulder was going to hit me in the face, but I think maybe the Pirates of the Caribbean ride was just a little more fabulous." We all laugh as Kelley narrates her thoughts on the last ride.

After Indiana Jones, we head to the *Honey, I Shrunk the Audience* show. Then we eat lunch at the food court. I finish the meal with a delicious chocolate ice cream bar in the shape of a Mickey head. We split up after that. My group heads to Matterhorn Mountain, explores Mickey's Toontown (and visits Minnie, for Amers), rides It's a Small World, then meets up with the rest of the team at Pirates of the Caribbean We end our ride time exploring the Haunted Mansion.

I feel like a giddy little kid as I look up into the misty night sky. A light sprinkle has been drizzling down almost all day. The sprinkling has not bothered us one bit because first of all, sixty-five-degree rainy weather is a heat wave compared to home right now, we have our baggy Rocky travel gear to keep us warm, and lines have been short to nonexistent. It does feel magical, even if that sounds corny. My eyes are pulled down by a glint that has just come into view. The parade ends with enthusiastic waves from familiar Disney characters. Now it is time for Mickey's Electric Light Show. Suddenly I remember being here as an eight-year-old like it was yesterday. A jolt of joy shocks through me. I give my nearest teammate a big squeeze.

Jeri reacts with a "Hello, little friend," and hugs me right back.

Minnie Mouse! Shye, me, Jeri, Amers, November 2003

184

* * *

"Thanks, Jamers!" Michele gives me a hug after pulling out the charm bracelet and fancy lotion from the package I gave her.

"You're welcome, Chelers." I hug her back. "And thanks for the shirt."

Michele's Christmas present to me is a dark-maroon shirt that reads "Out of Control." I have no idea what she is insinuating.

"Yeah, thanks guys," Isaac chimes in.

My present to Isaac is a DVD player, and he gifts me the DVD *Eight Crazy Nights*. We push the boxes and wrappings back by the tree and turn our heads in unison in response to a high-pitched, "Yoo-hooooo!" sailing up the stairs.

We all recognize the familiar greeting and smile toward the carpeted stairwell. Matt slowly lumbers up the steps, with Heidi, Kaitlynn, Travis, and Wicks in tow. Matt briefly scans the room then walks purposely toward Isaac, wrapping him in a giant bear hug. Matt buries his head in Isaac's chest, murmuring how much he loves him and has missed him. I chuckle quietly and let out a happy sigh.

College basketball schedules are brutal, turns out, so I feel extremely lucky to be able to get at least a little time in Chester for Christmas break. At noon on Friday Kat and I drove Maci's car to Fort Benton because she got a ride from Ryan.[132] Zana picked Kat up in Fort Benton, and I drove solo the last fifty-four miles up to the Hi-Line. I arrived here in Chester just before five. Dad greeted me as I pulled up to our front door. I was so very excited to see my daddy. I gave him a big hug. He of course insisted on carrying all my luggage inside, including my giant netted bag bulging with laundry. Mom got home a few minutes after five, and I was equally happy to see her. I love my parents so much. They just get cuter and cuter every time I see them.

That night we went to The Grand[133] for delicious chicken. We met Coach Schlepp, Kellie, and cute Baby Kade. I got to talk to the Deckers,

---

[132] Maci started dating Ryan McDermott, a Carroll student originally from Shelby, after a raucous Carroll College annual softball tournament weekend the previous April.

[133] The Grand is one of (the few) restaurants in Chester. It is a bar-restaurant combo, with a full bar, jukebox, casino machines, and the best chicken around.

too, so that was a bonus. We were at the bar for three hours or so, and then the folks dropped me off at my Kaitlynn's. She and I dropped off a present at Scott's; I think he and Kaitlynn will get back together soon enough. Scott just needs to figure a few things out. Then I went to the Vandykes', and Kate came over later. She and I talked to Coach forever, and Isaac and Travis got home right before we left.

Today, I went to Heart Butte to watch ball. The boys are so fun to watch. Isaac works so hard. It *almost* made me remember when basketball was fun. Anyway, I rode to the game with VanDykes and Ghekieres. Then Emily, Chele, Jessica, and I came home in Emily's car after we ate in Valier.

I click back to the conversations surrounding me and realize there is a debate raging about what movie we should watch tonight. Immediately I reach over and grab the gift bag Isaac just gave me. I know exactly how to settle this.

Chapter 25

January–March 2004, sophomore year, Frontier Conference season, Billings, Montana

January 14, 2004

Sixteen months today that Jeremy and I have been together. That is a long time, and it is going to be forever. This week I have been trying to get back into the groove of school. My Historical Geology lab did not work out because little did I know, it required a prerequisite. So that was a pain. I finally got it all figured out and am now taking only eighteen credits. Monday I had two classes and practice. Practice went pretty well I suppose. Jeremy, Peter, and I went to *Brother Bear* at the Ghetto after that, and maybe I did some homework when we got back. Yesterday I had three classes, practice, and then Jer, Peter, and I ate at Jessica Workman's cute apartment with Jess and Jenny. Those two may be the sweetest human beings on this planet. For dinner we had chicken, rice, beans, garlic bread, and then watched *The Pirates of the Caribbean*. We said thank you and goodbye to Jess and Jenny, and then both "Jer Jers" [134] and I made a late Walmart run because they needed supplies for their Art Design class.

Today I had only one class before practice. I made a quick stop at the sub before my three-hour education class with Dr. DeSilva. That class is loooong. Sustenance is a must in order to stay engaged. But when Dr. DeSilva stops talking, purses her lips into this sly smile—like everyone should know what she is smiling about, though we are not always quite sure—stares meaningfully at the always startled-looking offensive lineman in the back, waggles her finger, and sort of scolds but really more coos, "Jaaaaames," it always makes class worth it.

I wrote Brent a very long email today. He has been having problems lately. I want to be there for him. I just do not always know how to do

---

[134] There was some tension surrounding which "Jer Jer" was the original: Jeri or Jeremy.

that. I am such a lucky person to have Jeremy, and I need to remember that. I need to be happy and treat people—everyone—well all the time.

January 19, 2004

My chin still looks disgusting. I broke it open diving for the ball during the Carroll game. We were up 31-27 at half. I went into the training room to get it gauzed and bandaged up so I could make it through the rest of the game. I made it through, but we lost by ten. One nice thing was that Jeffrey came in the training room to check on me. He was very concerned and sweet. Then my dad and Hendo took me to the hospital after the loss to get the chin all glued up. In hindsight I probably should have chosen stitches, but needles make me faint. Anyway, with the righteous black eye I got from the next game, I look pretty messed up.

We are now 0-3 in conference play. Thursday we played terrible against Westminster. Actually, only the first half was terrible. We dug ourselves into such a hole that it was too much to dig out. I feel like I personally played pretty solid. I found myself missing having JD as a coach. He might have been tough sometimes, but at least he gave me feedback. And he was the only coach who has ever taken the time to explain to me that, as a point guard, I should be utilizing the pullback dribble. He talked to me about the fact that I did not need to do that in high school, but as the competition is a level up in college, it is a must. That made sense and gave me a new level of understanding and confidence. Now why don't my other coaches tell me what they want from me? How can I do better if I do not know the expectations?

Anyway, Friday I finished class at eleven thirty, and Jeremy and I went to Big Timber to watch Rebecca play. Kath, Jimmy, and the kids were there, and it was so much fun. Then yesterday we had shootaround at ten. After that I went back to the apartment and played cribbage with Jer. He asked me if I was excited about the Krib and Keg tournament this year. I asked him why in the world would I be excited about something I knew I was going to lose? He tried to claim, "There's a fifty-fifty probability," blah blah blah.

Bull.

I have played Jeremy enough times in cribbage to know it is not fifty-fifty. I started keeping a tally to prove it. He kept trying to convince me it would be anybody's tournament. I reminded him that in the middle of last year's tournament he took a break to play some Frisbee, jumped over a fence, jumped back again, sat down at the wrong table, eventually found where he was supposed to be, and still won the whole thing, including the coveted "Krib and Keg champ" T-shirt. In the end I agreed to at least participate this year because I know how elitist the organizers are.[135]

Jeremy is really cute when he talks about cribbage, though.

I keep working my way through recent games played. We played much better against Lewis-Clark on Saturday. But not much better enough. We got up by a few early, but then we were down 17-29 at half. Amber and I hit back-to-back threes with 11:45 left in the second half to pull us within three, 42-45, but we just could not hang on. Lost, 60-68. Our boys, on the other hand, knocked off both Westminster and LC on that road trip. That was so exciting. At least one Bears basketball team is winning.

Today has been pretty laid-back since it is Martin Luther King Jr. Day. No classes on a Monday. Wonderful. Our team did have lunch together today, then we had a shootaround, and then I read and read and read. Tonight we had a delicious dinner to celebrate our roommates' birthdays; Andy's is today and Erin's is on Friday. It is fun to celebrate.

* * *

After opening the envelope from Mom I close my eyes and take a few breaths. I did not love playing against Michele and Chasi at Northern last weekend. Chas played especially great, scoring ten, with two threes. And I was happy for her, really. Michele had four, I think, but it was Valgardson, Bateman, and Vermandel who really dominated. We could not keep them at bay. We also got two technical fouls, between

---

[135] Jeremy, Logan, and Eddie Stack—point guard for the men's basketball team, health and exercise science teacher at Loyola Sacred Heart High School in Missoula, Montana, (Missoula, 2017) and head boys' basketball coach since 2014—organized a Krib and Keg tournament each spring. They were extremely picky about who could compete and were ruthless when it came to rules; if you missed a point to peg, they would take it from you with no remorse.

Coach Hendo and Amber, which let's just say did not help our momentum. Ashley had four threes for us, Amers had six assists, and that was about it as far as highlights. I got rocked by a Valgardson screen at half-court in the final few minutes of the game and wanted to cry. I have been icing my neck constantly. Ever since the accident it hurts all the time. I pop ibuprofen like PEZ. I open my eyes, reach into the envelope, and flatten out the article Mom sent on the kitchen table.

WEEKEND GAMES FEATURE FORMER HI-LINE STANDOUTS

by Ryan Divish, *Havre Daily News*, Friday, January 22, 2004

It will be a veritable who's who of Hi-Line basketball this weekend at the Montana State University-Northern gymnasium.

With the Lights and Skylights hosting Rocky Mountain College and Carroll College on Friday and Saturday, several players who starred in our local hotbed of hoops will be returning home to compete in front of family and friends.

It will be like old times during Friday night's Northern-Rocky game for people in Chester. At any given point during the game, four starters from Chester's 2001 Class C state championship squad could be on the floor squaring off against each other.

The duo Michele VanDyke and Chasi Buffington have played major roles for the Skylights this season.

VanDyke, who has started 15 of 20 games for Northern this season after transferring from the University of Montana, is averaging 8.1 points and 4.6 rebounds per game.

Buffington has appeared in all 20 of Northern's games this season after transferring from Sheridan College. She is averaging 4.0 points per game and made her first start of the season against Montana Tech last weekend.

The backcourt from the 2001 squad has taken its talents to Rocky Mountain College.

Sophomores Jamie Graham and Maci Tempel have become key contributors for the Battlin' Bears this season.

Graham, who was the point guard for the championship squad, has taken over the point guard duties from former Skylight and senior Jenny Balgua, who went down with an injury before the season started.

Graham is averaging 6.7 points, 4.2 assists, and 2.3 steals per game and has had some big performances including a 19-point, 5-steal game against Jamestown College.

Tempel has appeared in 16 games for Rocky this season and is averaging 2.3 points per game. Tempel has scored some points coming off the bench to relieve Graham and Rocky's other shooting guards.

Another key player from Chester's title squad will also be in attendance. Katy Engstrom, a redshirt freshman for the Skylight volleyball squad, played a key role for Chester's championship run.

Rocky also has two other players with local connections. Former Big Sandy all-state forward Katherine Bitz is seeing significant minutes for the Bears. Bitz, a sophomore, is averaging 8.2 points and 2.9 rebounds per game and has scored more than 20 points on two occasions.

One of Bitz' teammates is getting some solid minutes for Northern. True freshman Sheena Darlington has appeared in 18 games this season and has had flashes of brilliance while adjusting to the college game. Darlington is averaging 3.6 points and 2.1 rebounds per game, with highs of 10 points and six rebounds this season.

Also on the Rocky roster is former Havre High standout Jeri Matter, who has seen action in nine games. Matter, also a sophomore, is averaging 1.7 points per game and played in Rocky's last two conference games.

The local flavor won't be in just the women's games.

The men's games will feature a trio of former standouts returning to the area. Former KG star Jake Stuart will play his final college game at the MSU-Northern gymnasium on Friday night for Rocky.

Stuart, who transferred from the University of Montana, plays particularly well in front of Havre as evidenced by a 26-point outburst in last season's game.

This season, Stuart is fifth in the Frontier Conference in scoring at 15.8 points per game while averaging 5.8 rebounds a game.

Stuart's longtime high school rival, Jeff Graham of Chester, will take to the floor on Saturday night for Carroll College.

Graham, who played as a true freshman for Northern and redshirted at Carroll last season, has played in all 18 of Carroll's games and is averaging 5.8 points per game. Graham scored 11 points in Carroll's last game and is starting to see more playing time in the conference season.

Besides Graham, Joey Stuart, Jake's younger brother, is seeing some time as a backup point guard for Carroll. Stuart, who originally went to Carroll to play football, has appeared in 12 games

```
this season after returning to the hardwood. He is
averaging 1.7 points per game.
```

That's nice. I like how he tied all of us Hi-Line kids together. Thanks, Ryan. I wish I could see and remember the "bigger picture" of all this more often. Like in high school I never really questioned why we did what we did. Why we played. It was just the way things were. It was how we kept busy, how we kept in shape, how we connected with friends and coaches and teachers and community members. And there was a clear goal. Things here are so, I don't know, just different. The goals do not always feel clear. Obviously we want to make it to nationals, but in the meantime it can feel like such a grind. And we are connected to the community in a way, I suppose, but not in the same way. There is such emphasis on individual play and, who starts, how many minutes we get. Maybe it feels political or something? It can just feel complicated sometimes.

I skim the article again. It does remind me how connected we all are. It reminds me that no matter what we do, the relationships are the most important thing. Right? Yes, I have to believe that.

I sigh and toss the papers on the table. I close my eyes again and rub the top of my nose with my thumb and forefinger. We did get a win against the University of Great Falls that Saturday—after losing to Northern—so that was nice. Don't get me wrong, we tried to give it away and went into the locker room at half down by fifteen. Ashley and Amber had solid second halves, finishing with sixteen and fourteen points to lead us to our 85-62 victory. Stacey shot well off the bench, and Kelley played awesome. That is a beautiful thing about basketball, you have to look to tomorrow and keep plugging away.

February 7, 2004

Last weekend we went 1-1, which for us, was an improvement. First we played Western. We were down twelve at half then had a solid second half. But we have got to start out stronger. The game was a heartbreaker. We had our chance. Sunwall is such a stud. She had thirteen. And Schmitz[136] led them with fourteen. Amber, Kat, and

---

[136] Megan Schmitz, my future sister-in-law!

193

Kelley all had double figures, but it was not quite enough. Final score: 62–63.

We beat Tech 95–86 Saturday in a fast-paced game. Amber was steady, scoring twenty-six, and Ashley was about just as tough, scoring seventeen. I had a couple steals and eleven points, and Stacey hit three threes.

Then tonight we had Carroll at home. Oh, Carroll. I shake my fist at you. We played okay, and I know we could have beaten them—I do feel like we can truly compete with anyone in the conference, if we just made a few tweaks, or had a different collective attitude, maybe—but alas, we did not. Woody and Zoanni were tough, and we lost 58–69. We were down eleven at half as well. It seems pretty clear we need to clean up our first half performances. Not sure what that will take. For now, though, it is past midnight and I really need some sleep.

February 15, 2004

Amber told Coach Hendo where he could stuff it at practice last week. I am pretty sure my jaw dropped to the floor. It felt sort of like I wanted to cover my eyes, but I couldn't, because I legit could not not watch. I was proud of Hendo, though, because he kicked her out of practice. I love Amber and all, but she crossed the line. I know Hendo is such a nice guy. That is one of the reasons I wanted to come to Rocky and play for him. But sometimes you have to put the foot down.

Then we played LC State and Westminster again over the weekend. Lewiston, Idaho is not the best-smelling town I have ever been to. I have learned that stench is emitted from the paper factory there. I have also learned one does best not to dis the smell. It's "the smell of money,"[137] turns out. And even though the paper factory smell is nose-crinkling, the delicious waffle restaurant makes up for it.

Amber had to sit out for the first half of the LC game, due to the altercation at practice the previous week. Would I have sat her out at least an entire game if I were the coach, or perhaps the entire weekend? Maybe. But I cannot say that for sure. I know any individual situation is layered and complicated. Anyway, Kelley started in Amber's place and played outstanding. I was so proud of her. She went 8–13 from the field,

---

[137] Intermountain, 2022.

2-2 from the free throw line, and pulled down seven rebounds. It was not quite enough, though, and we headed into the locker room with a loss, 68-92.

That locker room was memorable for another reason. Hendo was super fired up and ripping into us. Another type of ripping was threatening my world. I was doing my best to keep my attention focused on him, nodding my head and mirroring his concerned and angry facial expressions. But there was this very unfortunate, untimely, ultra-awkward distraction. I started shifting uncomfortably on the already uncomfortable bench. Then I knew the situation was about to get completely out of hand, out of my control. I knew there was little I could do but thought perhaps there was some way to lessen the intensity. I remembered someone once telling me all about this scientific explanation for why certain sounds are so loud. The fact that they bounce off hard surfaces at a certain velocity, how softer surfaces make a difference, ways to diminish decibel intensity, things like that. So, while keeping my eyes locked on Hendo, I slowly reached down and cupped my right hand under and around my right cheek. My rationale was that if only I could simply separate the cheek from the bench that might eliminate the vibrato factor, and thus, prevent the extremely embarrassing alternative.

Right as I slowly lifted my entire right butt cheek and tilted my body slowly to the left—all the while keeping my eyes on Hendo's—a long, loud fart escaped and rang throughout the whole locker room. So much for decibel reduction. If anything, it was louder than I first feared. Coach Hendo stopped midrant and looked directly at me. Time stood still as his eyes locked on to mine. Finally I shrugged innocently and looked back with an I'm-sorry-slash-what-can-ya-do? face. The room was pin-drop silent. Uh-oh. I was not sure what he would do.

Coach continued looking at me for another second more. Then he lowered his shoulders, let out a big sigh, shook his head, and a small smirk crossed his face. Everyone nervously giggled as he addressed the room again, this time in a more relaxed and maybe even resigned tone. "Alright, now let's just think about what we can learn from tonight"—he turned toward the door—"and sharpen things up for our next game."

195

The second the door closed, the locker room erupted with laughter. There was a lot of eruption that night.

Thankfully we put together a great game against Westminster Saturday. We were up 44–31 at half. They made a quick run early in the second half, but we kept our composure and kept control. The final was 81–72. It makes for a much more pleasant bus ride home when we get at least one win.

It should also be noted that I love having Kevin and Yonkers on road trips. They always join in our shooting games at the end of shootarounds and keep me entertained.[138] Yonkers interviewed me at halftime of the Westminster game. I ended up dying laughing because he started asking about what kids do for fun when they live in Chester. I told him we would go to Subway. He asked me to repeat the answer, and again I told him where we went. He paused for a bit, furrowed his brow, and finally said, "Huh. I am surprised such a small town would have a subway system."

I then explained to him I meant the sandwich shop, not an electric train system. I have no idea what New York City is like, but I also get such a kick out of his story about moving out to Montana. He got the job at the college over the phone, never having visited Montana. Then he started looking for a place to live. After studying a map of the Billings area, he decided on a space that looked like a nice "suburb" with a reasonable "commute" and settled on a rental in Huntley.[139]

February 22, 2004

The Argos came to play us here on the nineteenth. Remember how we outscored them by thirty-eight a mere month back to beat them by twenty-three? Yeah, neither do I. This time they were beating us at halftime. And then they were beating us when the game ended. By twenty. Then two nights later Northern beat us 67–76. Usually I love palindromes. That night I hated them.

---

[138] Kevin Jurenka was a student-trainer and thus accompanied us on road trips, tending to both men and women basketball athletes. "Yonkers," or Pat, was Rocky's radio announcer during my time at college.

[139] Huntley is located ten miles northeast of Billings. It was named for the Huntley Irrigation Project, which was the second US Bureau of Reclamation irrigation project. Billings may be the biggest city in Montana, but it does not have "suburbs" or a "commute" that mimic those near New York City in any way.

The redeeming quality of the weekend was that Michele and Chasi got to stay overnight with us, and Matt, Diemert, Jeff Cicon, Cory, and Geoff Osterman came and stayed, too. We played games and laughed all night. Thank goodness for good friends.

March 1, 2004

We had an intense and fun game against Tech last weekend. We were down 32-40 at half. That sadly felt familiar. But then we got hot the second half. We hit eighteen of thirty field goals for a double-digit win. Amber led with thirty-three, Ashley had twenty, I had eleven, and Kelley had ten.

My parents sent me a sweet card to encourage me before postseason play started. My mom told me that no matter what happened in the playoff game, she thinks I am and always will be a winner in every aspect of my life. Mom writes me letters all the time, but not Dad. Maybe I will hang his letter up.

> Hi Baby,
>
> Well, it's tourney time, and everything starts over now! You know about "crunch time" more than anyone. You have become the "Battlin' Bear" leader both on and off the court, and everyone will look to you to run the show and get everyone positive and on the same page. This is a tall order, but there is no one more able to handle this role than Jamie Graham!
>
> We are extremely proud of you in all aspects of your life. Your accomplishments on the court are great, but that is just part of what makes you so special. Very few athletes get the opportunity to do what you are currently doing! It is long, physically draining, mentally taxing, and pressure packed. But, enjoy the moment, as it will be over too soon!
>
> Look yourself in the mirror on Friday after the game and tell yourself you gave it all you had, win

or lose! We will see you Friday! Have fun and play hard!

Your only boyfriend,
DAD

I reread the letter from my dad several times. The message is hitting me in a funny way now. Growing up, I always thought the message from everyone was: WIN. I mean, I know that was the message, and it remains a primary goal before taking the court each game. But when I read Dad's words now, I hear something different. I hear the emphasis on being a positive leader all the time, no matter the situation. On being intentional in encouraging teammates and getting everybody on the same page. Focusing on finding ways to keep people together.

I know my dad played sports, too, but to be honest I have never sat down and tried to picture what that maybe felt like for him; it always seemed arbitrary, like a different lifetime, like those experiences are buried in the past. It seems obvious now, that of course those experiences are not arbitrary and are not buried, not for him. They are a part of my dad's story. They shaped his view of how to live life, and through him, those experiences are shaping me, too.

So I have been thinking about Dad's words a lot. And even though we did not end up with a "winning" record, I feel like the season was still worth the time, effort, and energy.

We lost our final regular season conference game to Western 63-71. Then we found out Great Falls barely beat us out of the number-six seed. Apparently since UGF beat Westminster in regular season play (which we did, too, so I do not entirely get the rankings), it bumped us down even further. So for the first round of the conference tournament we got to play . . . (drum roll, please) . . . Western!

We played Western for the fourth flipping time this season. You know that saying, *It's hard to beat a team three times in one season?* (In my head, an old man with a screechy southern accent is saying that.) Well after we played Western I made up this new saying: *It's easy for Western to beat Rocky four times in one season.*

And that was all she wrote, folks. Season over. Goodbye, sophomore season. Goodbye, 10-20 record. Goodbye darkness, my old friend. That might be going a bit overboard. But it is depressing when a season ends. I guess that makes sense, after what Dad said about the season being long, physically draining, mentally taxing, and pressure packed. Those inevitable ups and downs are the nature of any season, I suppose.

I need a nap.

Chapter 26

March 2004, sophomore year, difficult decisions, spring break,
Billings, Montana; Cody, Wyoming

"I get it," I say to Maci. I really do get it, but still it makes me sad. Maci and I sit together at a lunch table at the sub, and she tells me what I have already guessed. "Ryan and I have decided we don't want to do the whole long-distance romance anymore."

My head nods, my throat constricts, but I force myself to keep it together. Maci and Ryan have gotten very serious this year. I had a feeling she was considering transferring to Carroll to be with him. She drives over to Helena any chance she gets, and they are on the phone nonstop. For a second I try to picture how I would handle living in a different town than Jeremy. It takes less than a second to confirm I would do most anything to avoid it.

"I get it," I say again.

For how difficult basketball was for me this past season, it was even more so for Mace. Her playing time was spotty at best. I swear I could visibly see her losing her love for the game, one weekend at a time.

I have said it before. College sports are a grind. From October until March (mid-March if you are lucky, but I have not personally experienced that yet) it dictates your schedule. It takes an intense level of discipline and commitment. And in our case, the payback does not always feel equal to the pay-in.

Someone asked me a while back if I have a job while at college. I told them, for a college athlete, your sport is your job. Some might not buy that, but it certainly takes up the same number of hours as a part-time job. With at least three hours of practice a day—counting lifting, film, meetings, other sporadic team obligations—and then weekends leaving on a bus Thursday afternoon and getting home in the wee hours of Sunday morning, I would argue it is more comparable to a full-time job. You always see "student" come first when a reference is made to "student-athlete," but it often feels like those two words should be reversed. There are many benefits, of course. Sometimes it is just more difficult to see the benefits than others.

I look across the table at my teammate of over ten years. Half my life. We eat in silence, looking up after taking a bite, chewing and catching each other's eyes, smiling slightly. A lot is being communicated during this lunch. More than I could begin to put into words.

* * *

"I'm sorry, babe." Jer rubs my shoulder and kisses the side of my head.

My tears drip slowly onto his T-shirt. It is not that this is so shocking, but it does feel a little shocking, and it makes me sad. I have now had very similar conversations—with Kelley and Shye—to the one I had with Maci the other day. Kelley and Shye are not transferring schools, but they are not going to play basketball next season.

I continue with my pity party. "They are my funniest friends! If next season has as many depressing points as this past season, how will I make it without my funniest friends?!"

Jer squeezes me tight then releases his grip a bit, so we are now eye-to-eye. "I know it is hard," he says understandingly. He always tries his best to help me see the positives. "But Kelley and Shye will still be around. You will still have classes with Kelley, and you will still hang out with Shye."

I know what he says is true, but I am in a whiney mood and continue to whine. "But they will not live on campus! How often during the season do I have time to see anyone who does not live on campus?" I immediately answer my own question before allowing Jeremy any time or space to respond: "Not very often!"

He closes his mouth, opens it again with raised eyebrows, and then seems to think better of it and closes his mouth again. This is one of those moments where the best way for him to help me is to not say a word. There is nothing he can do to fix it. I can see in his eyes that he has several things he is debating saying. He instead continues to keep quiet and pulls me back in close to his chest.

* * *

"Wacky waving . . . what?" Amanda asks dubiously.

Without skipping a beat Peter, Kevin, Jeremy, and I enthusiastically reply in unison, "Wacky waving inflatable arm-flailing tube man!"

We all look at Amanda expectantly. She looks at each of us one by one, expression unreadable. Then she states simply, "You Rocky people are weird."

The five of us sit in a circle in Greg and Ann's basement living room in Cody, Wyoming. Amanda drove to Rocky yesterday and watched our boys' playoff game with me last night. Our boys played so hard, but they came up short against Northern. And that was it for them, too. Season over. It always feels so abrupt. Like your days and time and thoughts are filled with so much basketball, there is this huge build up, and suddenly it is all completely cut off. I do not know if there is any way to avoid that drastic drop-off that comes with a season ending. I always feel depressed for several days after.

Anyway, it was fun having both our basketball teams on campus last night. The Jorgensen apartments were rocking until the wee hours. I am dubbing last night the official-yet-unplanned kickoff to spring break.

This morning came quickly. Jeremy drove the five of us to Sheridan. We went straight to St. Peter's—walked in just as the bells were chiming—and got to worship with David. After church David treated us poor college students to a most delightful brunch at Oliver's. Then we made our way over the mountains[140] and are now staying here in Cody for a couple nights.

Ann made us a delicious roast for dinner, complete with her famous buttery mashed potatoes. Then we all watched *The Jerk* together. Watching any movie with Ann and Greg is the best because of their infectious laughs. Ann and Greg went to sleep after the movie, and now we are teaching Amanda how to play Slaps. After her comment about us Rocky people being weird, I look at her and laugh. "Okay, babe," I suggest, "how about we transition to the hot tub? Then maybe we can give Slaps another chance."

---

[140] The Bighorn Mountain Range is about 150 miles long and thirty miles wide, located in north-central Wyoming. Driving distance from Sheridan to Cody is about 145 miles.

* * *

This week has been wonderful. Lots of sleeping in, lots of good food, and lots of cribbage and pinochle. We stayed in Cody for two nights and had a lot of fun eating, sleeping, going to the rec center, hot tubbing, and just relaxing. Then we drove back to Billings and dropped off Peter, continued north and dropped Amanda off in Roundup,[141] and then I drove the rest of the way up to Chester while Jeremy and Kevin slept. It was nice being in complete control of the radio.

When we got to my parents' house, Kev had dinner with us and then headed east on Highway 2 to his family farm.[142] My brother made it up a little later in the evening, and apparently Jeffrey and Jeremy are now best friends.

This morning Jeremy and Isaac went on a run. Why would anyone want to go on a run for "fun"? It is beyond me, but I try not to judge. Then tonight we all went to The Grand for dinner. Not much beats the chicken at The Grand. Coach Schlepp, Kellie, and baby Kade were there, and the Hamels also joined us for a while. Mom and I got home at ten thirty, and the rest of those crazy kids are still going strong. There was lots of talk about weddings and in-laws tonight. Pretty funny.

* * *

"You're not invited," Diemert tells me bluntly.

"I didn't want to go," I retort back.

I explain to these boys—standing on my parents' front doorstep—why I greeted them at the door so fast, lest they get the wrong idea and think I was waiting for them. "I am on my way to Heidi's. I had no idea you were coming here."

Yesterday Jer and I spent the day in Havre with Chasi, Michele, and Kaitlynn. Today we spent all day in Great Falls, as my brother was coaching a junior high team from Chester, and Isaac and Travis were playing on another team. Mom and Dad took us all out to Golden

---

[141] Amanda's parents moved to Roundup after she graduated, after living and serving in Chester for twenty-two years.

[142] Kevin's parents, Tom and Marilyn, still live on their family farm, twenty-two miles north of Hingham. They farmed and raised cattle for years and now are happily retired.

Corral. We just got home around nine, about a half an hour ago. I was about to head out the door to meet Kayla at Heidi's when I ran into these three. These three classmates of mine who are looking for Jeremy, not me, thank you very much. I call Jer's name and hear him skipping up the stairs. "Have fun," I well-wish the boys and head out the door.

* * *

"This is exactly what I needed." Heidi lets out a relieved sigh and closes her eyes.

I look up toward the beautiful star-sparkling sky from the wonderful vantage point of Kayla's parents' hot tub. Kayla's family farm is twenty miles south of Chester. For how few lights there are in Chester competing with the stars, there are barely any out here. The three of us rendezvoused at Heidi's and decided a hot tub night was in order.

"I just saw him." I jump right in to what is on all of our minds. I explain, "He was with Cory and Colt, and they were picking up Jeremy."

Heidi opens her eyes and asks how he seemed. I tell her Matt did not say much, which is not anything out of the ordinary. He had his hands in his pockets and was sort of chuckling at Colt. "They caught me off guard," I continue, "because I literally ran into them heading over to meet you two. So I offered Matt a sympathetic smile, patted his arm quick, and left."

Kayla asks Heidi, "And how are *you* doing?"

Heidi closes her eyes again. A tiny tear trickles down her cheek. It takes her a minute before she can get any words out. "I don't know." She offers a weak smile. "Tired."

Kayla and I nod in sympathy. "You haven't had much time to process," I state.

"Right." Heidi agrees. Her voice grows stronger. "The last several days have been a blur. I know it is the best decision in the end, but for now . . ."

We wait patiently while she collects her thoughts.

She finishes the sentence in a whisper. "For now it is really, really hard."

Again we sit in silence, each lost in our own thoughts for a few moments. Then I look over to Heidi again. "Well, the best way to

204

process is sharing all the thoughts out loud with friends. We have no other plans tonight. So why don't you let it all out?"

Kayla nods in agreement. Heidi sits up a bit, wipes both her hands over her eyes and down her cheeks, then takes in a big breath. "Okay," she begins, "so here's what happened . . ."

Chapter 27

April–May, 2004, spring semester, Billings, Montana

"Tell me the truth," Logan asks again.

I peer through the rearview window as we sit idling in the Hardee's drive-thru. It is just past two in the morning. My phone woke me up just under an hour ago, and I made what is becoming a familiar trip to pick up these dancing fools from The Wild West. Jeremy, Logan, Kevin, Kyle, and Peter have been frequenting the dance club this spring. They generally meet many of the Rocky soccer girls and have a blast dancing for hours.[143] Kasey[144] has become Jeremy's official dance partner. Sometimes they go to the Red Door, too. According to Peter, Jeremy's karaoke rendition of Michael Jackson's "I Want You Back" has become a fan favorite.

Logan looks at Jeremy with that one eyebrow-knitted, chin-tucked-down look that communicates he means business. Jeremy rubs his chin and looks up toward the ceiling.

Peter interrupts with more urgent business: "Quick, spicy chicken sandwich or hot ham and cheese?"

"Just order them both." Logan quickly makes Peter's decision for him, apparently eager to get back to his important question.

Logan elaborates on his hypothetical. "If you boarded your flight, looked up in the cockpit, and saw that one of them was your pilot, would you exit the plane and book another flight?"

Logan, Jeremy, Peter, Kevin, and Kyle live for these hypothetical-situation discussions. Their current discussion explores whether or not

---

[143] The Rocky soccer girls were predominantly foreign students. The head women's soccer coach, Richard Duffy, started at Rocky as an assistant women's coach in 2001. He took over as the women's head coach in 2002, started the men's program in 2009, and is still coaching at RMC today.

[144] Kasey Fischer played basketball and soccer her first year at Rocky, and then she played just soccer after that. Those soccer girls were a blast to hang out with and were always up for a good time!

they would be passengers on a plane flown by some of Kyle's aviation classmates. [145]

Inside the vehicle all suddenly goes quiet. Everyone is thinking hard about this potential future scenario.

A scratchy greeting breaks the silence and asks me what we would like to order. The silence is immediately replaced by simultaneous sandwich requests. I do my best to sift through and relay the orders to the poor guy working the drive-thru graveyard shift. Then I slowly pull toward the pick-up window while the intense discussion continues around me. I smile and shake my head. Silly boys.

* * *

I successfully dropped off all the silly boys safely. Now I open the door to our apartment quietly. The dancing glow of the TV surprises me as I slip in our apartment as silently as possible. Erin and Andy are asleep, but Kat is sitting wide awake on our couch. [146] The TV volume is all but audible, but Kat is not paying it any attention. She instead has her entire attention focused on pieces of some silver tube-like apparatus. A plain, rectangular, brown box is propped against the couch. An instructions packet sits open on the floor. Kat looks up and smiles at me. "Hey, Jame."

With a look of curiosity I respond, "Hey, babe."

I take a step closer in an attempt to study the picture on the box. "What ya got there?"

Kat picks up the instruction manual and holds it out to me. I look down, and it finally clicks. Seeing the box brings a memory to mind. The other night I came in late like this, and Kat was glued to the TV, fixated on an infomercial. The receipt on the couch catches my eye. My mind calculates how many boxes of Cooler Ranch Doritos we could

---

[145] Rocky is known for its aviation and equine programs.

[146] For the sophomores who were able to live in the Jorgensen apartments, we had to have four people to an apartment instead of two. So for the 2003-2004 year, Kat and I also lived with Erin Olind, a volleyball player and business management major from Whitehall, Montana, and Andrea Robinson, an aviation major and George Straight-loving cowgirl from Malta, Montana. Our schedules were very opposite, and many weekends during basketball season Jeremy and Peter hung out with Erin and Andy way more than they hung out with us.

buy for that price. For some reason, a judgmental, parental instinct suddenly kicks in. "Katherine Renee! We do not need a Shark!"

I gesture toward the corner in the living room where our used Maytag vacuum cleaner—that Grandma Joyce found at her church garage sale—sits. As if this proves my point, for some reason I am compelled to add, "See? I know the commercial about the Shark is very cool, but we do not need that fancy thing!"

Kat looks back at me with a surprisingly serious expression on her face. We rarely, if ever, have disagreements. I know people sometimes have trouble finding a compatible roommate in college, but we were lucky right out of the gate. We have been able not only to live together but we have navigated shared basketball schedules and mutual friends, survived a move across campus where we added two additional roommates, managed to compromise on chores like cleaning the bathroom and doing the dishes, and managed to figure out all the complicated ins and outs of living peaceably with another human. Are we really going to have our first intense argument about something as insignificant as a vacuum cleaner?

A strained silence hangs in the air. Kat and I stare intensely at one another. We are like a married couple having a spat. She lowers her chin slightly, seriously. I tilt my head to the side a millimeter and squint my eyes in curiosity. What is she thinking? Is she going to yell at me? Have I gone too far?

Finally, Kat breaks the silence. "Jame." Her voice is low and steady.

I hold her stare, unsure of what she is going to say.

She continues slowly, as if trying to get me to understand something extremely important. As if what she is about to say will explain everything. "Jame. It sucks up bolts."

We both continue to look at each other for a few quiet moments. And then we simultaneously keel over and burst into hysterical laughter.

* * *

It is the most beautiful spring day. I walk out of the library and breathe in the fresh April air. I think I always naively assumed all of Montana had weather like Chester's. Thankfully I was wrong. Experiencing the Billings climate has been a most pleasant surprise. Snow and ice actually melt, there are not weeks straight of below-zero highs, colorful leaves stay on trees for more than five minutes in the fall, and there must be at least some moisture in the air because my skin doesn't feel like sandpaper here if I don't immediately apply lotion after a shower. "See ya later!" Megan[147] calls, heading toward the parking lot.

I wave to Megan and walk toward the apartments. I let out a sigh of relief, mentally ticking off the final papers and exams one by one. It is hard to believe that in a mere week from today, we will all be going our separate summer ways. At least this year Jeremy and I are separating together. That sounds strange. What I mean is, even though we have to separate from our friends, Jeremy and I are going down to Texas together for the summer. Jeremy will intern again for Jake, and Jake says he will figure something out for me. I will work wherever, as long as I do not have to be away from Jeremy ever again.

As I stroll past Fortin I see a Frisbee flying high in the grass in front of Jorg. I grin as I see a long, tanned arm snatch the disc easily out of the air. Jeremy tosses the Frisbee across the lawn to Peter, and Peter assists Logan for a goal. The teams switch sides, and Jeremy throws the "kickoff" downfield. Then I can see what is going to happen next. Oh, no. I instinctively cover my mouth and try to close my eyes. Too late.

A sickening *clang* rings in my ears.

I watch—because you can't not watch—as a red-haired kid attempts a great catch but instead runs directly into the light pole by the second set of stairs. Everyone playing ultimate Frisbee stops in their tracks, watching their fellow player collide then slide down the pole. We collectively hold our breath until the player holds up one arm and gives everyone a "thumbs up" from his prostrate position. Kyle jogs over and pulls the dazed kid up. Everyone cautiously gathers round to check for damage. Apparently everything is okay, because before you can say, "Watch out for that pole!" the game has started right back up.

---

[147] Megan Kidwell, from Bridger, Montana, was in many of my education classes and was always a favorite classmate of mine. She was the first person who ever sent me a text—while we were in class—and I remember thinking how ridiculous texting seemed. I was sure it would never catch on and that people would always call first if they needed something.

Suddenly, though, Jer turns and sees me walking. That familiar bolt of excitement shoots through me. It feels like we are thinking the exact same thing at the exact same moment. I drop my books on the grass and run toward him. He splays his arms out wide and throws his head back in delight, bracing himself. Kind of like Kerri Strug, but not really, I vault into his arms, wrapping my legs around his waist.

He spins me around, and I laugh and laugh.

Chapter 28

May-August 2004, summer break, Texas, Mexico, Jamaica

May 17, 2004

Greetings from Port Maria, Jamaica. Yes, we are here, and it is amazing. I didn't bring the journal I had been using, so this notebook will have to do. It has been so long since I have journaled that I don't even know where to start. Let's see. Quick recap:

Um, I'll go with Easter. I went to Chester Thursday after my morning classes and got to see all my friends. That first night I even saw Brent. It was nice because we didn't go into the big talk about us and what happened and the past and all the hard stuff. I like to think it was a good step for us as Brent and Jamie, friends. Then I went to VanDykes' and hung out with Isaac. Isaac is currently dating Brittney Kolstad. I have a feeling this could be his first love. He is doing great in track, revving up for Divisionals, and just turned seventeen. Ah, to be seventeen again.

The rest of Easter break was a blast. I ate most every meal with the VanDykes, since my parents were in Big Timber. Then Katy, Matt, Wade, the Clark twins, Jeff Cicon, Heidi, Cory, and I hung out at my house for hours. Zeb, Diemert, Maci, Kayla, and Brenton joined us later. Chasi, Mike, Eric, Doug, Jason, and Darin also made some appearances. I loved seeing all of those people and laughed a lot.

I went to Big Timber Saturday morning and got to watch Becca play in the Easter Classic tournament in Reed Point.[148] I had lots of good times with the fam, and then Sunday after church I headed back to Billings to finish off the school year—crazy. It was really sad saying goodbye to my mom and dad. We have said goodbye before, of course, but never with me going to another state and knowing I won't see them

---

[148] Reed Point—twenty-four miles east of Big Timber—is a small Class C town rich with basketball history and has held the Easter Classic since 1994. The tournament draws many teams from around Montana year in and year out.

for three whole months! That goodbye felt way worse than them dropping me off for college. It is one thing to know you can see each other in just a few hours, if needed, but that will not be the case this summer. So we shall see how things go.

Finals week went okay. The important thing is that finals are over. It was hectic finishing up all the final projects, papers, and exams, and it was just as hectic getting packed and saying goodbye to everyone at Rocky. Christopher John came through Billings Tuesday night, so he, Maci, and I hung out with Jeri, Andy, Erin, Kat, Jeri, Shye, and Jacqui. That was a nice way to finish the school year. And it was weird realizing college is now half-over.

Then Jer and I did not have to say goodbye to each other! That is the way I like it. We said goodbye to Peter, Logan, Kevin, Kyle, etc., and then headed to Sheridan. Thursday, May 6, 2004. A day that will live "in famy." (I do not think that is the opposite of *infamy*, but that's okay.) That Thursday we watched the final episode of *Friends*. Bittersweet, the end of an era, and all that. We hung out with Jer's dad and sisters and left the next morning: destination, Tyler, Texas.

Jer and I drove and drove and drove some more. We finally arrived at Jake's house around supper Saturday night. Jake took us out to eat. Turns out we go out to eat for most every meal. Fine by me. The first couple weeks here have been good, except for the fact that we are still not sure if I have a job. Also, I have been sleeping on a futon in Jake's living room. Yesterday we went to church, and then we packed a bunch of college students in two vans and headed to Houston. I had a really big problem in Houston. We went bowling, and I bowled a 199. It was devastating. All I had to do was bowl a four or more on my last ball, and I somehow bowled a three. Yes, three. I will not go any deeper into it, because I will just get mad.

This morning we left at five for the airport, did all the security checks—which takes a lot longer now, after 9/11—and flew to Jamaica. It was very cool flying over the water for the first time; the water and island are so beautiful. We sorted all our luggage after landing and boarded this tiny, sort of sketchy bus. We ate at Burger King where I got a meal for 250 Jamaican dollars, about four bucks American. Then we drove on this very tight road—on the *wrong* side of the road—for almost four hours. I was pretty sure we were going to die. Luckily, we did not die. Now we are at this lovely hotel, the Tradewinds Resort, that has the most amazing view.

We swam for a while after we got here, took a hike around these rocks surrounding the beautiful ocean, and were served a delicious three-course meal with the best fruit punch I have ever tasted in my life. Now it is time for Bible study.

May 18, 2004

Today was wonderful. God is great. We woke up to see the sun shining over the beautiful sea. We were served eggs, bacon, sausage, and *fresh* fruit: bananas and papayas. It started to drizzle when our bus driver, Trevor, took us to Port Maria around eight. People here are most definitely not in a hurry. We did some excessive bus sitting, due to the rain and lack of supplies. Then we ended up visiting with old, sick people in an infirmary. A doctor visits them maybe once a week. We hugged some people and shook some hands. People's faces would just light up at a single touch. It was wonderful and sad all at the same time.

After that, we picked up trash for a while at our eventual work site of the future dental clinic we are here to help build. But it started raining harder. The locals made it clear that there is *nothing* to do when it rains. People walk slowly everywhere and just sit outside houses and stores and talk and play dominoes. We had brown paper bag lunches with chicken, beef, or goat curry. Since Jer, Daniel, and I were serving everyone we ended up with the goat for lunch today. I have a feeling we will be eating goat a lot this week. [149]

Because of the rain, we only barely got started on digging the ditches for the foundation. People did not mind one bit that we got little work done. They were simply so thankful and in no rush. So we came back to the hotel, swam, ate, played games, and had our Bible study. We focused on 2 Corinthians 2:5. Our bus driver Trevor comes tomorrow morning at seven thirty. Hopefully we can get some work done.

---

[149] We did, indeed, have goat curry every day. It has taken me many years to try curry of any kind since.

The Green-Clad Kicker

May 19, 2004

Another great day. It was long and fairly taxing, but great. We had eggs and swordfish—and some other things—for breakfast. We also had incredibly fresh grapefruit and pineapple juice. I can already tell I will miss the fruit when we leave. Then we loaded up on the bus and got to the work site by eight. It never did get unbearably hot. It was better than picking oats in the Montana wheat fields because there were breezes and even some raindrops. We dug trenches all day long, after first picking up garbage. It was muddy, which made things sticky, made tools heavy, and there was a lot of concrete to break and dig up. For a couple hours in the morning I got to spend time in the nursery school, where there were kids ages three to six. Many of them had never seen a white person before. They chanted, "White pee-pull!" and called us "Whitey," but they were not being offensive, just curious.

I got to work in a classroom and sing some songs. The rooms are all open, with only three walls, so it gets pretty noisy. Some of the boys would run up and touch my arm really fast since my skin is strange to them. The girls all tried to hold my hands. They were the most beautiful kids. I read them *Cinderella*, and we sang lots of songs. Then we played lots of games outside. It was so wonderful. A man came by and gave us some passion fruit to try. There is a lot of unemployment, so a lot of people are just chilling all day. They seem happy and so laid-back. It feels refreshing.

After work we went to James Bond Beach. That was really cool. Then we came back here and showered before our lovely dinner. I even tried some spinach soup, so good for me. We played dominoes and had Bible study. Now, time to sleep.

May 20, 2004

I cannot believe it is already Thursday. It is kind of sad. We woke up early this morning to the sound of rain. What a beautiful sound. But it put a damper on our morning plans. After breakfast we went and checked out the work site. It was insane. Our two-feet deep trenches we worked so hard to dig yesterday were completely filled with water. We stood around, eventually went back to the hotel for a few hours, and then went back to the work site after lunch. They got a water pump, but there was still not much we could do. So people brought us coconuts to drink from, Jamaican bananas, corn on the cob, and banana chips.[150] We walked around town for a while, and everyone stared. We got lots of "Hellos," and someone told Scott to make sure to wear sunscreen.[151] After our walk we were surprised to see a man digging the trenches with a machine, which was fifty times faster than us doing it by hand yesterday. Maybe that should have been frustrating, but it wasn't because everyone here is so laid-back. It feels nice. Americans are always in a hurry and don't seem to enjoy life in the same way.

May 23, 2004

More rain. Trevor told us it has rained more this past week than he remembers in the past ten years. I enjoy it. Yesterday we did some shopping in Ocho Rios. We went to Dunn's River Falls. It was definitely beautiful, but treacherous. We all joked about the ambulance and infirmary we saw when we pulled in. But it was no joke. Daniel cracked his chin open and needed three stitches. Then I slipped and fell backwards on a huge rock over a steep ledge. Luckily Scott grabbed my arm and pulled me back up. Jer hit his head while we were wading and swimming in the bottom pools. But other than that . . .

Today we worshiped and led parts of worship at a Methodist church in Port Maria. We thought we were maybe going to be late for the nine thirty service. Luckily the word "late" does not exist here in Jamaica. And I love it. The service consisted of a lot of singing. There were a lot of prayers, announcements, and some readings. Our group sang two songs, Jake shared for a couple minutes, Stephanie shared a testimony, and then my perfect Jeremy shared the message. He started by busting out an offertory song. It made me cry. He is so amazing. He talked about how we had to get out of the water at a certain point at the falls yesterday, yet we knew there was more, that there was a pure and beautiful source somewhere above, and he compared that example to God. He did an amazing job.

---

[150] A friendly man named Kat brought us the coconut, and other foods, and pointed up to a mountain to show where he had hiked, climbed a palm tree, and chopped the coconut down with his machete.

[151] Scott Austin was a fair-skinned college student, the son of Jake's youth director partner Miss Teri, and played football at Rice University.

After the *first* part of the church service we ate a potluck lunch. There was not much food, not like the potlucks we are used to, but the people here went and ate elsewhere in order to serve us. So amazing. We worshiped some more after that, rested back at our hotel, had dinner, played games, and then we had devotions, my favorite part of the day.

June 2, 2004

We made it safely back to Texas last week. I called my parents right when we got back, and it was so good to hear their voices. I know I have not been gone that long, but I really miss them. We have not done much constructive since we have been back, unless you call playing cards, going to the movies, and watching VH1, *The Best of Will Ferrell,* and *Blue Collar Comedy Tour,* constructive. I think maybe I am homesick. I have never really felt homesick before. I am so glad I am with Jeremy, of course, but this feels like my first time truly being away from home. And it is not clear exactly what job I am going to do here, or where I will stay for sure. Sometimes it feels like I am sort of like the third wheel with Jake and Jeremy or something, even though I know Jeremy is so glad we do not have to spend this summer apart. I really miss all my friends, and I miss Chester. Welcome to the real world.

I called my parents again last night and cried a little. I tried not to. Dad was like, "We will come get you, or get you a plane ticket." He kept saying, "Jeremy and that other guy better get off the pot or tell them you are coming home to your daddy, because he misses you. I do. I miss you." What a cute dad. I assured them we would figure something out.

Monday we slept late and then worked out. We spent the afternoon at Miss Teri and Glenn's and had a Memorial Day picnic. I told Miss Teri my situation (get a job or go home), and she said Jake had discussed putting me on the church payroll, unbeknownst to me. Then we went to the football field so Jer could kick, talked about things, and I felt a lot better.

Tuesday was my first official day on the job. I get to be a youth intern with Jeremy and Daniel and do what they do and go where they go. Yay. Daniel is quite hilarious. Now he and Jeremy have bunk beds in a room right by Jake's room, and I have graduated from a futon to a

216

bed. The boys all sleep in one wing of the house, and I have the other wing all to myself. Jake's sweet Weimaraner, Maggie, has started sleeping on the foot of my bed, and my allergies have magically been pretty good.

There is tons of weight equipment in the room next to mine, as well as a full sports court outside. It is fabulous. I have been following all my weight workouts and have been shooting a ton. I have to wait until after ten at night to shoot outside, and even then sweat just pours. I have also had my first experience with real bugs. A giant orangey-brown beetle thing scurried across the sports court when I was chasing down a rebound, and I almost wet my pants. That thing was not only faster than fast, but it was giant. It was ten times as big as any beetle I have ever seen. Later I went to peel back the top of an Oreo bag and all these cockroaches marched out, one after another. That was before the snake slithered across the wood floor in the living room. Jake said he probably needs to call the exterminator. Welcome to Texas.

Yesterday was a good day. "Work" is laid-back and fun and includes doing some office tasks, but mostly hanging out with middle schoolers and high schoolers. There is a lot of time here to work out, which I was slightly worried about at first, so that is a relief. I talked to Heidi last night, which was so great. I miss my friends. Isaac finally called today and told me he got third in the two-mile at State with his best time ever. Then he got fourth in the mile, and the boys team finished third at State! Dad was happy. I am so proud of them.

June 9, 2004

Whew, we are busy. I cannot believe tomorrow is already Thursday. These weeks are flying by. We are having VBS this week. It is a blast. Jake and Daniel have been playing the guitar while Jeremy sings. I *love* listening to him sing. After VBS yesterday we got to go to *Harry Potter and the Prisoner of Azkaban*. It was of course amazing. Then we ate at Casa Ole's and worked out after.

I have also started teaching a cardio ab class for high school and college girls. It is really fun. We use canned goods for weights. Then we play a game, like volleyball or basketball or kickball, after the main workout. None of the girls have really been involved in competitive sports. They just have so much fun playing, even though they are not skilled. Kind of refreshing.

Then we always have middle school Bible study on Wednesdays and high school Bible study on Fridays. We go to different families' lake houses or swim in their pools, which is just as awesome as it sounds.

June 14, 2004

Jeremy and Jamie, twenty-one months today. How did I get so lucky? How did we get so lucky? Thank you, God. Jeremy amazes me more each day. It has been really special spending so much time in Bible studies together. Yesterday after college Sunday school we packed for the mid-high mission trip. Which is where we are now: Gore, Oklahoma, population nine hundred, staying and working at a Methodist Boys' Ranch. We spent today cleaning branches and rocks off the road near the woods. It was blazing hot. Then we went swimming at the lake. It is huge, beautiful, and so flipping warm! Tiber Dam has never been that warm, *ever.* We had spaghetti, played horseshoes, had Bible study, and now it is lights out.

August 6, 2004

It is Heidi Lynn's twenty-first birthday today! She is old! I cannot believe I slacked on writing in my journal basically this entire summer. It was an amazing summer. After finally figuring out where I was going to live and that I was going to have a job, things in Texas got a lot better. I have still missed my parents and home so much more than I ever could have imagined, but it has been bearable. The whole point of spending the summer in Texas was so that Jeremy and I could be together. I am glad we made it happen.

Let's see, after our mid-high (that's how the Texans say it, instead of "middle school") mission trip to Oklahoma—and a few little lice issues—we settled back in to a routine of mid-high and high school youth groups, all kinds of Bible studies, me teaching a cardio ab class three times a week, playing as much basketball and lifting as much as possible, going to the movie theater at least weekly, and eating out all the time. Pretty good little summer, I would say.

Our high school mission trip was working with this incredible group called Casas por Cristo. The entire ministry mission is focused on building houses for families in Juarez, Mexico. We drove in vans all the way down through Texas. And I thought Montana was a big state.[152] We stayed at a church in El Paso on our way and arrived early in the evening. El Paso just so happens to be where Brent is currently stationed. Brent and I keep in touch fairly consistently, but it was admittedly a little weird connecting with him about that trip. Of course I would not travel through and not let him know, but the plan-making was awkward. He was adamant that he did not want to meet Jeremy. No, thank you, he said several times.

So when we got to El Paso that evening, the plan was that Brent was going to pick me up from the church so we could have dinner somewhere. Jeremy handled everything incredibly well. I know it was hard for him, especially when Jake and Daniel kept asking to make sure they were hearing correctly, "So your girlfriend is going to dinner with her ex?"

I waited for Brent outside the church and hopped in his jeep around six. He took me to a local Mexican restaurant. At first the conversation felt strained. I kept asking basic logistical questions. He kept giving snipped, nondetailed answers. Finally when we got to the table I made some joke, and we both laughed. Then we sat down and settled into a comfortable space. The specifics of what we even talked about are blurry. It felt like, for me at least, having dinner with an old friend.

Right before Brent dropped me back off that night he quietly said, "I want to meet him."

I nodded, hopped out of the jeep, and ran in to grab Jeremy. He was playing dominoes with Jake and some kids but looked up the second I entered the room. I asked him if he would come meet Brent. He said, "Of course."

The interaction was only seconds, really—just a quick handshake then farewell—but it was a relief for me. And maybe a sign that somehow we can peacefully bridge past to present? That relationships can change but don't have to completely end? I don't know. One thing I am learning is it seems the more I learn, the more I realize I do not know.

---

[152] At its longest—north to south—Texas is right around eight hundred miles long, whereas Montana stretches 559 miles east to west.

219

* * *

"We made it!" I kiss Jeremy on the cheek as he parks the Honda in his dad's driveway.

Our drive back from Texas was more eventful than anticipated. First we snuck up to a game in St. Louis so we could watch the Cardinals play the Giants and Bonds—Barry Bonds. We had some difficulty managing the big city traffic but luckily made it through unscathed. Then the plan was to find the closest town outside St. Louis and spend the night in a hotel. Sounds simple enough, right? Wrong. It proved anything but simple, due to the fact that we were unknowingly traveling through Missouri during its annual Show-Me State Games weekend. A caravan formed, with travelers in the same boat (one vehicle was actually pulling a boat) as we were. There was this stream of headlights, everyone would pull into a hotel, one person would run in and check availability at the front desk, run back out and shake their head no, and then the string would pull back out and try the next town. Sometime around two in the morning we found a Super 8 with vacancy. That night, that Super 8 hotel bed was the most comfortable thing I had ever slept on.

The next day, the car's clutch started acting funny. When we were making our way through a toll station on the highway Jer maneuvered the clutch into second gear. We rolled through the toll—nervous about a full stop—and tossed a bunch of carefully counted change into the metal funnel. Later, when Jer needed a driving break, I hopped up behind him so we could switch drivers without pulling over. Finally we had to stop, not knowing if we would be able to get started again. Jer had an inkling that we should park on a hill so we could start the car back up in second gear. Luckily that worked. He is not only cute and good at kicking footballs and soccer balls, folks, but he has impressive car instincts, turns out. What a catch.

So we did not get stranded, thanks to Jer's quick thinking and slick driving skills. And we survived our first cross-country road trip together. (There was a time when I was pretty upset about his decision not to follow the google map we had printed out before leaving. He tried to calmly explain to me that the road he was taking was parallel to my road, but I was not having it.) I think every couple should go ahead and take a long road trip together and see how they fare. Just in case.

THIRD QUARTER

"Do all things without grumbling or arguing."

—Philippians 2:14

2004–2005 RMC Battlin' Bears

Chapter 29

September–November 2004, junior year, back to school again, Billings, Montana

School has honestly been pretty great so far this year. Busy, but good busy. My schedule consists of almost all education classes. Seventeen credits including a thirty-five-hour practicum, which is a blast. My practicum is in a third-grade classroom where I teach lessons every week. The students are so cute. I love them. Also, it is fun learning about different teaching methods and philosophies. Who knew there were so many things involved in teaching kids? It is pretty amazing connecting human development and psychology research to the actual art of lesson planning.

I think I will be a good teacher. I hope so. The other day I led a science lesson for my third graders. We were all standing in a circle outside on the grass, squeezing eggs as hard as we could. Miraculously, no eggs broke. Hopefully the kids now understand the miracle of the egg and how the eggshell protects the embryo but also breaks easily when the chick needs to hatch. (And let's be honest. It was also the easiest experiment I could find. Science still intimidates me.)

This semester I also attend two classes—science methods and social studies methods—at MSUB.[153] My advisor told me the science and social studies teaching classes are only offered at Rocky every other semester, and if I did not find a way to take them now it could make scheduling tricky for next semester. Scheduling details are overwhelming, so I am just going with it. The MSUB campus is nice. I am surprised how much I enjoy experiencing how things are done at a different place.

We started preseason practices on September seventh. It is strange not having Maci, Kelley, and Shye around. Maci is at Carroll, of course, but I am struck by how difficult it is to hang out with Shye and Kelley,

---

[153] Montana State University Billings, formerly Eastern Montana College.

people who are still in the same place as me but not involved in the same things as me. Makes me sad. Maci sent me an email a few weeks ago:

J- Hey how have you been?? How were first classes and all of that? I actually do like it here, last week was a little weird, it seemed like some people would look at me with a question like "what r u doing here" but I have since gotten over that! Anyway I like all of my classes. I am taking 18 credits which i don't know if that was a good idea or not, but hopefully then I will be done in 4 1/2 years instead of 5. But I like all my professors. The science one is a little boring and monotone, but I also don't like science so that doesn't help me out at all! What else... oh I am not going to walk on, I think I just need to have time to myself and work out on my own, it is going to be weird but I'm glad with my decision. And if I truly miss it that much then there is always next year! I have talked to Carly a couple times though and it is awesome to have her here even if it is just to talk to. Um... it is amazing how much time I have to do nothing, but then I have to think of it as I need to work so I can pay for an apartment and gas money and food and all that fun stuff. Ryan and I bought a washer and dryer, so we were pretty amped about our first "big buy." I love not living on campus and living with Ryan. We are only about 2-3 minutes away so it is great! He is amazing. The summer was great living together and it has only gotten better since we have been at school. I'm also glad that I don't have to worry about the driving anymore! But I did go home last weekend and got to see a lot of people, parents and my grandparents and such so that was nice. My parents were glad since that was the first time in 2 1/2 months that I had been home. Hapi came to Chester also and those boys are so so so cute, they are crawling and moving and JR is crazy, so it was hectic but so much fun! Anyway I am ranting on and on, oh one more thing, I've been writing Shye, how is that whole thing going???? Is Kelley playing??? Fill me in on some news!!! And tell everyone hi for me especially Peter and

224

Jeremy and Shye and Jeri and Alex, and all those junior
girls!!!! Talk to you soon! Love you and miss you!!!!

Maci T

I am happy to hear that Maci sounds so happy. Her email confirms
my suspicion that everything just changes all the flipping time. And I
don't like it. Take this season, for instance. It already feels very different
from last year.

A huge bonus this season is that Jenny and Rae Dawn are back
playing. Those two work so hard all the time. They lead powerfully
through their actions. Our preseason conditioning has also been a lot
harder than the past two years, which is encouraging. It has been
interesting trying to figure out where I might best fit on this team. My
three-point shot has never been better. It feels a bit wild, to be honest,
how accurate it is. Every summer I have followed a strict shooting
workout and have always been an okay outside shooter. In high school
there was really no need for me to shoot much outside since we fast-
breaked 90 percent of the time. The past summer was no different as
far as shooting workouts, except for tiny tweaks like always planting and
pivoting on my inside foot as well as adding billions of push-ups to my
days. Apparently those tiny tweaks made a huge difference.

Anyway, the team is different in many ways this year. What will my
role be? How will I figure that out? Jenny is the obvious go-to point
guard. Mentally I have been trying my best to prepare for that. I feel
confident I can do a great job being her backup and can accept that role.
When we split to scrimmage I have noticed Hendo often matches up
Steph, a freshman point, opposite Jenny. Not quite sure how far to read
into that. It feels obvious to me I should be ready to shoot first, which
has not been the case before. So many pieces to put together. Ah! My
brain gets overloaded with so many thoughts. Probably I need to take a
big breath.

* * *

"Achoo!" I cover my mouth with a Kleenex and wipe my reddening
nose, again.

"Sorry you caught a cold, babe." Jer rubs my shoulder tenderly.

225

"Just another example of how me and geology don't mix," I grumble pathetically.

Jeremy tries to suppress his grin. We have been in a physical geology class together this semester. I took geology because I needed the science credits and it felt least likely to push me over the edge. And yes, I am happy that I finally have a class with Jeremy—the first time since general psychology my freshman year—but it is driving me nuts that he has a better grade than I do.

Our relationship is still great. The tough thing is we do not get to see each other much. He is of course busy with football, I have basketball plus the practicum, and he took a part-time youth leader position with Uncle Gary at American Lutheran Church.[154] So I guess that should be another reason I am glad we have geology together. The reason I have this dumb cold is because our class went on a freezing-cold field trip to Wyoming to look at all these rock formations. Jeremy was so interested and excited and telling me all of these things. I was cold, thought the rocks all looked the same, and while my teeth chattered I thought to myself, *Yet another reason my family spends time in climate-controlled gyms.*

Jeremy hands me a glass of orange juice. "Here you go, Jamer," he says sweetly.

I smile a small smile despite wanting to remain cranky and whiny. "Thank you. How is your knee?"

Last week he dislocated his kneecap. Gross. He straightens his leg and studies it for a second. "I think it is getting better."

Our focus shifts from his knee to the entrance when the apartment door springs open. "Hi, guys!" Kat greets, balancing grocery bags.

Jer immediately hops up to help. "Hi, Kitty! What's for dinner?"

He asks this in a joking manner, but Kat's response is completely serious. "Steak!"

This brightens my mood. "Yum! Thanks! And I could make green bean casserole, if you want."

---

[154] Jeremy got this job working with my uncle through his roommate, Travis Dregne. Travis had worked in the position the year before. It was such a funny coincidence, Jeremy finding a job with my uncle through his roommate and not me.

Green bean casserole is one of the dishes I can manage. It is up there with dill pickle rollups, um, toast, and . . . well, that is about it. Earlier today my mom told me it is snowing in Chester and that it is coming our way. Everyone knows what that means: it is almost time to watch *Home Alone* for the first time this year! Just thinking of the steak, green bean casserole, snow, and *Home Alone* is enough to sweep away my frustration with this cold, and with geology.

Chapter 30

December 2004, junior year, preseason, Billings, Montana

Jeff and I sit on the big, red, cushy chairs in the lobby of our hotel. Somehow schedules magically aligned, and my brother and I are staying in the same hotel as our teams are playing in the same preseason tournament in North Dakota. Pretty random, but pretty cool.

We have been sitting out here for a couple minutes. Our team ate at a nearby Perkins, and Jeff said they ate at some steakhouse. I told him, "Ooh, look at you fancy Western boys eating at a fancy steakhouse."

We didn't make a formal plan to come out here to the lobby to chat, but this is nice. Jeffrey and I do talk on the phone now and then, and we of course see each other in Big Timber for holidays and such—and sometimes our schedules line up so we are together in Chester—but that is about it. I saw him more when he was dating Jenny and would visit Billings to see her.

Sibling relationships are likely all complicated at times, I would assume. It has always been just the two of us. Even though we did most things together as a family growing up, I was with Mom a lot and he would be with Dad. It also always seemed like we had our own friend groups and our own schedules for the most part. But he is a good brother. I look over at him and realize he is in the middle of telling me a story. This happens sometimes. He gets really excited and goes on about so-and-so and such-and-such, and I will rack my brain trying to put together the puzzle pieces. Who is Johnny? I think. Oh, that must be a softball friend.

He stops fairly abruptly and looks at me expectantly. I quickly think through as many sound bites as I can remember. I look at him with a very interested expression, nod, and give a nice safe, "Oh, wow."

Jeff and me in our Western and Rocky uniforms

This seems to satisfy him. We both look out the double sliding glass doors to the entrance and watch the big, beautiful falling snowflakes outside. There is a fireplace roaring next to our chairs. Montana is cold, but it feels like North Dakota might take "cold" to a whole new level.

I start thinking about the last conversation I had with Jenny. How sad I felt, listening to her work through various thoughts and emotions surrounding her relationship with my brother. They started dating when she and Jeff started college at Northern and I was a senior in high school. Over two years. Jeff has always been a serious relationship kind of guy. I of course think about his relationship ups and downs with Maci and trying to manage that as his sister and Maci's friend. Things felt similar with Jenny. Not only was I again on a team with my brother's girlfriend, but of all my high school teammates, Maci ended up being the one who played with me in college. So Jenny and Maci's relationship was another added layer. Is it fair to say relationships are complicated? Does that even begin to scratch the surface?

It feels like Jeff wants to share something else. I prepare myself to really lock in and concentrate, so I can do my best to follow him through his next story about people I may or may not know. When he looks over at me, I sense he has something else on his mind. Now he is looking right in my eyes. Big breath. I press my lips tightly together, telling myself to keep my judgy thoughts to myself. I bite my lip; I am not certain I can trust myself to be gracious on this topic I am sure he is about to bring up.

Oh, boy. This is what I was afraid of. Jenny is the best. I liked her when I first met her, and now that I have had the chance to be her teammate and we have formed our own friendship, I love her. I fear no matter what Jeff says about this new girl he is dating I will not feel happy about it. My sudden stubbornness on this subject surprises me. I generally pride myself on being open to meeting new people and finding their good qualities. But now I feel skeptical and negative and defensive. He turns his shoulders toward mine and looks me squarely in the face. Here it comes. "Himes," [155] he opens, more serious than usual.

I study my brother. Does he look nervous? Hesitant? It is hard to tell for sure. I notice my guard is still up. I pray I will not blurt out some reactive response that I will later regret. My eyes meet his, and he goes on. "Megan is really awesome."

---

[155] Ever since taking his first Spanish class in junior high, Jeff—and many of his friends— has most often referred to me as "Himes," his nickname for me derived from shortening the Spanish name "Jaime," pronounced "hi-may."

I pull in a long steadying breath through my nostrils and let it out slowly, skepticism rising. But I do not interrupt.

"She is your age but redshirted as a freshman. She went to Great Falls High and played basketball and softball."

Jeff Graham and Megan Schmitz

231

Well la-dee-flippin'-dah, my sassy inner voice responds. My mouth remains shut, though. Keep it together, Jamie. Just listen.

"And she is the oldest of five kids."

Now he is looking at me expectantly. Oh jeez. What should I say? Finally I manage, "Huh," then raise my eyebrows for emphasis, "cool."

Really eloquent, Jamie. Nice job. Then he hits me right in the heart. For as quickly as my defenses went up, what he says next drops them just as quickly. "Himes, I know you are going to like her. She is just like you. She's so nice and everybody loves her."

He continues to gush. The next thing he says is what really gets me. "Himes, it's like now I understand why Jeremy and Jamie are so happy."

A sigh leaves me, along with my skepticism and doubts. I smile at my brother and say, "Well she sounds great. And I am happy for you."

As I give him another smile I realize she really does, and I really am.

* * *

"Oh, no!" Gretchen scream-whispers in reaction to the piercing phone that breaks into our gigglefest.

I look toward the phone, and then read the red numbers on the digital clock next to the phone. Holy moly. Is it seriously almost two in the morning? Time flies when everyone in the room is telling hilarious stories and everything feels extra funny. I do not remember the last time I laughed this hard this long. After dinner, Jenny, Rae Dawn, and Workman knocked on our door dressed up in these ridiculous outfits. This spurred the rest of us to immediately join in, no questions asked. Everyone went to their own rooms, and we spent what felt like hours wearing different clothes in crazy ways and knocking on each other's doors, including our coaches'. Everyone was in fits.

The craziness eventually died down and people split and went to their respective rooms for the night. In our room, however, the craziness did not die down. In fact, it went the other way and things have since gotten completely out of control. My abs are sore, and I am sweating almost as much as when I play basketball. Almost.

Jeri, Gretchen, and I exchange anxious looks when the phone continues to ring. The three of us are stock-still and suddenly silent. I am closest to the phone. Urgently, Jeri mouths, "Act tired!"

I curl my shoulders up, squint my eyes as if I can barely keep them open, and pull the corners of my mouth apart and down, barely stifling a yawn. I grab the receiver and slowly pull it to my ear. As if in a daze I rasp tiredly in confusion and disorientation, "Hellooo?"

There is a brief pause. Then what first sounded like exasperation and anger quickly fades to resignation and perhaps even amusement. Coach Hendo's voice tells me the message the phone ring has already communicated. "It is time to go to sleep now."

"Yes, sir," I immediately oblige. Then I add quickly, "Night, Coach."

"Goodnight, Jamie."

We love to dress up

* * *

"No, that sounds great," I tell Aunt Shirley, as we wait to board our plane to Fairbanks, Alaska.

"You sure we won't be messing up plans?" my aunt asks again.

I smile and assure her one more time. "Not at all. Like I said, I asked my coaches what the itinerary for our trip was, and told them you and Uncle Dick would be more than happy to take us to a few places.

They said that sounded great. I honestly don't think they had anything planned, besides the games."

"Well then we will keep you busy!" Shirley assures excitedly.

"Okay," I tell my aunt, "we are about to board. See you this evening!"

"Sounds good, Jamie. we are looking forward to it!" She replies.

I push the antenna down on my Nokia, firmly hold down the power button, and zip the phone into a side pocket of my duffel bag. This is routine for all of us during most of our preseason games, that we shut off our phones or else pay for it with crazy roaming charges. Last year our big preseason trip was to sunny California. This year we are going the opposite direction. My uncle told me they lose more than twenty minutes of daylight each day in Fairbanks right now.

"Final call for flight A473, services to Seattle," the announcement for our final boarding call rings through the air.

* * *

When I first saw this Alaska trip on our preseason schedule I got really excited. My aunt and uncle have lived up in Alaska since 1969. There was an incentive for new teachers to teach in "The Bush," and Dick and Shirley graduated from Western, got married, packed up, and headed north![156] They have lived here ever since, but this will be my first time seeing their house. My cousin Shannon is a doctor in Anchorage, and we play there for our second game. So this trip works out perfectly for me.

"Brrr!" Workman squeaks and pulls on her hood as we hop out of our rental vehicles, now parked at 1073 Solitude Way.

We all follow suit, pulling up the black hoods of our Rocky travel gear. Before approaching the door, I take in our surroundings. This proves difficult because it is already dark out. But I am still so glad to be here, at the door of my aunt and uncle's house for the first time. The porch light gives a small stretch of visibility, and I look across the snowy front lawn to see if I can spy any moose tracks. No tracks, but Coach points up toward the night sky. "What is that?" I ask.

Coach Hendo gives an excited, awe-filled response. "It's the northern lights."

A sweet sense of peacefulness washes over me. We all stare up in

---

[156] Akiachak, Alaska

silent admiration. Seconds, maybe minutes, pass before anyone makes a move. A chill bites my cheeks, and I look over at the inviting front door.

Aunt Shirley opens the door and greets us graciously. "Hello, girls! I'm Jamie's Aunt Shirley, and this"—she motions toward the living room—"is Jamie's uncle, Mr. Wiegand."

A feeling of giddiness replaces the chill, and I lead my team up the stairs and inside. I give my aunt a hug as my teammates and coaches stream in and pull off their shoes. Uncle Dick[157] shakes hands with Coach Hendo and Coach Mouat, and then he pulls out a Rocky roster and starts asking each girl to share her name and position. He has Stephanie sit down next to him and begins talking and asking about Wolf Point. Meanwhile, Shirley makes an announcement. "I just made spaghetti and garlic bread, because it's easy to make, and it should be a good meal for you girls to have before playing in your game tomorrow. Just grab a plate from over there, and you all can sit at the dining table, or here in the living room, or wherever is comfortable. So go ahead and help yourself."

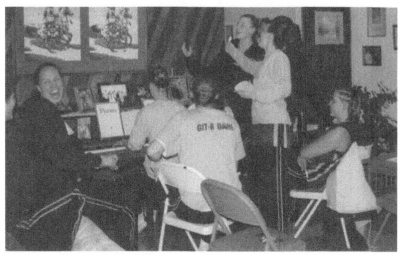

An impromptu sing-along in Aunt Shirley and Uncle Dick's living room after dinner, November 2004

---

[157] Uncle Dick was a standout football and basketball athlete who graduated from Wolf Point, Montana. He rodeoed in college at WMC, Dillon, and that is where he met my aunt Shirley. Shirley often referred to him as "Mr. Wiegand."

235

We all say thank you and do as we are told. As I heap the spaghetti and bread onto my plate I smile and look around this fun scene. Everybody is chatting and seems content on this blustery Alaska evening, safe inside this cozy house. What a special night.

* * *

Well, we are flying back from Alaska to Billings with two more losses, making our preseason record now 1-4. The Nanooks, of the University of Alaska Fairbanks, jumped ahead 19-49 in the first half, and the final was 49-84. If only we could have held them scoreless in the second half, then we would have tied. Ha. We had thirty turnovers, and they killed us on the boards. Our game against the Anchorage Seawolves was not quite as brutal. We only trailed three at half, 28-31, and the final was 58-66. Both teams were NCAA Division II, but that fact does not make losing feel any better.

Huddle before the University of Alaska Anchorage game, November 2004

I personally had a great trip, though, losses aside. Aunt Shirley and Uncle Dick took us to this muskox farm that was so cool. The muskox live at this large animal research station run by the university. They were amazing to see and learn about. There were also a bunch of reindeer, also known as caribou. We learned all about how the animals are used

236

for research and educational projects regarding biological principles, biomedical sciences, and best practices as far as teaching wildlife protocols. Super fancy things, and more exciting than it may sound. A little mouse scurried under our feet, so if we were not paying attention before, we were after that.

Then we had so much fun when Dick and Shirley took us to North Pole, Alaska. We all saw more reindeer, drove down Santa Claus Lane, Kris Kringle Drive, and Mistletoe Lane, visited Santa's workshop, and even sat on Santa's lap. It legit got me so excited for the Christmas season. Our team laughed so much together. I really surprised Mouat by busting out some sweet dance moves in front of the vehicle he was driving one night, when we were getting food and the radio was blaring. We did have one little mishap involving our entire team and this very unlucky lady who was not amused having to spend forty-five minutes in a hot, cramped elevator with an entire college sports team. Besides that, everything was pretty good.

North Pole, Alaska, November 2004

Dick and Shirley not only came to our game against the Nanooks, but then they flew to Anchorage and watched us against the Seawolves. Also, those may be the coolest mascot names ever. Then I got to spend the night with Shannon and Riley Rae when we were in Anchorage.[158]

---

[158] Shannon is my cousin, the oldest daughter of Uncle Dick and Aunt Shirley. She was a doctor in Anchorage then. Riley Rae is her and her husband Mac's sweet daughter.

Aunt Shirley and me in Alaska, Nov 2004

Riley Rae is barely four months old, and she is the cutest, chunkiest baby girl. It was so special staying with my relatives.

I look out the window at the billowing white clouds. I have a feeling when I look back someday on my college basketball days, this trip will likely beat any game when it comes to most memorable moments. Mouat's laugh cuts through my train of thought, and I glance over at him. Headphones on, portable DVD player in lap, he continues to giggle at yet another episode of *Friends.* I smile and close my eyes for a little snooze.

* * *

I walk toward a table near a window on the north side of the sub and set down my tray. This year I find myself eating many meals alone in here. Lots of my friends live off campus now, and the ones who live in Jorg insist that buying and preparing their own food is much better than being on the meal plan here. Jeremy, Peter, and Kat especially get all excited about cooking new things. Weirdos. I will take food prepared for me any day, thank you very much, and have no interest in shopping, cooking, or trying new recipes. I have got Top Ramen, Easy Mac, and Campbell's alphabet soup down to a science—with good old PB&Js on the side—when I am forced to eat in my apartment. Otherwise, the sub is my first choice.

Recently I have discovered there is frequently a *Billings Gazette* sports page sitting on one of these back tables. I pick up today's copy, take a bite of my Cheerios, and read.

ROCKY WOMEN TOP DSU, 70-63

PERIMETER PLAY HELPS LADY BEARS TO 3RD VICTORY OF SEASON

By Bill Bighaus of the Gazette Staff

238

Jenny Balgua said Rocky Mountain College's perimeter shooters "were due for a good game" — and the Lady Bears came up with one on Saturday night. Balgua, a senior point guard, hit 24 points and Rocky drilled ten 3-pointers in beating Dickinson (N.D.) State 70-63 at the Fortin Center and avenging a 14-point loss to the Blue Hawks last month.

"We had a little bit of that killer attitude going for us tonight," noted Rocky coach Brian Henderson, whose team improved to 3-9 on the season. "We came out looking to stick it to somebody. You've got to have that."

The 5-foot-6 Balgua, who usually plays with a lot of determination, scored the last five points of the first half to put Rocky ahead 35-32 at halftime. The Lady Bears never trailed in the second half and led by as many as 11 points, 54-43, on a short jumper by Balgua with 9:50 to play.

"We're just starting to play a lot better as a team," said Balgua, who had eight rebounds and three assists to go along with her 24 points. "We played hard against (Montana State University in a 72-61 loss on December 10) and that gave us a lot of confidence. We've just been playing a lot smarter."

DSU threw a zone defense at Rocky, and the Lady Bears responded by connecting on 10-of-27 3-point shots. Rocky passed the ball around well on the perimeter in getting its open looks. "It was nice to see the ball movement tonight," said Henderson. "We didn't anticipate seeing that much zone, but the girls did a good job of taking care of the ball and relaxing."

The Lady Bears committed just nine turnovers. Rocky also shot 41 percent from the field. "Our perimeter shooters were due for a good game, and this helped us out a lot," said Balgua, who was responsible for a game-high four 3-pointers. "We were due for a good, solid win, and to win a close one like this is fun."

Reserve Jamie Graham chipped in with nine points—all on 3-pointers. Gretchen Wall and Katherine Bitz added eight points apiece. Bitz handed out seven assists, and Stephanie Neubauer—who nailed two 3-pointers—had six assists.

DSU, which beat Rocky 82-68 in Dickinson on November 26, received 21 points from April Tormaschy and 14 points from Omoh Odiye. Stacey Milanovich, one of DSU's starters and leading scorers, was recently ruled ineligible for academic reasons. She had scored 12 points in the earlier win over the Lady Bears. The Blue Hawks, whose season record fell to 4-9, closed within 66-63 Saturday night on two free throws by Tormaschy with 56 seconds left. Rocky, however, came right back with Neubauer feeding 6-4 Sarah Bills for a basket underneath to make it 68-63 with 36 seconds to go.

Balgua closed out the scoring by making two free throws with 8.5 seconds remaining. Rocky, which has played just three home games so far this season, will be back on the road at the University of Saskatoon Tournament December 29-31. The Lady Bears will play the University of Regina on December 29. Those three tournament games will be Rocky's final warm-up before Frontier Conference action starts on January 6.

"We needed this win to go into the Christmas break, and we need to go to Canada and get three more," said Balgua. "We're playing better. Our

```
chemistry is coming together. It's always better
to peak later in the season than earlier."
```

I fold the paper back up, set it down on the table, and take a drink of my apple juice. I chew while I reflect on the article. We have had another brutal preseason schedule, with the majority of our games on the road. Last year was the same way, and I guess I should not have been holding my breath that this year might have been the opposite.

Yes, I am a reserve this year. Playing time and general rotation expectations have not yet been discussed with me this season. I am doing my best to just roll with it. Has going from a starter to a reserve who doesn't know when—or for how long—I might get in messed with my confidence? Perhaps. But I am so glad to have Jenny and Rae Dawn back. And I realize I am not the only one who feels confusion surrounding her role. This whole figuring out your role thing is tough, mostly because it seems to be ever-changing. So I really try my best to play hard and stay encouraging. That is something I can control.

I also note that ineligibility is not something the Rocky women's team ever has to worry about. Several of us always seem to be on the dean's list, and I was even inducted into some new honor society a few weeks back. Hendo preaches the importance of studies coming first, and I know he takes academic records very seriously while recruiting. I admire that about him. Sometimes I get tunnel vision, and it feels like basketball is the most important thing. It is good to be reminded every once in a while that basketball is not the most important thing.

* * *

Our team counts down in unison, "3-2-1 . . . Happy New Year!"

Whatever enthusiasm we were able to muster quickly dies down as we continue on Highway 16.

A green sign comes closer and assures that we are almost to I-94 and under two hours from Billings. In theory. The bus plugs cautiously along on the snow-packed roads, so it is hard to tell when we will actually make it back on campus. I think about my baby boy, and how kissing him at midnight on this night has again been thwarted by basketball. Oh, well. After I am done playing college ball I will do everything within my power to be able to kiss Jeremy on as many New Year's Eves as possible, I resolve.

"Yes!" Jeri's nudge and triumphant exclamation shift my focus away from fantasizing about kissing Jeremy.

"I made it to the Top-Secret Area!" she explains proudly.

"Sweet!" I respond, genuinely thrilled.

Compelled to dispense as much helpful knowledge as possible I add, "Remember, Yoshi can swallow fireballs."

"Got it," Jeri responds, all business.

One good thing about these long bus rides is there is a lot of time to sleep, read (I finished *The Da Vinci Code* in one weekend a while back), and play video games. Jeremy let us borrow his Game Boy Advance, so now we have two, and Jeri and I have played *Yoshi's World* nonstop since leaving for Canada on Tuesday.

Now it is technically Saturday morning, and if I am honest, my eyeballs feel dry and bloodshot. Sometimes that is the price you have to pay for Nintendo glory. Jeri's five-year-old nephew Dylan was with Jeri's sister and parents at our hotel in Canada. Dylan and I played a lot of *Yoshi's World* together. Dylan started calling me "Game Boy Girl." I am totally okay with that. [159] Jeri is back to it, concentrating hard while navigating the Top-Secret Area. I look down at my screen to determine my next plan of action. Let's see. Yes, I think I better stock up with a couple Super Leafs before I dare enter Ludwig von Koopa's castle.

---

[159] Jeri's nephew Dylan and his grandma, Judy, were two of our biggest fans all the way through college, attending many games with Jeri's sister Jennifer and father Ed. Grandma Judy—mother of six and grandmother to eleven—reminded me so much of my mom as she was so sweet, encouraging, caring, and always wore a smile. She died in 2019. When Dylan was thirteen, he was diagnosed with Hodgkin's Lymphoma. Dylan eventually died on August 15, 2021, at the age of twenty-one. I still have those Game Boys and when I see them, will always remember sweet, smart-as-a-whip Dylan and his wonderful Grandma Judy.

Jeri and me with her nephew, Dylan

Chapter 31

December 2005, junior year, role seeking, Billings, Montana

"Come on in!" Coach Hendo responds to my nervous knock.

I take a couple steps over from the door to a chair facing him and his important-looking desk. I sit and try to look as calm and pleasant as possible, considering how shaky my knees are. I worry my voice will come out just as shaky and attempt a steadying breath. "Hi, Coach. Thanks for meeting with me."

"You bet," he easily responds. Then, "What's up?"

I poise my shoulders, lengthen my neck, and feel suddenly confident and clear on what I want to share. One more short breath, and I begin. "Well, um."

Come on, Jamie! What happened to confident and clear? Jeff and I went through this entire conversation on the phone last night. I told Jeff everything that has been keeping me up at night, and he told me I need to be straight with Hendo. He told me I should ask why I didn't even play until the final two minutes in the game the other night. I almost tear up just thinking about that game.

Grandma Joyce and Aunt Kath drove all the way over to Billings for that game, and so did Jeremy's dad. I had never been sat like that before. There had been no injury, no insolence, nothing I could put a finger on. Then when Coach Hendo motioned for me to hop in at the two-minute mark at the end of the game—when it was clear we were going to lose—I momentarily froze. After a few frozen seconds I hopped off the bench and felt like I had no idea what to do. It was such a bizarre feeling. I felt embarrassed. Obviously I know a lot of people don't play until the end of blowout games, and I do not mean to sound all holier-than-thou. I am just saying, I mean, I am saying that it felt strange and surprising to me. It really threw me off. I did not know how to make sense of it. Still don't. Recalling those events reminds me why I am here.

Coach Henderson continues looking expectantly at me. I look him straight in the eyes and start again, for real this time. "So I was totally mentally prepared to back up Jenny. All summer I had that in my head, to be ready to back Jenny up and be ready for a different role than last season."

Hendo nods slightly, so I continue.

"I have so much respect for Jenny. I am glad she is back, and I am grateful to get to play with her. She's the best."

Coach still seems to be listening, so I tell myself I need to get to it. Finally I spit it out.

"I was prepared to back up Jenny." I pause. "But Steph?"

Then my words stop, overridden by my swirling thoughts. Nothing against Steph. She is a good ballplayer. She is a freshman, a little shorter than me, a good ball handler. Confident, quick. Good defender. The thing is, I like to believe I know when people are better than me. And if anything, we are pretty equal, skill-wise. Only I am a better shooter, I started every game last season, and well, I believe that presently I am a stronger leader. Because, because I just am. Coach VanDyke and Coach Schlepp always made it clear that I was the encourager, the floor general, the leader. That was my role. That is still my role. Right? Son of a B. Since when do I doubt myself? Why can't I figure out what my role is here and now?

I feel so frustrated that I am not able to express this clearly to my coach. I have thought this through so many times. I need to be honest with him. I continue. "Backing up Steph, I was not expecting that." I look down briefly then right back up. "It feels like you recruited over me."

There. I said it. A flood of relief runs through me. It feels good to get that out in the open. Now he can explain his strategy, his plan. I search his eyes, trying to guess what he might be about to say. Maybe he will give me some really specific feedback, some suggestions for me to work on so I can stop wondering whether or not I am doing what is expected of me.

To say his response surprises me would be a gross understatement.

245

"You have been turning the ball over too much."

Wait, what?

My body automatically pulls back and stiffens, from leaning forward in anticipation to pressing back against my chair in disbelief and frustration.

My mind flips instantly to stats I have studied from the last few games. *I* have been turning the ball over too much? First of all, I have not had enough minutes to turn the ball over too much, and I know for a fact Jenny and Gretchen—two starters—have averaged thirteen turnovers between the two of them in the last three games. I also currently have the best free throw percentage on the team and am shooting 44 percent from the three-point line. Close to 10 percent better than I have ever shot from the arc (thank you billions of pushups last summer). Do my coaches here even look at the stats? Unbelievable. Coach VanDyke and Coach Schlepp were always straight with me. They gave me clear expectations and goals. I have no idea what to do with this.

I realize Coach is still talking. "Do you want to be a two-guard?" he asks, as if repeating himself.

Blood boiling, I force myself to keep it together. I give a clipped, obligatory response: "Sure," and quietly exit the office.

Immediately following this extremely disappointing meeting with Coach Hendo, I head out to the court for practice. After a few warm-up drills, I proceed to turn the ball over three times in a row while we set up half-court to practice our set plays. Would we call that a "self-fulfilling prophecy," or would we merely call it, "letting the Man get me down?"

For all the times I have watched *Empire Records,* how am I still letting the Man get me down? I know better. This is maddening. My throat constricts, a telltale sign. *Do not cry, Jamie. Knock it off. This is not who you are. You are a great ball handler. Don't let somebody else's flippant statement mess with your mind.*

I take a deep breath and stand up straight. I slap the ball, hold up two fingers, pass-fake, and make a sharp pass to Rae on the wing.

* * *

"Jeez, why does he always yell at you?" Jeri approaches me and watches Hendo disapprovingly as he walks back to the baseline.

She is not wrong. If there were stats kept for who gets ripped on most in practice, it would definitely be me. I guess the thought had not occurred to me before. Jeri is not done with her rant. I smile because, well, Jeri's rants are hilarious. "It's not like you are ever not working your butt off. And also"—she continues with even more conviction—"if he's gonna yell at someone, he should yell at someone who plays more."

I can hear that familiar tone that is a sign Jeri feels an injustice is occurring. I want to hug her for her loyalty and defensiveness. Something clicks. Maybe this is part of my role here. I look toward the baseline at our coach, who is clearly frustrated with how practice is going. "Maybe he yells at me," I consider, then look back at my teammate, "because he needs someone who can take it."

* * *

"Hi, Jamie Marie! How was practice?" Peter's sweet greeting strikes a chord I have been trying to ignore for the last two hours.

Before Peter looks my way he makes a request to his sous-chef. "Brother,[160] would you please hand me the sea salt?"

Jeremy hands Peter the small, glass container and then turns my way. "Hi, Jamers!" His tone of voice changes from excitement to concern when he takes a good look at me. "You okay?"

Jeremy sets down his spatula on the kitchen counter and walks toward the doorway. When he is close enough to reach I drop my tennis shoes and fall into his open arms. We stand there for a minute or so, Jer communicating care and concern simply by holding me, and me releasing a mix of emotions through some drippy tears. Eventually Jeremy leads me to the couch and we sit down. I break the silence, "It smells good in here. Kat had to rush after practice to meet a study group. I don't really have dinner plans."

My statement gives Jeremy and Peter permission to speak freely again. They look relieved. "Well look no further," Peter motions to the

---

[160] Peter and Jeremy began consistently referring to each other as "Brother" at some point during college, and they still do to this day.

active, sizzling stovetop. "We are concocting a chicken veggie stir-fry. And if that doesn't sound appealing, we have plenty of bread, canned juice, and government cheese left from your grandma's latest drop-off."[161]

I wipe a tear away and giggle. "Anything sounds great," I say. "Is anybody else coming over for dinner tonight, or is it just you two?"

Jeremy and Peter exchange glances and grins. I look from one face to the other. "What's so funny?" I ask.

Jeremy starts to explain, but his attempt is overridden by laughter. Peter goes on to explain. "We were over at Jenny and Kevin's apartment a bit ago, but it remains to be seen whether or not Kevin will be joining us."

Jeremy laughs even harder, and their shared delight is contagious. I giggle softly in anticipation as Peter continues with the story.

"Jenny is visiting her parents, and Kevin is a little busy tonight, it seems, as he is preparing for his parents to come over for a visit soon. When we walked in and called out to him, he invited us to join him in the bathroom. Of course this gave us pause, but he assured us it was safe to join him."

Jeremy continues to laugh, and Peter chuckles as he continues tending to the cooking. They seem to be enjoying keeping me in suspense. I know they want to draw this out. I know they want me to beg them to continue. Fine, I'll play along. "Okay, so Kevin told you to join him in the bathroom," I ask-demand, "and then what?!"

"Well," Peter gestures toward their kitchen sink, "apparently Kevin had gotten behind on the house chores."

Jeremy's laughter reaches a full octave higher after Peter mentions the house chores. Now I am officially curious. "*And...?*"

"So Kevin was washing what appeared to be every single dish, cup, and piece of cutlery in a very full and very sudsy bathtub."

The scene Peter paints causes laughter to burst from me. Clearly grateful to see me smiling, Peter continues with the cheering-up.

---

[161] Grandma Joyce sent us poor college kids home with food bank boxes every time we were through Big Timber, or anytime she made her way to Billings. We enjoyed many meals because of this generosity and always noted how nice that was of her to think of us.

"Jeremy also told me your coaches recently took your entire team to the theater to the movie *Miracle*. Is that true?"

This question feels out of left field. "Um, yeah, they did." I confirm. "Why do you ask?"

"Whose idea was it?" Peter probes further.

I shrug. "I'm not sure. Maybe Coach Mouat thought it was a good idea?"

Peter shakes his head, rests his left fist on his hip, elbow pointed out, and flips the rice with his spatula-laden right hand. Jeremy is apparently catching on to Peter's point before I am and continues in his laughing fit. "So your coach thought it would be a good idea to take you all to see a movie called "miracle" in the middle of your season."

Peter 'tsk-tsks' as he stirs. When he sums up his point with three final words, I join Jeremy in hysterical laughter, despite myself and despite my frustration with the ups and downs of this basketball season.

Peter shakes his head dubiously from side to side. "What a D."

Thank goodness for friends who know how to cheer me up.

249

Chapter 32

January–February 2005, junior year, conference season, Billings, Montana

Jenny addresses us in our Fortin locker room. "Alright, ladies. We finally get to be back on our home court. First home conference game."

Thank goodness we finally get a game at home. Thirteen of our first sixteen games have been away. We are kicking off the conference season tonight against Northern. It was okay playing Northern last year. Okay and a little weird. There was this mix of fun-weirdness when playing on the same floor as Chasi and Michele but wearing different uniforms than them.[162]

It would have been nice if Michele would have transferred here after leaving the University of Montana. I smile slightly recalling that weekend—the spring of my freshman year—when Michele visited Rocky for a recruiting trip. Hendo put me in charge of taking Michele out to a nice dinner. Very trusting of him. So that night Maci, Jenny, and I tried our best to convince Michele to transfer to Rocky. Carly also came to Billings that weekend, and she tried to convince Michele to transfer to Carroll. In the end, Michele didn't listen to any of us and chose Northern instead. I have to believe that she will always remember her visit to Billings fondly, though, when we wined and dined her at Olive Garden, spontaneously belted out "I'm with you-ouuuu!" at the top of our lungs when Avril Lavigne came on the radio, and then hung out the rest of the night at some random person's house that Jenny's roommate Tammy was house-sitting for, where we played cards and laughed and laughed.

"Forget the losses," Jenny continues, and I make a concerted effort to focus on Jenny's words, "and concentrate on looking forward. We are a different team now."

---

[162] After our freshmen year of college, both Chasi and Michele transferred to Northern.

We all nod and huddle together in our, well, our huddle. Rae Dawn prompts us. "Lady Bears on three. One, two, three—"

"Lady Bears!" we shout and hustle out onto our bright and shiny green-and-gold home court.

It always feels so nice running out onto a home court. I had almost forgotten how nice. No pep band tonight. That is a bummer. But Van Halen's "Jump" streaming from the speakers comes in a close second to a live pep band. I hustle to touch the half-court line with my toe and notice Michele jogging to the back of her team's layup line. I cross the line, into enemy territory, and give her a nice hearty smack on the bottom. She turns with a grin. We both automatically lift out our arms and our elbows tap, something they have done hundreds of times before. Then we turn back and join our separate team lines.

The game starts out feeling a little helter-skelter. Both teams bobble a few passes and commit a few messy turnovers early. Finally everyone settles in for some steady back and forth. Somehow we pass the ten-minute mark of the first half. Gardner, a guard for the Skylights, hits her second three. I look up and the scoreboard surprises me. We are down 8–18. Alyssa outlets to Jenny who sprints coast-to-coast for a quick layup. On the other end, the six-feet-four-inch wingspan of Bills thwarts a Reome jump shot attempt. Gretchen grabs the blocked ball and gets it to Jenny. It feels like we are taking some momentum back.

The rest of the first half is intense, with lots of pressure defense and fights for boards. We are down three as we jog into the locker room. I glance up at the stands and see my dad walking toward the exit with Peter and Jeremy. I smile to myself. A while back Jeremy told me Dad caught them off guard by asking to go to their apartment for a Busch Light at halftime. Apparently Peter started saying something like, "Oh, sir, I am not twenty-one," and Dad cut that BS off and just told them to get him a beer already.

The second half starts off fast-paced and pretty even. I get in off the bench here and there. When on the bench I try to stay locked in and support my teammates on the court by calling out screens, calling out help side, and giving consistent encouragement in general. While on the bench together, Amers and I frequently strategize and comment on what great coaches we would make.[163] With under ten minutes left in the game we are up 48-38. Michele jukes, jives, and puts in an and-one to stop the clock. She makes her free throw—I am tempted to shout, "Where was that in our final in 2001?"[164] but decide I will save it for after the game—and has that killer-instinct look in her eye I have seen so many times. Uh-oh.

Sure enough, Michele goes crazy in the span of five minutes, scoring nine points. Then Heny hits a three to put them within one, 59-58. Amy and I both look at each other, and I know we are thinking the same thing: *Call a time-out.* After a few seconds Hendo makes the T sign with his hands. The ref blows her whistle and signals the players to their respective benches. Hendo draws up a play to hit Bills inside. We nod our heads and offer quick encouragement like, "Let's go, ladies!" "We got this!" "Stay composed and finish!" as the huddle breaks.

Gretchen inbounds to Rae, who hits Jenny on the right wing. Jenny lobs it up to Sarah as she comes off a low-block screen from Root. Sarah catches, turns, shoots, and . . . foul. The ball bounces off the back iron, but it puts Bills to the line and gives Valgardson her third foul. Bills knocks down both free throws. With 5:36 to go, we are up 61-58.

It is fun to have a close game for the fans that made it out on this subzero night. No one scores for several possessions. Then Root banks in a twelve-footer, putting us up 63-58. Heny hits a fifteen-footer on the other end, we answer with a bank shot by Root, and then Reome hits a huge three for the Skylights. Both benches are going wild as Jenny confidently pulls up and drains a three. Gardner responds with a pull-up three of her own. Copycat. We put on full-court pressure and Rae

---

[163] Amy coached in the Billings West high school girls' program—under Montana-born former WNBA player Greta Koss, as well as a few other coaches—for a total of ten years. I coached in the girls' program in Big Timber, Montana—under former Northern Skylight Kim Finn, who played when Northern won the national championship in1993—and currently coach in the boys' program at Hill City High School in South Dakota, first under Nate Bayne and now Laramie Harvey.

[164] In 2001, our senior year at Chester, Michele had a chance to win the state championship game against Harlowton with an and-one with 2.1 seconds left. She had just tied the game with a putback after rebounding her first two attempts. The free throw bounced long but thankfully we won the game in double overtime (Graham Duprey, 2020). It never gets old, teasing her about that.

almost comes up with a steal. Instead she unfortunately comes up with a foul. That sometimes happens with Rae. She has never been accused of holding back. The whistle allows for all of us in the gym to catch our breath.

The first free throw goes in, then Jenny pulls down the rebound as the second free throw attempt clanks off the iron. She is swarmed by an attempted trap, but the whistle blows and stops play. With 28.6 seconds to go Jenny jogs to the line. She knocks down both free throws. Atta girl! Their coach calls a time-out right away. We gather close. Hendo does not reach for his whiteboard. Instead he addresses us excitedly. "Alright, great job. Let's put some pressure on them as they inbound. Get in their faces, but do not be overaggressive and do not reach."

He gives Rae a quick smile. "We have the lead. Just keep the ball in front and play disciplined, straight-up defense. Don't let them get off an open three; keep a hand in their faces, especially Heny, Gardner, and Reome. If they get it inside, play straight-up. Even if they score two, we are still up one with possession. Do not foul. Let's get this first home-court conference game win!"

We are all fired up as we shout, "Bears!" and prepare for the final seconds of the game.

Our defense pressures their every move. Dribble, dribble, pass. Pass-fake, dribble, dribble, pass. Screen, roll, nothing there. Kick out to the wing, quick reverse, another quick reverse. Heny puts up a three and leans into Rae Dawn, whose hands are straight up. The ball spins freely, demanding everyone's rapt attention. All eyes follow it diving down toward the hoop. Clank! That clank is music to my ears. Bills pulls down the board like a beast and tosses it out to Jenny. Jenny gathers herself and looks at the ref, surprised, when the whistle goes off.

I look up at the scoreboard: 5.8 seconds to go. If there is a travel called I am going to lose my mind. A suspenseful silence holds us for a few moments. Then the ref looks toward the Skylights' bench and makes a quick T sign. Ooh, bench technical. Looks like their coach did not like the no-call on Heny's attempt to draw a foul. Emotions can make us crazy when it comes to sports.

Our crowd goes crazy. Nine players line up behind half-court while Jenny coolly hammers in the last two coffin nails with one free throw. Swish. Then another. And that is all she wrote, folks.

Winning is fun.

* * *

January 25, 2005

Last week was okay. We beat UGF 72–58 after the Northern win, but then practice was a bit rough. It was that time of the month for pretty much everyone, so we were all on edge. Coach Mouat all but tossed us a bunch of chocolate candies at the end of practice. It was really funny. We left for Dillon Friday morning and had a shootaround there at noon. I got to see Jeffrey and Amanda for a second, but Jeff had class and Amanda had to referee out of town that night. But it was good to see her. Our game did not go so great; we lost by almost fifteen because we had to foul at the end. Dad, Mom, Kathy, Jimmy, and the kids were there, though, so that was awesome. Jeff had a great game that night, and they beat our boys. It is always weird to be rooting for one person on the opposing team.

We rode on our bus over to Butte late that same night. The Tech game was much better. We had a good shootaround and a very fun lunch. Our game started out not so great. We were down twelve with three minutes to go in the first half then went on a 17-2 run. I was put in with forty-nine seconds left in the first half. We were up two at that point and I hit a three coming off a screen on the left corner with eight seconds to go. That was nice. It can be difficult being ready to go when you never know if or when you will go in, but I think I am getting better at it. At being ready all the time. We won by ten, and our bus ride home was very fun.

Sunday was nice. We slept in, had breakfast, I cleaned both apartments—because I swear the boys never even think about cleaning anything—and then Kat, Jer, Peter, Kevin, Aubyn, Jess, and I went to Pioneer Park. They all played tennis while I read and ate snacks. It was an unreal sixty-five degrees outside. So crazy. The temperature fluctuated one hundred degrees from last week to this week. Montana weather. Schizo.

Monday morning a strange number came up on my phone. Guess who? Yes, Brent called from Afghanistan. He actually sounded pretty good. He said he has been lifting and has gained fifteen pounds, which is crazy as he usually loses weight while deployed.

Yesterday I had three classes. Jeremy and I (mostly Jeremy) made delicious enchiladas for dinner. Jeremy had a youth group event, so Jeri and I went to the movie *Ladder 49.* We cried the entire time.

Today I had class until noon, ate lunch outside, took a nap, and then did homework until practice. Which was not actually practice, turns out. We sat in the locker room and went around the room saying one nice thing about everyone. That is, it would be one person's turn, and then everyone else said one nice thing about that person. It took over two and a half hours. But it was awesome. People said so many really caring and kind things about each other. Gretchen even said that meeting me on her recruiting trip was basically the reason she wanted to come to Rocky. She is so sweet. Anyway, for a fleeting moment I thought about staying another year, but I really think I am ready to move on. This is a great team for my last basketball team memory.

* * *

The rest of the season has gone okay. Could be better. I list out the games and scores on my science methods notebook:

*Carroll 71-88	*LC State 56-76
*Westminster 72-64	*UGF 82-76
*Northern 73-90	*Tech 77-68
*Western 53-61	*MSUB 44-66

I look at the opponent and score of each game and recall tidbits and memorable plays. Westminster was by far my favorite game. I felt completely "in the zone" and had sixteen points, six assists, and five steals. Gretchen had a breakout game, with nineteen points and solid defense and rebounding. The other games we played fairly steadily, with sparks of greatness flickering throughout.

Regardless of the scores, I will say I am proud to be on this team. We are hard workers, we are respectful and disciplined, and we treat each other well on and off the court. I may not always agree with my coaches' decisions, but I know they have the best of intentions. Dad reminds me that they are learning, too. That any good player, good coach, good teacher—or whoever—should always seek ways to learn and grow. That thought had not really occurred to me before. I always thought adults had things all figured out. The closer I get to "adult" status, however, the further away that thought flies from my mind.

* * *

"You did everything right," Dad tells me, as he kisses the side of my sweaty head.

I bury my head in his chest and try to speak, but mostly sob. I started sobbing in the locker room while Coach Hendo was telling us how proud of us he was, how enjoyable it was coaching us this season. I continued crying while hugging each teammate, and then while taking a long, hot shower. I thought I had it together but started the waterworks again when I saw my parents waiting for me outside of the locker room.

"I saw you tell Coach Mouat to have them run that backdoor play," Dad continues, "and that three-pointer was in and out; it was a great shot and the right call."

It is no use trying to reply with coherent words. Our season—my final season, forever—just ended with a heartbreaker against the Carroll Lady Saints in the Frontier Conference tournament. We were down 38–55 early in the second half. Then we switched up our defense and started zone pressing. We went on a crazy 27–8 run and led 65–63 with just under four minutes to go. It was back and forth after that, with little scoring, but Woody had a couple huge steals, and Hall and Forney went 4–4 from the free throw line down the stretch. Jenny and I both had threes that just would not quite drop with around a minute to play. If either had gone in it would have tied it up.

But it was just not our night.

I briefly recall the mood I was in after our first tournament game the previous night. It was a great matchup against Northern, neck and neck the whole game all the way through regulation. We got up one in overtime. Jenny took a huge charge against Heny. We won 64–62. I was sitting with Michele and her team during the LC-UGF game, before we played each other, and her teammates were all talking about beating

Carroll, as if there was no chance Rocky might be a factor. So it was extra fun beating Northern in OT.

It feels crazy how quickly my feelings and emotions have changed from last night to right now. I suppose that is part of the attraction of sports. Getting to feel so many extreme emotions in such short spans of time. Right now I feel completely exhausted. I hug my dad a little tighter, Mom rubs my back. I close my eyes and exhale.

Goodbye, basketball.

Chapter 33

March 2005, junior year, spring break, Billings, Montana; Cody, Wyoming

"We should go on a walk one night while we are here, before sunset. Does that sound nice?" Jeremy's question pulls me away from my basketball reels that continue playing—without permission, mind you—whenever I have a free moment.

I look over at my cute driver and smile. My eyes turn and peer out the front windshield in search of the next little green mile marker. I see a turnoff to Chief Joseph Scenic Byway. "Oh! We are getting really close!"

This is just what I need. I need to "get out of Dodge," or whatever they say. The last few days were draining. I cried a lot and slept a lot. Why does finishing a season take so much energy? Of course I caught a cold. Why do you always immediately get sick when a season ends? And of course I wish I were flying to Jackson, Tennessee, with my team, preparing for the national tournament. But apparently that was not in the cards.

"I can't wait to eat my mom's mashed potatoes." Jeremy has been talking about food for the last twenty miles of our drive from Billings.

I smile at this comment. It is not the first time I have heard it. His stomach always begins to control his thoughts if he hasn't eaten in a few hours. "Your mom does make the best mashed potatoes," I reply.

Cody, Wyoming is just under two hours almost directly south of Billings. Jeremy and I have become quite familiar with this peaceful drive. Usually we make the trip with a car full of friends, but this time it is just the two of us. Ann and Greg have some hallway painting we are going to do for them. I am terrible at painting and also, I hate painting. But Jeremy likes to paint. So we are going to paint. Maybe doing something completely different will be therapeutic for me, after months—years, really—of focusing so much on all things basketball.

Painting or not, I am most excited to be in a different physical space. There is such relief in simply driving out of town. There are some patches of snow here and there, but the roads are bare. The antelope have kept a safe distance as well. I really try to concentrate on the scenery, to enjoy this peaceful ride. But it intrudes again. "Ah!" I exclaim.

Jeremy turns his head slightly in my direction but is unperturbed and unsurprised.

I rehash my frustration out loud. "I cannot believe that three-pointer I took on the top of the key did not go in! It was legit in and out. If I would have made that, we would have won."

I have always had a hard time stopping my brain from playing different scenes from basketball games over and over again. Who knows when that will stop? I heave a sigh and cross my arms while leaning back huffily in my seat. Jer continues tapping in time to the music with one hand, and with the other he sweetly rubs the top of my leg, not saying a word. He pats my knee and gives me a sympathetic close-lipped smile. "I'm sorry, Jamer."

My eyes close. I let out a long exhale. The tension holding up my shoulders releases and they drop. My shoulders, especially my right shoulder, hurt most days. So does my neck. Maybe this will be a chance to finally rest them. Maybe my body will have a chance to heal.

Jer downshifts as we approach the Cody city limits. Another thought occurs to me as I picture Ann and Greg's house. It makes me smile. "That hot tub is calling my name."

* * *

"Thanks, Ann." I pull on the fuzzy black gloves Ann hands me.

"That wind makes it really cold, especially when the sun starts going down," Ann reminds us, in classic caring-parent fashion.

I adjust the cap she lent me and turn toward Jeremy. He is extra bouncy this evening and apparently very excited to go on this walk. I have decided that he has more energy than the average human, and since we were painting and eating all day, he must really need to get outside and get some exercise. I have been feigning disinterest, as he has been talking about how we can look at all of the different rock formations and rock types, blah blah blah, but it is hard to be disinterested in anything if it means being with Jeremy. In this case, I do believe he is genuinely interested in all of that geology stuff, but I also think he likes to bring it up as often as possible because he ended up with an A in our geology class, and I got a dumb B+.

Jeremy has the door open and says, "Goodbye, Mom! Goodbye, Greg! See you all in a little while!"

They wave and tell us goodbye. I grab Jer's outstretched hand and follow him toward the giant, red rock formation ahead of us. "Let's go up there."

He points west toward the horizon. That looks very far away. Don't get me wrong, I like to exercise, but my family has and likely never will be labeled "outdoorsy." We prefer warm gyms. He grabs my hand to control the pace. "Come on!" he urges enthusiastically.

We traipse across Ann and Greg's backyard and cross to more uneven terrain. I have to admit, these red rock formations are pretty beautiful. Jeremy stops in front of me, reaches down and picks something up. He places it in my gloved hand. "Shale," he states, matter-of-factly.

"I believe you," I respond.

He smiles and starts walking again. The incline intensifies pretty quickly, so I focus more closely on where each foot lands. I think we have officially shifted from "walking" to "hiking." My breathing and heart rate have picked up. Am I already out of shape? It has only been a few days since I played my last game.

Jeremy stops several more times on the way up. Each time he turns to show me what he has collected. He flips it over and over in his palm. Sometimes he tells me a fact. Sometimes he asks me if I know the name. He stopped asking after I responded, "It's a rock," for the third time.

I may not be super interested in everything he is, but it sure is cute how excited he gets about different things. I think this is one of my favorite things about him, that he is always up for trying something new, learning something new, and meeting someone new. I only hope I can keep up with him.

After what seems like hours—but likely has only been twenty minutes or so—he stops. I nearly ram into his backside, since I have been paying such close attention to my steps and not stumbling. It takes me a second to gather myself. When I get my bearings I draw a quick breath. The beauty really is . . . breathtaking. Jeremy points across the sky. "Walk a little ways farther over there," he instructs, "and you can get a really good view of the sunset."

I follow his instructions. He is right. The layers of colors are incredible. I don't know that I have ever seen so many hues of reds, oranges, and yellows. I am about to tell him as much when he poses another question. "What do you think about this rock?"

I giggle to myself. Okay, I will try to make a real guess this time. I think I can actually identify shale. Um, maybe some gneiss? Before I make any move I feel a pull on my hand. The pull turns me around so I face him. It takes me a second to make sense of the scene. What is he . . . ? Why is he . . . ? *Oh*!!! Oh, my goodness. I cannot believe he surprised me!

"Jamie," Jeremy addresses me in the most sincere, slightly shaky, tone.

He has assumed "the position." His left knee balances on the rocky earth, while his right knee props up his right elbow, a pink velvety box in hand. I can tell he is talking, but things are feeling dizzy and slow motion-y, and it is difficult to discern what all he is saying. Something about how much he loves me, wants to be with me forever, et cetera. My mind instead plays back his initial question: *What do you think about this rock?*

I hear myself excitedly exclaim, "Good one!"

Jeremy's expression mimics the one he made when I was quizzing him about loving football and being like Kathy Ireland's character in *Necessary Roughness* that night we first kissed, over two and a half years ago. I realize he is looking for more than, "Good one!"

I skip forward and throw my arms around his neck. "Yes!" I shout emphatically. "Yes! Of course, yes!"

YES YES   YES
YES 3-7-05   YES YES
                                        YES
YES   The day the love of my
        life asked me to marry him
                                    (3-08-05 Tues

Slack slack slack, of course.
Anyway, I'm poly to sleep soon, but
yesterday was quite a day. I went to
Cody w/ Jeremy Sunday afternoon. We
talked about going on a walk a few times,
so we decided to the next day. We painted
a hallway in the house for the end of
the morning → 4 or so. Then we took
showers & went to the Sierra Trading
Post; I got my mom some cute pants
for YOGA, since she's really into that
now. It's so cute. Anyway, Jen asked,
"Are we still gonna have time to go on
a walk?" I said yes, yes. So we went
back to the house at 5:30 or so, &
Ann & Greg were home. I got some
gloves & a hat from Ann, & Jen got his
stuff on. We decided to take a hike
up the red rocky hills in the back of
Ann & Greg's house. We climbed and
crawled & kept naming rocks; Jeremy
really likes rocks. So, we got to the
top, the very top, just at sunset. I

My journal entry, March 7, 2005

* * *

I lie in my childhood bed and open the letter Mom left for me when I got home today. I drove all the way home from Cody today, singing along to my CDs and sneaking glances as my sparkly fourth finger that was wrapped around the steering wheel. I kept replaying our walk yesterday, reminding myself we are now officially engaged, and smiling and smiling. Mom and Dad just left my room, after kissing me goodnight. Just like old times.

Now I focus on the letter with the distinctive script that addressed this letter to *Ms. Jamie Graham*. My strategy has been to save this letter to read just before I go to sleep, because Grandma Barb's letters always make me happy. A yawn escapes as I unfold the paper.

> Big Timber, Mont.
> March 4, 2005

Dear Jamie,

Just a little note to thank you for the rose for Valentine's Day. That was very sweet of you. We were happy to see that you had a good game a week or so ago. I should remember whom you were playing but I don't. It's very frustrating to forget, especially when I used to have an excellent memory. Grandpa gets disgusted because, as he says, "I can't do a d*mn thing!" Then he gets cabin fever, so we try to visit someone or go someplace. But that's hard because so many of our friends are dead. We did go up to the assisted living to see a couple friends today. We joined one as she and several other residents were watching a video of scenic areas in the U.S.A.

Our friend Betty is in St. V.'s with a stroke. It isn't as bad as Grandpa's was, so that's good. She was watching The Oscars and she saw double — the same scene on top of another. She had read that that was a sign of a stroke. So she had her neighbor

263

take her to the PMC.[165] After they saw the one side
of her face sagged, they loaded her up in an
ambulance and sent her to Billings.

Well, I just got Grandpa to bed and I think I'll hit
the hay too. Thanks again. Hope we'll see you one of
these days.

P.S. I steamed open the envelope and will put
this in a new envelope, since I remembered you will
be in Chester next week for spring break.

With hugs and kisses
Grandpa & Grandma B.

Aw. Well I don't know if I would say everything in this letter makes
me happy. The thing is, though, even when Grandma writes about
frustrating or sad things I can still hear her steady, calm, positive,
outlook. She always seems serene, even amid sadness or frustration.
She takes everything in stride. I read the letter once more then set it
down on my bedstead. I click off the lamp and blink a few blinks into
the darkness. Then I let my heavy eyelids close. My prayer before I fall
asleep is for God to help me someday learn how to live life the way
Grandma does.

---

[165] Pioneer Medical Center—the hospital, clinic, and assisted-living facility in Big
Timber, Montana.

Chapter 34

April 2005, junior year, decisions, Pranksgiving, Billings, Montana

T he rest of our time in Cody together was wonderful. That night, after Jeremy proposed, we walked down the Chugwater formation arm in arm. Jeremy plucked the beautiful, sparkly, white gold engagement ring from its perch inside the pretty, pink, dainty, velvet box and placed it on my glove-warmed left finger. On the wonky-looking finger I broke deflecting a basketball years ago. I was right, my future husband did not care about my incorrectly healed finger. He loves me for me. Just as I am.

Ann and Greg were anxiously awaiting our arrival, as Jeremy had filled them in on his plans. We all hugged, and we told them the story. Then I spent an hour or so calling as many family and friends as possible, to share my most exciting news ever.

The next day I drove to Chester for the rest of the spring break week. Turns out my eyes are easily distracted by this shiny thing on my finger, so I had to remind myself to focus on the road and not the ring. I just kept smiling and smiling all the way home, thinking about becoming Mrs. Jeremy Duprey. Has a nice *ring* to it. Indeed.

Now I am back in my bedroom at Rocky. The weather has been gorgeous this week. I love spending spring in Billings. Everything buds so much earlier than in Chester. We have been frequenting Pioneer Park, mostly playing Frisbee golf. And the other night we—along with many of our neighbors on either side of us in this apartment complex—planned and executed a most lovely progressive dinner party. Jenny and Kevin provided sangria. Jeremy and Peter put together a fancy cheese, meat, and cracker tray. Kat, Jeri,[166] and I provided garlic bread and a

---

[166] Jeri joined us as a roommate during our junior year.

fruit tray. Kayla and Adam made lasagna, and Burke, Jake, and Brett made a chocolate cake with rainbow-chip frosting. It was a blast. [167]

Tonight Kat and Jeri went to a movie with Jeremy, Peter, and I think a few other people, but I did not feel like going out. Especially because we are all heading to Red Lodge tomorrow. I need to rest up. [168]

I reach out to pull a brown hair tie out from under a textbook flopped sideways on my dresser. I hook the band with my finger and pull harder than I mean to. The book teeters briefly before toppling to the floor. I sigh. Maybe this is a sign that I finally will organize this unruly mess. I squat down to retrieve the book. As I reach for the book, I notice the crisp corner of a plain, white envelope poking out of a notebook stuffed full of basketball papers. Curious, I leave the book for now and instead pull out the envelope.

A Rocky Mountain College logo and address is printed in green in the top-left corner. My name is scribbled across the front with an unfamiliar script. That's funny. I don't remember seeing this envelope before. I vaguely remember packing up random items—including a few papers— from the locker room after our last game. Then maybe I added the pile to this crazy clutter. Hard to tell. Details from the last weeks are blurry.

Finally I manage to flatten out the professional trifold. It is an email printout addressed to Coach Mouat, subject: Jamie Graham. He must have slipped this envelope in with my other basketball papers. It only takes reading the greeting for me to hear the letter-writer's voice and for both a smile and throat lump to form.

Jamie,

> *Hi there little buddy! How are you doing? I was just writing to wish you good luck this weekend! I have a feeling that Rocky will come home victorious! You guys have had a*

---

[167] Somehow we lucked out and had apartments next to many friends: Kevin Jurenka and Jenny Balgua lived right next to Jeremy and Peter; then it was Kat, Jeri, and me, followed by Kayla Neubauer and Adam Sanchez; and the last room in our fun string held Jeromey Burke, Brett Wilson, and Jake Stuart. I don't remember who first had the idea, but I am so glad we organized several progressive dinners.

[168] Each year we spent a weekend or two down in Red Lodge, Montana. Most of the time was spent at Snow Creek.

great season so far, and I am confident that you can win this weekend and move on to Nationals.

I know that this year has been frustrating at times, and that is understandable. However, you can always look back with no regrets because you are without a doubt, a class act. You have handled adversity with grace and have proven to be the best teammate anyone could ever ask for. You are selfless, kind, hardworking, and hilarious. Perhaps you are unaware of this now, but later you will realize what everyone who has ever had the privilege of playing the game with you has already come to know: You are fabulous in every sense of the word. You have forgotten this—you are a great player, Jamie G. You are a joy to play with, and your ability to see the court, pass, shoot, and defend are admirable. I think you have lost your confidence to do this somewhere along the way. Find it. It is true!!!!! However, something much more important must be addressed!!!!! You are a fabulous person, and I mean that with everything in me. You are one of my favorite people, and your sense of humor, kindness, and loyalty do not go unnoticed. In ten years from now, one year, one hour, whatever, your teammates may not remember anything you have done on the basketball court, but they will recall fondly everything you have done for them as a friend. And that is the most important, and I still think of you and laugh out loud.

Back to basketball—you will do great. Your hard work will pay off. I honestly believe, although I can't speak for you, that you can leave the court with no regrets. You have done everything that has been asked of you, and you have done it with HARD WORK and determination. Go get um' little friend.

GOOD LUCK!!!

Love,
Kelley

By now tears are streaming. I have to blink furiously in order to make out the words in the final paragraph. Somehow knocking over that book does not feel accidental. This is exactly what I needed to hear. I read a phrase near the end again: *you can leave the court with no regrets.*

I feel pretty certain Kelley was not talking about leaving the court of our last game this season. Tears well and spill over again. I close my eyes.

A scene pops up in my mind's eye and begins to play, like watching a movie. The scene shows me walking slowly off a shiny, lacquered, hardwood floor. The background is dark and blurry. A mass of people stand on the far end of the court. I watch myself walk steadily and calmly away from the throng. My head is tilted slightly down—but my eyes look determinedly forward—and I tug lightly at my sweaty green uniform, untucking jersey from shorts. My hair is pulled back in a messy bun, sweat sliding down my hairline and temples. My basketball shoes noisily and resolutely trudge—making a hollow echo-y sound—across the squeaky wooden floor. I take in a big breath, hold it for a few seconds, exhale deeply, and walk right off the court. I do not glance back even once.

* * *

Ah, sweet, sweet water. I guzzle greedily from the fountain by the exercise room in the Fortin Center. That mixed feeling of exhaustion and exhilaration you get after a hard workout flows through me. The feeling gives me the confidence to approach Coach Henderson. I wipe my mouth and walk across the tile toward him. He is standing facing the staircase of the weight room, watching other players ascend. I reach out and tap on his arm to get his attention. He turns my way.

"Hey, Coach?" I ask, and barrel on, so as not to lose my nerve.

"Can you and I grab lunch tomorrow? Maybe Red Robin?" I suggest hurriedly.

His eyes flicker, and I am not sure, but that flicker seems a little sad. He manages a smile and nods. "Sure, Red Robin sounds good."

"Okay," I continue, "I finish class at MSUB at 11:48.[169] Does it work to meet around noon?"

---

[169] I took two education classes at MSUB that semester, as Rocky only offered them in the fall. It was not my original intention to rush or take extra classes, but after taking those two classes I realized I would be able to finish a semester early, which would mean deciding whether or not to play basketball.

Hendo looks thoughtfully at me, as if considering many things. After what seems like several seconds he kindly responds. "Sure, Jamie. See you then."

I give him a close-lipped smile. Then I wave my dorky Jamie wave and walk back toward the locker room.

* * *

Hendo is already at a table when I enter the restaurant. He waves. I smile and walk his way. Ever the gentleman, he stands and pulls out my chair. A memory of him holding the door for me on the way into the Fortin Center during my recruiting trip flashes through my mind. I specifically remember thinking, *What a nice guy.*

"Hi, Coach," I open.

"Hi, Jamie," Coach politely responds.

"Thank you for meeting me," I continue.

"You're welcome."

We both smile, I sort of shrug, and then the waitress brings us menus. Thankful for something to focus on, I study my menu as if it is the first menu I have ever laid eyes on. Hendo follows suit. He is letting me take the lead. He really is the nicest guy. Last night I attempted to visualize this situation and practice. It sort of sounded okay in my mind. The problem is, though, that I struggle getting the words out of my mind so that they make sense and don't mumble or rush or get too emotional, and all that.

I take a breath. I set my menu down and look across the table. Coach mirrors my actions. His patience and kindness create a safe and relaxed atmosphere. I smile gratefully at him. Finally I gather up the courage and open my mouth. "Coach," I lead.

"What can I get you two today?" Our well-meaning yet slightly brusque waitress interrupts my big moment.

The shift in focus causes me to awkwardly sputter out my order. "I would, uh . . . um . . . I'll have the . . ."—I pick up my menu again, scan, and point—"yeah, the bacon cheeseburger, please."

"Okay," comes the quick response, "and how would you like that cooked?"

"Um . . . ," more "ums" spew. "I guess medium well."

The waitress scribbles something on her notepad and turns toward Coach Hendo. He politely reaches for my menu, stacks it with his own, and hands it to the waitress as he orders. "I'll have the same. Thank you."

"You bet." The waitress gives us a typical Montana response and rushes off toward the kitchen.

Unable to come up with any fun small talk, I square my shoulders and try again. "Coach. I came here to talk to you about next season."

A sad smile spreads over his face, as if he is attempting to look indifferent and composed but cannot quite pull it off. That dang lump forms in my throat again, and even though I do not want them to, my next words catch. "I . . . um."

Oh for crying out loud. Well, that is exactly what I am trying to avoid. Come on, Jamie. The point of practicing this in my head last night was so that I would not cry out loud. As I look across at Hendo, though, I know he already knows. Still, I owe it to both of us to lay it out clearly.

I think back through the past months and all the back-and-forth that has been waking me up in the middle of the night. All the possible scenarios, all the pros and cons. There were times when I felt so sure I knew what the best next step was for me, only for those thoughts to be flipped upside down with doubt two seconds later.

Like after my fall meeting with my advisor last September—where we went over classes taken, classes needed, and credits left to finish my degree—and the conversation I had with my parents immediately after. I realized I was unexpectedly on track to graduate early. It would allow me to student teach in the fall instead of the spring, which has always appealed to me, so I could see how best to start out a school year. The only problem with that plan was—and it went without saying—that it would mean I would not play basketball my senior year.

Or like when I met with the student teaching advisor, and she laid out options for where I might be placed. After that conversation it felt sensible to focus on student teaching and be finished with basketball. But then we played Carroll at home, and I was so emotional in the locker room afterward. I broke down sobbing and I told Jeri, "I don't want to quit, Jeri! I'm not a quitter. I don't want to quit!" and she just hugged me and let me bawl.

Not play basketball? At first it sounded crazy. But the more I thought about it, the more the insanity of the idea wore off. Then it started sounding practical. It started sounding like an idea that would make the most sense as far as prioritizing my chosen profession, my vocation. It started to feel like the responsible, "grown-up" choice to make.

But was I ready to be a responsible grown-up? *Am* I ready?

Anyway, so here I am. Sitting across from my coach of the last three years, the coach who recruited me and offered me an opportunity to play the sport I love for a little while longer after high school. The coach who held the door for me and told me how much he valued hard-working, encouraging people who would put their education above their sport. And I know he was being sincere.

He tilts his head slightly and attempts a reassuring smile. Finally I get everything out. "I, um, have decided to student teach next fall, which means I will not play basketball, and I will graduate in December."

There. I said it.

My eyes well up. I try not to let the tears spill over, but it is no use. Coach tears up, too, and teases, "Did you invite me here so we could cry together in public?"

This makes me laugh-cry. "I'm sorry," I say. "I have been going back and forth. It has been really hard. My parents and Jeremy all have said over and over that they support me whatever I decide. Which I appreciate, but that hasn't helped make the decision any easier. I just, I mean, I think this is the right decision. "But . . ."—it takes a few seconds to compose myself and keep the recent throat lump at bay—"but it has been really hard," I finish in a whisper.

I reach for and unravel a roll of silverware and use the napkin to wipe my eyes. Hendo starts apologizing. "I'm sorry. I should have encouraged all of the things that I loved about your game when you played in high school. You were put in some tough positions. I know I messed with your confidence. I should have communicated better. I'm sorry."

He grabs his own napkin and dabs at his eyes. Aw, this is not why I brought him here. I did not intend for him to feel like he needs to apologize. The decision has been made. I just wanted to share it directly with him. I offer him the most convincing "I'm okay, promise" smile I

271

can muster. Then I say, "Coach, it's okay. I don't have any regrets. Thank you for giving me the chance to be at Rocky. If I could do it all over again, I would choose Rocky every time."

And I mean it.

* * *

Ah, Pranksgiving. According to Jer and his friends, Pranksgiving is arguably the best "holiday" of the year. I am unsure of its exact origin, but this is somehow the third Pranksgiving in under two years; apparently Pranksgiving is a biannual holiday.

The boys just rushed in here to our kitchen to tell me all about their latest flash of brilliance. Yesterday they poked hundreds of plastic forks in the front yard of the house down the way on Poly Drive where Shane, Dustin, Dylan, and Zach live. The day before that they swapped all of Fischer's and Styles'[170] bedroom furniture with their own living room furniture. Fischer and Styles retaliated by hiding a bunch of hard-boiled eggs in Logan and Kyle's basement, and then the boys dumped and smashed packets and packets of ramen noodles into the girls' carpet. I also heard stories of baking soda in toilet bowls with vinegar in the tank, a Keystone Light "beer-amid," and J-Rod's car being Saran wrapped.

Just now the boys rush in and are so excited because they stapled hundreds of Dixie cups together on the kitchen table of a girls' soccer apartment and filled all the cups up with water. They are also talking excitedly and simultaneously about a stack of phone books or something? It is hard to follow. As they rush out of the apartment I yell to Jeremy I have never been prouder to be his fiancé.

True to Peter, Jeremy, Logan, Kyle, and Kevin's history of no-nonsense-rule compliance when it comes to really important things— like Krib and Keg tournaments, or games of Slaps—there are official rules for Pranksgiving. Not only that, the rules are typed up, printed, and posted. All participants receive a copy and must abide.

Almost as quickly as they faded, I now hear a loud clambering of heavy footsteps outside coming toward the door. The boys must have

---

[170] Kasey Fischer and Andrea Styles were best friends and both on the ski team. They were very good friends with Jeremy and his crew and somehow put up with all the boys' nonsense.

struck again. I shake my head and grin and try to refocus on my homework. Speaking of homework, Jeremy and his friends spent the majority of last week watching March Madness games at Hooligans. They were oddly obsessed with Tyler Hansbrough from the University of North Carolina. They lovingly referred to him as "Cow Eyes." I went down to meet them at Hooligans a few times between classes, but I have no idea how many—if any—classes they attended that week. Come to think of it, how are they passing their classes? Hopefully there are no surprises come semester-grade time, because Jeremy is supposed to graduate in just a few weeks.

Graduation in just a few weeks? That thought tightens my stomach. Graduation means ending. I listen again to the childlike excitement of the stampede happening outside my door. Are we ready for this to end?

 **Chapter 35**

March 27, 2004, twenty-first birthday, Big Timber, Montana

I f you would like to talk about this infamous event, please contact me, and I will decide how much information to disclose.

Chapter 36

May 2005, junior year, Jer's graduation, Billings, Montana

"Where are my snacks?" I feel Peter pulling on my shirt sleeve.

I am sitting on the second tier of bleachers on the south end of the Fortin gymnasium. Peter sits one tier below. I usually do not feel strange in gyms. Today I feel strange in this gym. First, I am sitting in the bleachers instead of licking the tips of my fingers and wiping my shoes, preparing for a practice or game. Second, the hardwood is hidden by reams of some sort of black, shiny material. Third, there are rows and rows of folding chairs lining the court.

Peter has now pulled open the canvas bag I hold. He asks, "What about my games? I want to play a game."

I giggle. "Give me one second. Just be patient."

I dig down into the bag and feel around. My hand finds a small, rectangular plastic container. I present Peter with the possibility. "What about a Ritz Cracker Handi-Snack?"

Peter narrows his eyes and contemplates his first option. "Um, no thanks."

I giggle a little harder and try again. This time I pull out a small aluminum foily-feeling packet. "How about some Gushers?"

"Yeaaaaaaah, now you're talking," is the response I receive.

I tear open the top of the bright-yellow packet and hand it to Peter. He happily accepts, plucks out one small, red candy and chews. After he swallows he looks up, as if discerning his satisfaction level, and reports, "Mmm. Tasty."

"Glad you like them." I smile and give his back a little scratch.

"Oh yeah . . . a little to the left . . . up, up . . . right there." Peter does love a good back scratch.

People continue streaming in, and the bleachers are getting quite full. I look up at the large clock on the wall. Just a couple more minutes until the ceremony is scheduled to begin. I have never been to one of these here before so I am not sure what to expect, punctuality-wise.

I look back down at Peter. "What game do you want to play?" I query.

"Um," Peter says, "how about Game Boy?"

I think about it for a second. "That might be a little too distracting. How about a coloring book?"

Now it is Peter's turn to think for a second. Then, "Sure."

I feel around inside the full canvas bag yet again until I find the Care Bears coloring book. Then I smear my hand across the bottom until I feel a colored pencil. I pass both items to Peter just as he is finishing his last Gusher.

"Thank you, Jamie Marie."

"You're welcome, Peter Bennett."

I grab myself a packet of Gushers just as the Rocky concert band begins its melody. As the first three chords play the gathered audience rises instinctively. Peter and I rise as well, along with Jeremy's parents, sisters, and grandparents who are also in our corner cluster. Ann has her camera at the ready. I watch the black, square hats bob in two lines as the graduate hopefuls enter the arena. Since the letter *D* is near the beginning of the alphabet I know I should spot him soon: Christie, Rob . . . ; Daniels, Jesse . . . ; Duprey, Jeremy.

There he is! Ann's camera clicks quickly and excitedly behind me. Jer's Grandma Ruth takes a few pictures as well, as does his Grandpa Ron. His Grandma Donna, Grandma Pammy, Grandpa Dick, and Grandma Ann all look on proudly. A warm feeling spreads throughout my body. A snorty, happy-sad combo cry escapes my mouth. I cover it and continue to watch Jeremy walk bouncily down the aisle, grinning all the way.

When the song finishes, the guests of honor take their seats in unison. We all follow suit. My mind flips back three years ago, to my high school graduation. So many parallels: a community gathered around a class of students packed into a space used primarily for sporting events; student musicians sharing their gifts of music-making; a class who has met said requirements clothed in uniform dark caps and gowns, eager for commencement to commence, but more importantly, for it to conclude; family members observing with pride, wonder, and a million emotions in between.

I focus my attention back to today's ceremony, to Jeremy's college graduation. To my fiancé's college graduation. Cute fiancé. These last three years have been so full of big changes. Leaving my parents. Moving here to live with new roommates, new classmates, new teammates. Leaving my hometown. Leaving my friends. Leaving my first love. Starting classes that would teach me how to become a teacher, but more importantly, teach me how to understand people and the world better, and to—hopefully—become a functioning and contributing member of society. Talk about pressure. Becoming part of a new basketball team. Learning how to play for new coaches. Meeting the love of my life. And now I sit here and feel like the big changes have somehow only just begun.

How can that be?

A loud burst of applause interrupts my thoughts. I guess that is that. I did pay attention to some of what was said, but it was difficult for me to focus. I clap and cheer as Jeremy's name is called across the loudspeaker: "Jeremy Michael Duprey."

Yes, I decide for the thousandth time, that last name is perfect.

FOURTH QUARTER

*For everything there is a season, and a time for every
purpose under heaven.*

—Ecclesiastes 3:1

Jeremy and me walking out of the church,
right after the wedding ceremony

Chapter 37

April 22, 2006, post college, Billings, Montana

My dad positions his left hand near his tuxedo pocket. His elbow extends, and I thread my right arm through the triangular opening. Dad has not been looking forward to this moment. Jeremy had not been looking forward to asking my dad about getting to this moment.

I found out Jer purchased the ring before we left for Texas, almost two years ago May. He hid the ring behind a couple books on his bookshelf, and it took him until the end of March to find time—and the courage—to bring it up. According to Jeremy, he and my dad were driving to watch Rebecca and the Big Timber Lady Herders play a volleyball game in Columbus. I had a game that same night and was not feeling great so just Jeremy and my dad drove together. The radio was on, but after several stammering "ums" and "uhs," my dad turned down the radio and huskily asked, "Do you have something to say, son?"

The memory makes me smile. Everything today makes me smile. Yesterday I was a mess. The rehearsal and rehearsal dinner were so nice, but everything made me cry. I was worried my eyes would be swollen this morning after crying so much. But I woke up today feeling more excited than I ever remember feeling. I have not cried once. I feel so happy and content. One thought has been playing on repeat in my mind: *I just want to marry Jeremy!*

After finishing my awesome student teaching experience last fall—at Blue Creek Elementary—I worked there as an aide for several weeks and coached basketball for a fun group of sixth-grade girls.[171] Kat and I also coached the freshmen girls at Billings Central Catholic High

---

[171] I student taught under Mrs. Ann Solie in a fourth-grade classroom.

School.[172] Then I lived in Chester from Christmas up until this past week, substituting, coaching fourth-, fifth-, and sixth-grade basketball, helping Mom with some wedding plans, and enjoying time with my parents. We drove from Chester to Billings this past Wednesday. I was so excited to see Jeremy that I could hardly handle it. The wedding details have been fine, and I have felt very little stress about the wedding itself because *I just want to marry Jeremy!*

I squeeze Dad's arm as we watch the procession pave our way. He is clearly focusing very hard on keeping his composure. I look toward the entrance to the sanctuary and smile at Miss Teri as she lines up each wedding-party pair and cues them when it is their turn to walk.

My smile grows and heart swells when David's guitar softly starts playing James Taylor. I really feel like I might burst when Jeremy sings the first verse and chorus.

> *There's something in the way she moves*
> *Or looks my way or calls my name*
> *That seems to leave this troubled world behind*
> *If I'm feeling down and blue*
> *Or troubled by some foolish game*
> *She always seems to make me change my mind*
> *And I feel fine anytime she's around me now*
> *She's around me now*
> *Almost all the time*
> *And if I'm well you can tell she's been with me now*
> *She's been with me now quite a long, long time*
> *And I feel fine*

Ryan escorts Ann while my brother escorts my mom. Ann and my mom are each handed one of those fancy church candlelighters. They

---

[172] Billings Central Catholic High School is a private Catholic school (Billings Catholic Schools, n.d.). Kat and I coached under head coach Scott Severance, who was the head coach at Rocky from the 1996–97 season to the 2001–2002 season, just before I got to Rocky. He started teaching in the business department at Rocky in 2000 and still teaches there today. He has continued with coaching, as he coached high school girls' basketball at Central and Huntley Project and has been coaching the Broadview-Lavina boys' basketball team since 2017.

walk up together—in their pretty flowy dresses—and light the candelabras lining the altar. Cute mamas.

Next it is time for the wedding party. Jeff escorts Rebecca, Brian escorts Chasi, Joshua escorts Maci, and Ryan is getting approving nods as he escorts both Shye and Jeri. Michele and Isaac come next, looking sharp in pink; Amanda and Kevin don light blue; Heidi and Kyle walk together in matching purple; Kat and Logan wear green; and Kaitlynn and Peter bring up the rear in their yellow—or "butter" as Peter keeps reminding me—dress, bowtie, and vest. It is so fun watching our favorite people walk into a room full of our family and friends.

My little cousins are more than ready for their turn. Megan, the flower girl, is a pro at keeping little brother Mitchell in line. Mitchell followed me around for a long time when we were doing pictures earlier today. We had a ring bearer pillow for him with two rings tied up to it that were just for show. That was not going to cut it. He was the ring bearer, thank you very much, and he had been preparing for months to carry the *real* rings. So we swapped out the cheap silver knockoffs for the real deal. Everyone of course oohs and aahs at Megan and Mitchell because they are hands down the cutest people in attendance today.

Jeremy and David finish the last verse just as Megan tells Mitchell where to stand, and all assume their positions on the steps near the altar.

> *And I feel fine anytime she's around me now*
> *She's around me now almost all the time*
> *If I'm well you can tell she's been with me now*
> *She's been with me now quite a long, long time*
> *Yes, and I feel fine*

The music shifts. The energy shifts. I feel a flow of peaceful excitement. "Peaceful excitement." Oxymoronic? Perhaps, but somehow that is how I feel. The first gentle notes of my favorite Phil Aaberg song, "High Plains," plink lightly and ring melodiously throughout the sacred space. Music makes everything better. After a few measures, Miss Teri smiles and gestures that it is finally our turn. I turn and look up at my dad. He brings his right arm across to his escort arm. He lovingly rubs the top of my right hand. If he tries to say anything I know he will cry. I lean my head against his shoulder so he can give me a forehead kiss. Then we both take in a breath and step forward into the sanctuary.

My eyes lock on to Jeremy's. His deep, brown-green eyes sparkle as he attempts to still his nervous-excited bounce. We grin at each other. Each step takes me one step closer to my groom. Closer to my future. I think about the scripture David helped us choose for our wedding ceremony from the book of Ruth:

> *Where you go, I will go,*
> *And where you stay, I will stay.*
> *Your people will be my people, and your god, my god.*
> *Where you die, I will die, and there I will be buried.*

I hope we will be able to remember these words from this day forward.

Here we go. Time for kickoff!

Jeremy and me dancing at our wedding, April 22, 2006

Dupreys, Grahams, and Pendleys wedding picture, April 22, 2006
(Photo by Jay Eklund)

Wedding party, April 22, 2006 (Photo by Jay Eklund)

NOTES ON PEOPLE

Aaberg, Phil: A fellow Chester native and Grammy- and Emmy-nominated composer.

Anderson, Doug: A year younger than me and brother of one of my brother's best friends, Jason. Doug attended MSU Billings College of Technology from 2003–2005. He would often come over in the afternoons and watch daytime TV with my roommates.

Anderson, Jason: Classmate and best friend of my brother.

Anglin, Clint: My second cousin. A police officer in Billings.

Anglin, George: My dad's cousin's husband. We call him "Uncle George."

Anglin, Jarred: My second cousin. A police officer in Billings.

Anglin, Melanie: My dad's cousin. We call her "Aunt Mel."

Arifin, Cady: A year younger than me. Competed against me in high school sports and graduated from Kremlin-Gilford.

Austin, Glenn: Glenn was married to "Miss Teri." Glenn passed away on April 28, 2019.

Austin, Scott: Miss Teri and Glenn's son. Scott played football at Rice University from 2003–2007. He went with us on our college mission trip to Jamaica.

Austin, Teri: Miss Teri was one of the youth directors at Marvin United Methodist Church, where Jeremy worked for two summers and I for one. She read the scripture readings at our wedding.

Balgua (Holly), Jenny: A teammate of mine at Rocky. Dated my brother for two and a half years.

Bayne, Nate: A teacher, coach, and writer from Spearfish, SD. I had the privilege of coaching boys' basketball at Hill City with Coach Bayne for a year before he got married and moved to North Dakota.

Berg (Bartel), Megan: A teammate at Rocky who graduated high school from Lewistown, MT. Megan married a football teammate of Jeremy's, Dylan Bartel.

Bighaus, Bill: Bill was a beloved sportswriter who retired from *The Billings Gazette* in 2014 after twenty-three years.

Bills, Sarah: A teammate of mine at Rocky and one of the best shot blockers I have ever seen.

Bitz (Prowald), Katherine "Kat": My college roommate and teammate.

Bitz, Galen: Kat's dad.

Bitz, Henry: Kat's brother.

Bitz, Matt: Kat's cousin who went to Rocky with us.

Bitz, Zana: Kat's mom.

Boggs (Coulter), Shye: A college teammate and close friend. Jeremy and I have the privilege of being godparents to Shye's son Gentre, her oldest of six.

Boggs (Fix), Misti: Shye's sister.

Boyer, Dean: A close high school friend of Jeremy's who attended the same youth group.

Branae, Barb "Grandma": My maternal grandmother.

Branae, Gary: My mom's older brother.

Branae, Helmar "Grandpa": My maternal grandfather.

Branae, Linda: My mom's sister-in-law.

Brekke (Peterson), Miranda: A year younger than me in high school. A volleyball teammate and a very funny friend who always kept us laughing.

Bucklin, Vanessa: Fellow author who grew up in Conrad, Montana. Vanessa and I met after her husband Tyler gave her my first book for a Christmas present. As is the case with many people from small-town Montana, once we met we discovered we had several shared friends and connections.

Buffington (Jensen), Sharon: Chasi's aunt and a manager on the Chester girls' basketball team that placed second at State in 1979.

Buffington (Stonehocker), Chasi: High school classmate and one of my best friends.

Bumgarner, Zach: A good friend of my brother's. Graduated from Belt, played football at Carroll, and my brother roomed with him while attending Carroll.

Burke, Jeromey: A Rocky men's basketball player and one of my favorites. I coached against him a couple years when I assisted at Sweet Grass High School in Big Timber. He has coached girls' basketball and girls' and boys' golf at Columbus High School since 2015.

Campbell, Peggy: My aunt. Rebecca and Joshua's mom.

Cheatham, Ruth: Cousin of my father-in-law.

Cicon, Gail: Mom of Heidi.

Cicon (Browne), Heidi: High school classmate and one of my best friends.

Cicon, Rudy: Dad of Heidi.

Clark, Brent: My high school boyfriend.

Clark, Bruce: Brent's dad.

Clark, Matthew: Brent's brother and one of my good friends.

Clark, Mary: Brent's mom.

Clark, Mitchell: Brent's brother and one of my good friends.

Cochran, Ron: Sociology and anthropology professor at Rocky for more than thirty years.

Cook, Logan: One of Jeremy's best friends. Played football and skied at Rocky.

Corey, Terry: Athletic director at Rocky for nine years.

Coughlan (Bumgarner), Skye: High school girlfriend—and now wife—of Zachary.

Craig, Alexia: College teammate my freshman year.

Cuin, Patrick: Football teammate of Jeremy's.

Daniels, Jesse: Football teammate of Jeremy's.

Darlington, Sheena: Graduated from Big Sandy High School and played for three years in high school with Kat. She played basketball in college at MSU-Northern.

Decker, Christopher: High school classmate who joined the army right after graduation. He visited Maci and me several times during college, and we often wrote him letters.

Decker, Cory: Christopher's brother.

Decker, Scott: Christopher's dad.

Decker, Sherry: Christopher's mom.

DeSilva, Suneentha: An education professor—and my advisor—at Rocky. She was always so very sweet and patient with her students.

Diede, Ericka: Graduated from Valier High School and competed against me in all sports in high school. She played volleyball at Rocky and is a physician in Whitefish.

Diemert, Annie: A high school teammate of mine who was one of our senior leaders in all sports when I was a freshman. Annie died in a car crash on November 29, 1999.

Diemert, Colt: Youngest brother of Annie and high school classmate of mine.

Diemert, Kacey: Kacey was a year younger than me in high school and a cheerleader for our basketball team my senior year. Colt's cousin.

Divish, Ryan: Sportswriter from Havre, Montana who played baseball at Dickinson State, ND. He currently covers the Mariners for *The Seattle Times.*

Dregne, Travis: Travis roomed with Jeremy for a spell at Rocky. He also worked with the youth at American Lutheran Church with my Uncle Gary. Travis was a great roommate, and he had a wonderful girlfriend—now wife!—named Roelie—who also went to Rocky.

Duffy, Richard: Soccer coach at Rocky.

Dundas (Eaton), Jacqueline "Jacquee": Beloved English professor at Rocky who passed away from breast cancer in 2020. Jacquee taught at the middle school, high school, and college level for over fifty years. Her grandfather, Lewis Eaton, and his brother Ernest founded Billings Polytechnic Institute in 1908, which became the foundation for the present Rocky Mountain College.

Duprey, Alycia: Jeremy's sweet sister who is a professional jazz musician.

Duprey, David: Jeremy's dad. He was an Episcopal priest in Wyoming for over twenty years and now serves as a Naval chaplain.

Duprey, Jackson: Our ten-year-old son and the baby of the family. Jackson is up for anything and has such a loveable and easygoing personality!

Duprey, Jeremy: *The* green-clad "Kicker"!

Duprey, Jordan: Our fifteen-year-old daughter and firstborn. Jordan is confident, caring, and not afraid to speak her mind!

Duprey, Justin: Our thirteen-year-old middle child. Justin doesn't always have a lot to say, but he gets along with everyone, loves soccer, and when he does speak it often makes us all burst out laughing!

Duprey, Naomi: Jeremy's other sweet sister who is a senior program manager for seller relations at Amazon.

Duprey, Pammy: Jeremy's paternal grandmother.

Duprey, Richard: Jeremy's paternal grandfather.

Earl, Anna MD: My childhood doctor, and beloved Chester physician. She and her family were our wonderful next-door neighbors for many years.

Earl, Brett: Dr. Earl's husband. I babysat often for the Earls and always loved my breakfast table conversations with Brett many summer mornings.

Earl, Emma: Dr. Earl's firstborn. Emma and I watched a lot of *Blues Clues* together and made many trips to the Chester park and pool. Emma is studying to be a physician as well.

Earl, Isabelle: Dr. Earl's second daughter. Isabelle was small but mighty right out of the gate and is headed to law school.

Edwards, Kelley: A college teammate of mine. No one has ever made me laugh more than Kelley.

Edwards, Whitney: A 2022 Hill City High School graduate who currently plays basketball for the Dickinson State Blue Hawks. Whitney and I connected through Hill City Young Life and high school sports, and it has been a pleasure to encourage her on her own high school and now college journey.

Elliott, Mike: A football teammate of Jeremy's at Rocky. Mike could often be heard playing his guitar and singing in the dorms.

Engstrom (Saisbury), Kaitlynn: High school classmate and one of my best friends.

Engstrom, Kathy: Kaitlynn's mom.

Engstrom, Zeb: Kaitlynn's brother and high school classmate of my brother.

Erickson, Emma: Oldest daughter of Pastor Pete.

Erickson, Peter "Pastor Pete": My pastor through junior high and high school. Pastor Pete and I recently crossed paths vocationally in shared work of the Evangelical Church in America (ELCA), which has been such a gift. Pete officiated Jeremy's and my wedding.

Erickson, Tonja: Pastor Pete's awesome wife. Tonja always cooked delicious meals for us for high school youth group gatherings.

Evenhus, Doug: A college teammate of Jeremy's from Centerville, MT. Doug was on the Centerville football team that played Chester in the 1998 state championship game.

Fame, Adja "Maina": A college teammate from Senegal, Africa. Adja brought as much joy to our team as she did height and could often be found greeting guests at the Rocky Fortin Center front desk.

Feaster, Ryan: A close high school friend of Jeremy's. He was an usher at our wedding.

Finn, Kim: I was lucky enough to teach with Kim at Big Timber Grade School for seven years, and we coached girls' basketball at Sweetgrass High School together for two seasons. Kim is one of the most competitive, hard-working people I know.

Fischer (Watson), Kasey: Kasey played basketball at Rocky for a season and ended up focusing on just playing RMC soccer. Kasey was always up for dancing and filled in as Jeremy's dance partner many times when I was either underage or on a basketball trip.

Fisher (Uhrich), Savannah: A favorite high school teammate and a grade younger than me.

Frederickson, Colt: A high school classmate and friend of mine.

Fuller, Leif: A close high school friend of Jeremy's.

Gagnon, Cory: A high school classmate and friend of mine.

Ghorbani, Monet: Jeremy's cousin who is a U.S. diplomat. When she gets to come back to the U.S. for vacation, our home is her home.

Gonzalez, Julio: A Belizean student at Rocky who often hung out with Jeremy and his close college friend group.

Goodheart, Wendy: My wonderful high school choir teacher.

Goodwin, Dorothy: Jeremy's surrogate grandma from Sheridan, WY. Jeremy and his sisters spent many after-school hours at Dorothy's, and one of Jeremy's favorite memories is all of the Wheat Montana Bread she spoiled him with before soccer practice.

Graham, James Preston "Grandpa Jim": My paternal grandfather.

Graham, Jay: My dad's brother.

Graham, Jeffrey: My big brother.

Graham, Jim "Dad": My dad.

Graham, Joshua: My baby cousin on my dad's side.

Graham, Joyce "Grandma": My paternal grandmother.

Graham, Karen "Mom": My sweet mom.

Graham (Ullman), Kathy: My dad's sister.

Graham, Rebecca: My baby cousin on my dad's side.

Griffith, Amber and Ashley: College teammates of mine at Rocky for one season. The sisters from Miles City excelled at both basketball and golf at Rocky.

Griffith, Daniel: A youth intern with Jeremy and me the summer we worked in Texas. Daniel was one of our roommates and always kept us laughing.

Gunderson, Amy: Brent's cousin.

Gustin, JD: My coach my freshman year at Rocky.

Hagedorn, Matt: A football teammate of Jeremy's.

Hamel, Steve and Richie: Some of my parents' closest friends when I was growing up. Richie passed away from pancreatic cancer in 2009. I babysat for their sons William and Michael for years, and they were all like family to us. Richie was sarcastic and hilarious, and I still carry with me many lessons learned from her.

Hammond (Stuart), Ashley: I never got the chance to play with Ashley, but I respected her as a point guard for Rocky not only because of how hard she played but because of her positive leadership. She dated Jake through college and they married soon after they graduated. They have two kids who are close in age to our two oldest and live in Malta, MT.

Harvey, Laramie: Current Hill City High School head boys' basketball coach. One would be hard-pressed to find someone who is as committed to the game of basketball—and to student-athletes who want to learn the game—as Coach Harvey. I was lucky enough to coach under Laramie for two seasons at Hill City.

Hash, Rich: An assistant coach at Rocky who brought a lot of enthusiasm to our bench.

Hayashi, Takuto: A college classmate from Japan. Takuto and I shared many memorable meals together at the Rocky sub, and we still think of him often.

291

Hayden, Alisha: A great player for Rocky who graduated before I got to play with her. Alisha served as a student assistant at Rocky, and I always admired her poise and integrity.

Helvik, Justin: A college teammate of Jeremy's who graduated from Wibaux High School.

Henderson, Brian "Hendo": My college coach.

Heny (Hitz), Jaci: Jaci was a teammate of Chasi's at Sheridan College, and then again when they both transferred to MSU-Northern. Jaci, Michele, and I were all bridesmaids at Chasi's wedding.

Hoffman, Shane: A theater student at Rocky and a good friend of Peter and Jeremy's.

Honeywell, Yvonne: A longtime Sunday school teacher in Chester. Her youngest son Camon was good friends with my brother as they played baseball and football together growing up.

Humphreys-Loving, Peter: The best man at our wedding.

Jensen, Mike: A senior when I was a freshman. Mike was a great three-point shooter and played with my brother for two seasons in high school. He dated Chasi in high school and college.

Johnson (Moro), Desiree "Desi": A couple years younger than me in high school. Desi and I exchanged many "Dear Abby-esque" letters when I was a senior.

Johnson (Streit), Jillien: A basketball teammate of mine when I was a senior. I always admired how hard Jillien worked, and she found a lot of success in track.

Johnson, Benton: Quarterback for Rocky when Jeremy was a sophomore.

Johnson, Noah: One of Jeremy's best childhood friends.

Johnson, Wade: A high school classmate and friend of mine and one of the funniest storytellers I know.

Jurenka, Kevin: A groomsman in our wedding.

Jurenka, Marilyn: Kevin's mom.

Jurenka, Tom: Kevin's dad.

Keith, Curtis: A classmate and friend of mine in high school.

Kidwell (Charchalis), Megan: A college classmate. Megan and I shared many education classes together and was always such a fun person to be around.

Kimmet, Matt: A football teammate of Jeremy's from Laurel.

Kleinsasser, Eric "Klein": A senior when I was a freshman and good friend of my brother's. Eric was one of the most natural athletes I have ever seen. He was also an incredible baritone player in Chester's high school pep band and never needed music.

Kolstad (Anderson), Brittney: A couple years younger than me in high school. Brittney was one of my dad's favorite student-athletes and taught and coached track for several years.

Krohn, Aaron: Jeremy's Belizean college roommate his sophomore year.

Kudrna, Tanner "Tex": Redshirted for the Rocky basketball team his freshman year. We hung out with Tex a lot first semester of my freshman year.

Kunkel, Luke: A center for Rocky men's basketball team.

Larson, Roger: A football teammate of Jeremy's. Roger was a standout athlete at Kremlin-Gilford High School, and we Hi-Line kids hung out a lot in college, especially our freshman year.

Lebsock, Paige: A year younger than me and played for Rocky, but we never got a chance to play together. Paige was one of the most pleasant people to be around and was always studying for difficult science-y classes I was glad I didn't have to take.

Lehman (Petzold), Tammy: Jenny Balgua's best friend and roommate.

Lei, Rae Dawn: A teammate of mine with more grit and guts than anyone I ever played with.

Loukianoff, Natalie: A college team manager and great encourager.

Loving, Laura: A pastor, writer, and Peter's mom!

Ludwig (Chelmo), Jenni: A Chester High School graduate and member of the 1979 second place state basketball team. Jenni is also the mother of my high school friend, Patrick.

Lybeck, Shirely "Nan": Maci's beloved maternal grandmother.

MacDonald, Tristan: Tristan played at Rocky, but was younger than me and we never had the chance to play together. It was fun having Tristan at Rocky, as we had played against each other at the State C basketball tournament in the semifinals my senior year.

Matkin (Johnson), Kayla: A good friend and high school classmate.

Matter (Skelton), Jeri: A good friend and college teammate.

Matter, Ed: Jeri's dad.

Matter, Jennifer: Jeri's older sister.

Matter, Judy: Jeri's mom.

Mattson, Chris: A good friend of mine and my brother's. Chris is a multisport coach in Chester.

Mattson, Jeff: Chris's brother and one of my favorite storytellers. The Mattson family has farmed north of Chester for years, where Jeff and his family run the farm.

May, Curtis: Graduated from Joplin-Inverness High School and attended MSU Billings. Maci and I hung out a lot with Curt our freshman year.

McDermott, Ryan: Attended Carroll College and dated Maci for several years.

Melle, Kyle: A groomsman at our wedding.

Meyer, Carl: A college classmate who we hung out with a lot my freshman year.

Miller (Wiederrick), Alex: A friend and teammate my freshman year. Alex, Maci, and I all got to stand up together in Shye's wedding.

Morgan (Sangster), Tiffany: A teammate my freshman year. Tiffany was one of the players most severely injured in our van accident. Thankfully she healed and married Thomas soon after graduating from Rocky.

Mouat, Chris: Assistant coach my sophomore and junior year.

Nelson, Kali: A high school classmate of my brother's and good friend of both of ours. Kali and I played a lot of Barbies together when we were little, and our moms were close friends until Kali's dear mother Jan passed away from breast cancer in May of 2016.

Neubauer (Bacon), Kayla: A fellow education major and older sister of teammate Stephanie.

Neubauer-Zupan, Stephanie: A teammate my junior year who graduated high school from Wolf Point, MT.

Nevrivy (Warburton), Stacey: A teammate my sophomore year who graduated high school from Malta, MT. Stacey married RMC punter George Warburton. Jeremy always said George was one of the best punters he had ever seen.

Norby (Malkuch), Mandy: A teammate my junior year who graduated high school from Sidney, MT.

Nynas (Hackl), Suzette: Trainer at Rocky.

Olind, Erin: One of my wonderful college roommates.

Olon, Ruth: Jeremy's maternal grandmother.

Omar, James: A teammate of Jeremy's.

Osterman, Geoff: A high school classmate and friend of mine.

Parsons, Bob: A well-known and beloved coach from South Dakota.

Pendley, Ann: Jeremy's mom.

Pendley, Greg: Jeremy's stepdad.

Petrick, Brent: A standout athlete at Blue Sky High School, Brent redshirted for the Rocky men's basketball team his freshman year. He and I were in a bowling league together in elementary school. Brent ended up marrying a wonderful Chester girl, Amanda Kolstad.

Preeshl (Hersel), Kristin: A Kremlin-Gilford graduate who attended MSU Billings and teaches in Billings.

Pulst, Darin: A senior when I was a freshman and a good friend of my brother's.

Riggin, Scott: A good friend of my brother's. He dated Kaitlynn for several years through high school and college.

RMC Battlin' Bears JV (2002-03): Maci Tempel, freshman guard, Chester, MT; Katherine Bitz; freshman forward, Big Sandy, MT; Shye Boggs, freshman guard, Baker, MT; Jamie Graham, freshman guard, Chester, MT; Tiffany Morgan, junior guard, Cody, WY; Alexia Craig, junior guard, Las Vegas, NV; Megan Berg, freshman guard, Lewistown, MT; Alex Miller, freshman forward, Whitewater, MT; Becky (Rebecca) Wolf, Salt Lake City, UT; Jeri Matter, freshman forward, Havre, MT; Kelley Edwards, sophomore forward, Denton, MT; Liz (Elizabeth) Sulser, junior center, White Sulfur Springs, MT; Natalie Loukianoff, junior redshirt, San Mateo, CA; Kasey Fischer, sophomore redshirt, Redmond, OR; head coach Brian Henderson; assistant coach JD Gustin

RMC Battlin' Bears varsity (2003-04): Amy Schillinger, freshman guard, Billings, MT; Katherine Bitz, sophomore guard, Big Sandy, MT; Maci Tempel, sophomore guard, Chester, MT; Stacey Nevrivy, senior guard, Malta, MT; Jamie Graham, sophomore guard, Chester, MT; Kelley Edwards, junior forward, Denton, MT; Shye Boggs, sophomore guard, Baker, MT; Jessica Workman, sophomore forward, Centerville, MT; Jeri Matter, sophomore forward, Havre, MT; Amber Griffith, senior forward, Miles City, MT; Ashley Griffith, junior guard, Miles City, MT; Mandy Norby, freshman forward, Sidney, MT; Adja "Maina" Fame, senior center; Dakar, Senegal; head coach Brian Henderson; assistant coaches Chris Mouat and Alisha Hayden

RMC Battlin' Bears varsity (2004-05): Alyssa Root, Jessica Workman, Gretchen Wall, Jeri Matter, Sarah Bills, Mandy Norby, Katherine Bitz, Rae Dawn Lei, Jenny Balgua, Stephanie Neubauer; head coach Brian Henderson; assistant coaches Chris Mouat and Rich Hash

RMC Battlin' Bears JV (2004-05): Jenna Anderson, Cady Arifin, Tristan MacDonald, Lindsay Comte, Magon Jones, Kelsey Crampton, Becky Wolf, Tessa Barndt, Megan Mohr, Paige Lebsock, Beth Ueland, Tabitha Krack

Roberts, Jared "J-Rod": A Rocky skier and good friend of Jeremy's and his crew.

Roberts, Robin: My uncle.

Robinson, Andrea "Andy": One of my wonderful college roommates.

Rooley, Cindy: A librarian in Chester for years. She always read books with the best voices and accents.

Root, Alyssa: A teammate at Rocky with a great sense of humor and a huge heart.

Sanchez, Adam: A quarterback at Rocky and one of the two football players Kelley said I would be "allowed" to date.

Schillinger (Westrope), Amy "Amers": A college teammate and close friend.

Schlepp (Amosa), Amanda: My childhood best friend and godmother of our son Justin.

Schlepp, Brian: My brother's best friend and Amanda's older brother.

Schlepp, Kade: Coach Schlepp's oldest of three children.

Schlepp, Kellie: Coach Schlepp's wonderful wife.

Schlepp, Willie: One of my high school coaches.

Schmitz (Graham), Megan: My brother Jeffrey's sweet wife.

Schott, Kenny: My Grandma Joyce's kind neighbor who took perfect care of her lawn for years.

Severance, Scott: A business professor at Rocky who has coached Montana basketball for many years.

Smith, Donna: Jeremy's maternal grandmother.

Smith, Dustin: An aviation student at Rocky and good friend of Jeremy's.

Smith, Ron: Jeremy's maternal grandfather.

Solie, Ann: My mentor teacher who I student-taught under at Blue Creek Elementary. My favorite story of Mrs. Solie is where she found this delicious "energy drink" that she said worked miracles as far as keeping her calm and patient in the afternoons while finishing out the school day; she even shared it with the principal. Shortly after she discovered the drink, a student teacher was assigned to Mrs. Solie. The student teacher finally got up the nerve to ask her if she knew she was drinking an alcoholic drink—Sparks Energy—every day. Mrs. Solie was of course completely unaware, and that story still makes me howl.

Sparks (Morse), Jamie: A year younger than me in high school.

Stack, Eddie: A Rocky men's basketball guard who played with more intensity and hustle than most any player I have ever seen.

Stephens, Leif: A good friend of Jeremy's at Rocky their freshmen year. I met Leif through some Big Timber connection, and Leif was the first to officially introduce me to Jeremy. After much discussion with Leif's mom, Tracey, Leif and I later discovered that we are fourth cousins.

Stephens, Todd: Younger brother of Leif and, thus, also my fourth cousin.

Story (Odom), Jessie: A good friend of Jeremy's growing up in Sheridan, and one of Jeremy's first girlfriends.

Story, Ann: A good friend of Jeremy's growing up in Sheridan.

Stuart, Jake: A standout athlete at Kremlin-Gilford who was recruited to play at the University of Montana, then transferred to—and thrived at—Rocky.

Stuart, Joey: A standout athlete at Kremlin-Gilford who played football and then basketball at Carroll College.

Styles, Andrea: A Rocky soccer player who was always up for a good time and one of the most "chill" people I have ever met.

Sulser (Meier), Elizabeth "Liz": A college teammate my sophomore year and one of the kindest people I know. Liz was very badly injured in our van accident and did not play basketball after that season.

Tempel (Hausman), Mari: High school classmate and good friend.

Tempel (Shatto), Maci: High school classmate and good friend.

Thompson, Chance: A high school classmate and friend of mine.

Tomkins, Ann: Jeremy's paternal grandmother who passed away in 2005.

Tranberg (Repnak), Emily: High school classmate and one of my best friends.

Tranberg, John: Emily's younger brother.

Ueland, Beth: A year younger than me and played for Rocky, but we never got a chance to play together. Beth was great friends with Paige Lebsock and was also such a pleasant person to be around.

Ullman, Jim: My uncle.

Ullman, Megan: My baby cousin on my dad's side.

Ullman, Mitchell: My baby cousin on my dad's side.

VanDyke, Carly: The oldest of the VanDyke siblings. Carly was a senior leader on our high school team my freshman year and played college basketball at Carroll.

VanDyke, Isaac: One of Michele's younger brothers, and one of my best friends.

VanDyke, Jessica: The youngest of the five VanDyke siblings.

VanDyke, Linda: My high school basketball coach.

VanDyke, Michele: High school classmate and one of my best friends.

VanDyke, Travis: One of Michele's younger brothers.

Violett, Mitch "Mitchy": A couple years younger than me in high school and a good friend.

Violett, Teresa: A longtime elementary teacher at Chester and mother of Mitchell.

Wade, Travis: A friend who attended Chester until he moved to Conrad before he entered high school. Travis is also Chasi's cousin.

Waldo, Ken: A Rocky men's basketball player.

Wall (Moritz), Gretchen: A Rocky teammate my sophomore and junior year who had a strong inside game and the best laugh.

Wendland (Diemert), Heather: Graduated from Blue Sky High School and married my high school classmate, Colt.

Whisler, Mac: My cousin Shannon's husband.

Wicks, Patrick: A few years younger than me in high school and good friend.

Wiegand (Branae), Shirley: My sweet aunt who passed away in 2021.

Wiegand, Elliot: My cousin Shane's son.

Wiegand, Emma: My cousin Shane's daughter.

Wiegand, Richard: My uncle.

Wiegand, Riley Rae: My cousin Shannon's daughter.

Wiegand, Shane: My cousin on my mom's side who is a teacher in Alaska.

Wiegand, Shannon: My cousin on my mom's side who is a doctor in Alaska.

Wiegand, Shawn: My cousin on my mom's side who is a financial advisor in Alaska.

Wienert, Sean: A high school classmate of my brother's.

Wilson, Brett: A Rocky men's basketball player who graduated high school from Sweetgrass High in Big Timber. Brett was the epitome of a great teammate, and I loved watching how hard he worked and how much he loved the game.

Wolf, Becky (Rebecca): A teammate at Rocky.

Wolfe (Rohrback), Joanne: A Chester High School graduate and member of the 1979 second place state basketball team. Joanne is also the aunt of Matthew.

Wolfe, Matthew: A high school classmate and friend of mine.

Womack, Jake: Jeremy's youth pastor in high school and the godfather of all three of our children.

Wood, Greg: A Rocky men's basketball player who was so much fun to watch.

Woody, Emily: A standout at Carroll College and good friend of Carly VanDyke's. Carly brought Emily home to Chester a time or two, and I rarely stopped laughing when Emily was around.

Workman, Jessica: A teammate at Rocky who brought so much love and positivity to our team.

Zoanni, Tara: A Carroll College standout and graduate of Conrad High School.

SOUNDTRACK

"Damn Cold Night" by Avril Lavigne
"The Dance" by Garth Brooks
"The First Noel" traditional English Christmas carol
"Here's to the Nights" by Eve 6
"Here Without You" by 3 Doors Down
"High Plains" by Phil Aaberg
"If You Could Only See" by Tonic
"If You're Gone" by Matchbox 20
"(I've Had) The Time of My Life" from *Dirty Dancing*
Jars of Clay by Jars of Clay (self-titled album)
"Kiss Me" by Sixpence None the Richer
"Leader of the Pack" by The Shangri-Las
"Lucky" by Britney Spears
"Oh Holy Night" by Placide Cappeau & Adolphe Adam
"Picture" by Kid Rock & Sheryl Crow
"Pomp and Circumstance"
"Something in the Way She Moves" by James Taylor
"Somewhere in Between" by Lifehouse
"Strawberry Wine" by Deana Carter
The Hits - Chapter 1 by the Backstreet Boys (album)
"Wild Thing" by The Troggs
Weezer (band)

REFERENCES

Alaska Anchorage. 2022. Women's basketball. Retrieved October 5, 2022, from https://goseawolves.com/sports/womens-basketball.

American Rivers. "Yellowstone river: a wildlife paradise." 2019. Retrieved November 14, 2020 from https://www.americanrivers.org/river/yellowstone-river/.

Anderson, Erik C. February 16, 2018. Montana state-northern women's coach and helena high grad chris mouat q&a. Retrieved April 8, 2022, from https://406mtsports.com/college/frontier-conference/msu-northern/montana-state-northen-womens-coach-and-helena-high-grad-chris-mouat-q-a/article_aa24cb21-1f70-563e-ada-e25678cfe9c5.html.

Baseball reference: alex rodriguez. 2022. Retrieved April 7, 2022, from https://www.baseball-reference.com/players/r/rodrial01.shtml.

Big Piney and Marbelton. 2022. Retrieved April 7, 2022, from https://www.bigpiney.com/.

BigSkyFishing.com. 2002-2021. Chief joseph scenic highway. Retrieved September 4, 2022, from https://www.bigskyfishing.com/scenic-drives/chief-joseph.php.

BigSkyFishing.com. 2002-2021. Dillon, Montana. Retrieved June 3, 2021, from https://www.bigskyfishing.com/scenic-drives/towns/dillon.php.

Billings365. The History of the Billings Rimrocks. n.d. Retrieved November 23, 2020, from https://billings365.com/the-history-of-the-billings-rimrocks.

Billings Catholic Schools. n.d. Retrieved April 26, 2023, from https://billingscatholicschools.org.

(The) Billings Gazette. October 25, 2003. Jeremy duprey field goals 2003. Newspapers.com. Retrieved June 18, 2023, from https://www.newspapers.com/article/the-billings-gazette-jeremy-duprey-field/123142337/.

(The) Billings Gazette. May 7, 2005. 2005 rocky mountain college graduates. Retrieved November 11, 2022, from https://billingsgazette.com/news/local/2005-rocky-mountain-college-graduates/article_e8a639aa-8228-51ca-8ee5-a397bca7ade4.html.

Billings Public Schools. n.d. Retrieved November 28, 2020, from https://www.billingsschools.org/our-schools/high-schools.

Biola University. Be brilliant for christ. 2022. Retrieved September 14, 2022, from https://www.biola.edu/.

Bofinger, Alec. December 28, 2022. Broadview-Lavina coach scott severance has new perspective after bout with cancer. Retrieved May 14, 2023 from https://www.montanasports.com/high-school-sports/boys-basketball/q2-aow-broadview-lavina-coach-scott-severance-has-new-perspective-after-bout-with-cancer.

Buccaneers Athletics. 2021. Retrieved September 10, 2021, from https://www.dawsonbucs.com/landing/index.

Bureau of Reclamation. Projects and facilities: tiber dam. N.d. Retrieved November 2, 2022, from https://www.usbr.gov/projects/index.php?id=252.

Casas por Cristo. Juárez, mexico mission trips. N.d. Retrieved November 3, 2022, from https://casasporcristo.org/locations/juarez-mexico-mission-trips/.

Cedar Point. Life needs more getaways. 2021. Retrieved June 23, 2021, from https://www.cedarpoint.com/.

Circle of Care. Help, healing, hope since 1917. 2020. Retrieved November 2, 2022, from https://circleofcare.org/about/our-history/.

City of Billings. n.d. Retrieved April 19, 2023 from https://ci.billings.mt.us/1776/Explore-Billings.

Comics Kingdom. Zits. September 16, 2022. Retrieved September 16, 2022, from https://comicskingdom.com/zits.

Costello, Brian. n.d. The jerk movie review. Retrieved October 3, 2022, from https://www.commonsensemedia.org/movie-reviews/the-jerk.

Dan Brown. 2022. The da vinci code. Retrieved October 5, 2022, from https://danbrown.com/the-davinci-code/.

Duprey, Jamie Graham, and Joe Puckett. The yellow sports bra: a true story of love, faith and basketball. Aubade Publishing, 2020.

Dylan Scott Hendrickson. August 15, 2021. Obituary. Retrieved October 5, 2022, from https://www.hollandbonine.com/obituary/dylan-henderickson.

Ebert, Roger. December 25, 2001. Kate and leopold. Retrieved March 24, 2022, from https://www.rogerebert.com/reviews/kate-and-leopold-2001.

Educational Insights. 2021. Blurt: word game. Retrieved September 2, 2021, from https://www.educationalinsights.com/blurt-word-game.

Enjoy Wilcoxson's ice cream. n.d. Retrieved August 19, 2021, from https://wilcoxsonsicecream.wordpress.com/.

Faggan, Pete. April 15, 2000. To switch or not: area coaches react to current human rights dispute to shift girls' sports seasons. Retrieved April 12, 2021, from https://www.bozemandaily

chronicle.com/sports/bobcats/to-switch-or-not-area-coaches-react-to-current-human-rights-dispute-to-shift-girls/article_1f61fe09-7bdd-5c9a-9208-5c8dcb6aa380.html.

Falstad, Jan. February 16, 2014. Have you heard? no longer a wild west in billings. Retrieved October 4, 2022, from https://billingsgazette.com/business/columns/have-you-heard/have-you-heard-no-longer-a-wild-west-in-billings/article_384b8f85-b0c8-5453-8b07-42ab9a6b5c89.html.

Famous Movie Quotes. Empire records. October 12, 2010. Retrieved September 8, 2022, from https://www.quotesquotations.com/movies/empire-records-quotes/.

Fiduccia, Christopher. January 4, 2021. Retrieved July 7, 2022, from https://screenrant.com/funny-quotes-adam-sandler-billy-madison/.

Friends. The one where emma cries: episode 9.02. 2002. Retrieved July 16, 2021, from http://www.friends-tv.org/zz902.html.

Gazette Staff. May 30, 2017. Ronald perry cochran. Retrieved April 8, 2022, from https://billingsgazette.com/lifestyles/announcements/obituaries/ronald-perry-cochran/article_ec27f252-c398-55b1-9302-69365a156db5.html.

Guerrasio, Jason. Serendipity at 20: director reveals why jennifer aniston turned down the lead role and his decades-long regret that harvey weinstein forced him to digitally erase the twin towers from the movie. October 1, 2021. Retrieved March 22, 2022, from https://www.insider.com/serendipity-20th-anniversary-film-secrets-casting-rare-photos-021-9.

Have Daily News. August 25, 2019. Obituary: judith a. (turbak) matter. Retrieved October 7, 2022, from https://www.havredailynews.com/story/2019/08/29/obituaries/obituary-judith-a-turbak-matter/525153.html.

Havre Daily News. Shirley lybeck, obituary. Retrieved September 2, 2022, from https://www.havredailynews.com/story/2003/11/18/obituaries/shirley-lybeck-obituary/482408.html.

Hartley County, Texas. 2022. Retrieved March 24, 2022, from https://www.co.hartley.tx.us/.

History.com editors. Battle of the little big horn. December 2, 2009. Retrieved September 10, 2021 from https://www.history.com/topics/native-american-history/battle-of-the-little-bighorn.

History.com editors. This day in history, march 11, 2003: lawrence welk is born. November 16, 2009. Retrieved May 28, 2021, from https://www.history.com/this-day-in-history/lawrence-welk-is-born.

Hooligan's Sports Bar. 2022. Sports bar in billings. Retrieved November 10, 2022, from https://hooliganssportsbar. business.site/?utm_source=gmb&utm_medium=referral

Hurston Z. N. & Danticat E. (2021). Their eyes were watching god (Gift). HarperCollins.

Hysham Montana Chamber of Commerce. 2013. Retrieved January 29, 2021, from http://hysham.org/.

Intermountain Histories. 2022. Clearwater paper: lewiston's defining feature. Retrieved September 29, 2022, from https://www.intermountainhistories. org/items/show/178.

IMDb. Austin powers: the spy who shagged me. 2020. Retrieved April 26, 2023, from https://www.imdb.com/title/tt0145660.

IMDb. Dirty dancing. 2023. Retrieved April 20, 2023, from https://www.imdb.com/title/tt0092890.

IMDb. Necessary roughness. 2020. Retrieved December 17, 2020, from https://www.imdb.com/title/tt0102517/.

IMDb. Tommy boy. 2022. Retrieved September 16, 2022, from https://www.imdb.com/title/tt0114694/.

Independent Record. Recent history of highway speed limits in montana. (November 30, 2014). Retrieved July 9, 2020, from https://helenair.com/news/local/recent-history-of-highway-speed-limits-in-montana/article_a27bf2e5-ca02-5353-8499-57ac7068a777.html

Jamaica. Dunn's river falls and park. N.d. Retrieved November 2, 2022, from https://www.visitjamaica.com/listing/dunns-river-falls-and-park/30/.

Krishnankutty, Pia. The Prnt. Nokia's snake, the mobile game that became an entire generation's obsession. July 18, 2020. Retrieved April 14, 2021, from https://theprint.in/features/nokias-snake-the-mobile-game-that-became-an-entire-generations-obsession/462873/.

Lake Tyler. 2021. Lake tyler in east texas. Retrieved October 25, 2021, from https://www.lake-tyler.com/.

Levi's. SilverTab is back: huge news. Retrieved May 22, 2021, from https://www.levi.com/US/en_US/blog/article/silvertab-is-back/.

Lewis Clark State Warriors. n.d. Women's basketball. Retrieved September 29, 2022, from https://lcwarriors.com/sports/womens-basketball?path=wbball.

Lewistown, MT: Find Your Center. Explore. 2006-2020. Retrieved May 19, 2021, from https://www.enjoylewistown.com/eddies-corner.

Liggons, Jordan. April 21, 2020. Why we keep returning to 'love and basketball' 20 years later. Retrieved March 25, 2022, from https://www.theringer.com/movies/2020/4/21/21228610/love-and-basketball-20-year-anniversary.

Lyrics: Here without you. 2021. Retrieved October 11, 2021, from https://www.lyrics.com/lyric/15558958/3+Doors+Down/Here+Without+You+%5BAcoustic+Version%5D.

Mackenzie River Pizza. "Our Brand Culture." 2020. Retrieved December 5, 2020, from https://www.mackenzieriverpizza.com/story/.

Marvin United Methodist Church. 2021. Marvin youth. Retrieved October 21, 2021, from https://marvinumc.com/.

McDonald, Adam. I'll be–edwin mccain (Lyrics, Song Review and Meaning). March 26, 2016. Retrieved March 29, 2021, from https://justrandomthings.com/2016/03/26/ill-be-edwin-mccain-lyrics-song-review-meaning/.

McGlad, Caitlin and Price, Justin. May 10, 2018. Churches are putting faith in these old vans that could kill. Retrieved June 3, 2021, from https://www.courier-journal.com/story/news/investigations/2018/05/10/deadly-risks-old- 5-passenger-vans-echoes-carrollton-bus-crash/529909002/.

Melby, Richie. November 29, 2020. Frontier conference: no football yet, but msu-northern's new stadium 'the total university experience.' https://www.montanasports.com/frontier-conference/no-football-yet-but-msu-northerns-new-stadium-the-total-university-experience

Miles City Area Chamber of Commerce. 2021. Retrieved September 10, 2021, from https://milescitychamber.com/history/.

Miles Community College. 2021 Retrieved September 10, 2021, from https://www.mccpioneers.com/landing/index.

Missoula Catholic Schools. 2017. School info: loyola sacred heart high school. Retrieved September 29, 2022, from https://missoulacatholicschools.org/lsh-school-info/.

Montana's Historic Landscapes. Glendive, the yellowstone's first railroad town. November 7, 2014. Retrieved September 10, 2021, from https://montanahistoriclandscape.com/2014/11/07/glendive-the-yellowstones-first-railroad-town.

Montana. 2022. Huntley Retrieved September 28, 2022, from https://www.visitmt.com/places-to-go/cities-and-towns/huntley.

Montana State University Northern. n.d. Retrieved January 29, 2021, from https://www.msun.edu/.

Montana University System. Colleges and Universities. n.d. Retrieved November 28, 2020, from https://mus.edu/Universities/.

Montana: Wibaux. 2022. Retrieved September 2, 2022, from https://www.visitmt.com/places-to-go/cities-and-towns/wibaux.

Myers, Quinn. MEL Magazine. The inside story of 8-minute abs. 2020. Retrieved March 29, 2021, from https://melmagazine.com/en-us/story/8-minute-abs-inside-story.

National Association of Intercollegiate Athletics. Legislative briefs: varsity vs. junior varsity. 2021. Retrieved April 12, 2021, from https://www.naia.org/legislative/2013-14/releases/20130920iovxw.

Northwest College Trappers. n.d. Trapper athletics. Retrieved June 3, 2021, from https://www.nwctrappers.com/landing/index.

Olp, Susan. May 9, 2015. Losekamp has long history of music, theater, and maybe ghosts. Retrieved May 3, 2023 from https://billingsgazette.com/news/local/losekamp-hall-has-long-tradition-of-music-theater-and-maybe-ghosts/article_3cd10c30-790c-5543-a38e-6089c79056fe.html.

Penguin Random House Canada. 2021. Excerpt from my antonia. Retrieved June 3, 2021, from https://www.penguinrandomhouse.ca/books/25296/my-antonia-by-willa-cather/97805255 62863/excerpt.

Red Robin. 2022 Red robin billings. Retrieved November 10, 2022, from https://locations.redrobin.com/mt/billings/232/

Rock Doc Travel. Cody, wyoming. 2015. Retrieved November 8, 2022, from https://www.rocdoctravel.com/cody-wyoming.

Rocky. n.d. Retrieved November 21, 2022, from https://gobattlinbears.com/.

Rocky Mountain College. 2018. Flight operations. Retrieved October 4, 2022, from https://www.rocky.edu/academics/ academic-programs/undergraduate/aviation/flight-operations.

Rocky Mountain College. Jo swain. 2018. Retrieved September 13, 2022, from https://www.rocky.edu/academics/academic-programs/graduate/master-educational-leadership/faculty/jo-swain.

Rocky: Women's Soccer. 2022. Retrieved October 4, 2022, from https://gobattlinbears.com/sports/womens-soccer/ roster/coaches/richard-duffy/448.

Rocky. Rocky mountain college clara klindt athletic hall of fame: jake stuart. 2019. Retrieved May 4, 2023 from https://gobattlinbears.com/hof.aspx?hof=121.

(The) Ruth Cheatham Foundation. All you need to know about ruth's story. Retrieved May 9, 2023 from https://www.ruthcheathamfoundation.org/read-me.

Sampson, Elizabeth. March 22, 2022. 8 ways to explore the bighorns. Retrieved May 11, 2023 from https://travelwyoming.com/article/ways-to-explore-the-bighorn-mountains/.

Show Me State Games. N.d. Retrieved November 3, 2022, from https://smsg.org/.

Song Facts. 2021. Butterfly kisses: bob carlisle. Retrieved October 26, 2021, from https://www.songfacts.com/facts/bob-carlisle/butterfly-kisses.

Song Facts. 2021. If you could only see, by tonic. Retrieved March 29, 2021, from https://www.songfacts.com/facts/tonic/if-you-could-only-see.

Song Facts. 2021. Kiss me: sixpence none the richer. Retrieved November 3, 2021, from https://www.songfacts.com/facts/sixpence-none-the-richer/kiss-me.

Song Facts. 2022. Something in the way she moves. Retrieved November 13, 2022, from https://www.songfacts.com/lyrics/james-taylor/something-in-the-way-she-moves.

Southerland, Edward. November 13, 2018. Dairy queen: a texas icon? Retrieved October 27, 2021, from https://www.heralddemocrat.com/lifestyle/20181113/dairy-queen-texas-icon.

Sportsfanfocus. 2022. How long is a basketball game? Retrieved April 8, 2022, from https://sportsfanfocus.com/how-long-is-a-basketball-game/.

Schlitterbahn: Waterpark and Resort. 2022. Retrieved March 25, 2022, from https://www.schlitterbahn.com/new-braunfels.

T., Matt. September 6, 2019. Air dancers: the wacky flailing story of the inflatable tube man. Retrieved October 3, 2022, from https://tentandtable.net/blog/2019/09/06/air-dancers-wacky-inflatable-tube-men/.

Tait, Amelia. February 13, 2019. 'You've got mail' is about a millionaire destroying a woman's livelihood. Retrieved March 24, 2022, from https://www.vice.com/en/article/mbz7d8/ youve-got-mail-movie-relationship-bad.

Tallent, Aaron. April 9, 2019. The cast of 'major league:' where are they now? Retrieved April 7, 2022, from https://athlon sports.com/mlb/major-league-1989-cast-where-are-they-now.

Tiny's Tavern. 2021. Billings favorite place to have a good time! Retrieved June 3, 2021 from https://tinystavern.com/.

Travel Alaska. 2022. North pole. Retrieved October 5, 2022, from https://www.travelalaska.com/Destinations/Cities-Towns/North-Pole.

Tunefind. Friends soundtrack: season 9 2021. Retrieved May 31, 2021, from https://www.tunefind.com/show/friends/season-9.

Utah Tech. "JD Gustin." 2023. Retrieved April 19, 2023, from https://utahtechtrailblazers.com/staff-directory/jd-gustin/276.

United States Bowling Congress. n.d. Retrieved July 3, 2020, from https://www.bowl.com/Youth/Youth_About_Us/History/.

University of Alaska Fairbanks. n.d. Large animal research station. Retrieved October 5, 2022, from https://www.uaf.edu/lars/.

University of providence. n.d. Retrieved September 29, 2022, from https://www.uprovidence.edu/athletics/.

University of jamestown. n.d. Retrieved April 8, 2022, from https://www.uj.edu/.

University of mary for life. n.d. Retrieved April 8, 2022, from https://www.umary.edu/.

(The) University of Montana Western. 2021. Experience one. Retrieved May 31, 2021, from https://www.umwestern.edu/.

Vanguard University. We are vu. 2022. Retrieved September 14, 2022, from https://www.vanguard.edu/.

Vernoy, Lee. May 23, 2020. GOAT boys' basketball: north star's championship roots go back six decades. Retrieved May 7, 2023 from https://www.greatfallstribune.com/story/sports/2020/05/23/north-star-goat-knights-roots-go-back-60-years/5244973002/.

Vickrey, Marilyn Rae. 1997. St. john the baptist episcopal church. Retrieved April 7, 2022, from http://www.bigpiney.com/bigpiney/echurch.htm.

Visit Southwest Montana. n.d. Whitehall, montana. Retrieved June 3, 2021, from https://southwestmt.com/communities/whitehall.htm.

Vudu Fandango. Ladder 49. N.d. Retrieved November 4, 2022, from https://www.vudu.com/content/movies/details/Ladder-49/45409.

Welcome to the red door lounge. n.d. Retrieved October 4, 2022, from https://thereddoorlounge.com/.

Western Wyoming Community College. 2019. Women's sports. Retrieved June 3, 2021, from https://www.westernwyoming.edu/.

Westminster: Athletics. 2022. Retrieved March 22, 2022, from https://westminstercollege.edu/student-life/athletics.html.

Women's Basketball. 2022. University of alaska fairbanks athletics. Retrieved October 5, 2022, from https://alaskananooks.com/sports/womens-basketball.

YouVersion. 2022. Ruth 1:16-17. Retrieved November 14, 2022, from https://www.bible.com/bible/compare/RUT.1.16-17.

Zachary. February 22, 2018. There's no crying in baseball. Retrieved October 13, 2021, from https://www.throwbacks.com/league-of-their-own-facts/.

INDEX